Life into Space

An Introduction to Space Biology

Physiology Series

J. H. U. Brown, Ph.D., Consulting Editor
National Institutes of Health, Bethesda, Maryland

Life into Space

An Introduction to Space Biology

Charles C. Wunder, Ph.D.
Associate Professor of Physiology
University of Iowa, Iowa City, Iowa

 F. A. DAVIS COMPANY • PHILADELPHIA

Foreword

This small book represents one of a series of volumes prepared for the graduate and medical student to use in daily study. The volumes are designed to be more complete and to provide greater depth than the chapters pertaining to the material included in most textbooks of biochemistry, physiology, or pharmacology, but they are not designed to be definitive treatises in their respective subjects. The topics have been selected to present materials which may not be covered to the same extent or from the same viewpoint in standard texts.

In addition to this volume, the series to date includes:

Basic Endocrinology

Blood and Body Functions

Volumes in press include:

Biomedical Engineering

Volumes currently in preparation include:

Cells and Tissues

J. H. U. Brown, Ph.D.
Consulting Editor

Preface

The present work is an attempt to offer physical, engineering, biological and medical scientists an introduction to the considerations involved in applying their specialized knowledge to the problems of carrying life into space. Unfortunately, the need for scientists who are qualified to face these problems far outstrips the present supply of ideally trained individuals. With such limitations in mind, the author has undertaken in this book to better prepare scientists for further study of specific problems related to space biology. It may be that in the process the reader will develop a more sympathetic understanding of certain basic principles of knowledge which previously were beyond his interest.

The preparation of a text on space biology represents a unique challenge. In most areas of science the development of new knowledge proceeds at an orderly pace. The recent intensive emphasis placed upon space exploration, after decades of neglect, has created a situation in which demands are made for an organized body of knowledge in advance of the availability and screening of appropriate information. In some instances a significant amount of relevant and valuable information lies buried in unpublished reports. In other instances, articles have appeared which have not been subjected to the high level of editorial scrutiny possible for better-established and hence more orthodox scientific publications.

As measured by standards for the more established scientific areas, most leaders in the new discipline of space biology are essentially amateurs in attempting to apply knowledge or methods from their own established disciplines to this new one. Ecologists have begun to consider the response of man and other organisms to space environments. Respiratory physiologists are attempting to predict the effects of new gas mixtures upon the organism on the basis of experiments conducted at high altitudes and with deep-sea diving. Toxicologists and pathologists are seeking to determine the response of life to many adverse agents under a combination of conditions which, until recently, had been considered inconceivable. Evolutionists are wondering if the little that is known about the origin of life on this planet will reveal something of life which conceivably might have evolved on another planet. Rehabilitation experts are comparing the influence of forced immobilization and bed rest with the possible influence of weightlessness. Engineers possessing no formal training in biology are cooperating with botanists in attempts to utilize plants to recycle life-support materials. Astronomers are examining the habitability of other planets even before biologists can predict the extremes of conditions under which some exotic life form might exist.

As meaningful space experiments with living material have been almost nonexistent, the chapters of this book must deal largely with experimental information that has been obtained under Earth conditions. Investigators look forward to the day when space biology need not depend so extensively upon indirect information.

The diversity of backgrounds and levels of knowledge among readers confronts the author with still another challenge. The basic textual material is presented in a somewhat elementary fashion. Although intended for college graduates the material is presented in such a way as to be comprehensible to graduates of a good high-school science program. Information of a more advanced nature is included in certain tables, figures, and footnotes and need not be fully comprehended by those individuals seeking the more elementary presentation in the body of the text. Other tables, figures, and footnotes together with the parenthetical expressions are included for the purpose of introducing pertinent, basic information for those individuals who possess a less than ideal background either in the biological or in the physical sciences. So that the textual material may be useful to individuals of varying backgrounds without interruption for reference to other introductory scientific texts, considerable accessory material is included. Such inclusion is more extensive than is normally appropriate for works of this level of sophistication. The decision to do this was made with some reluctance. Hopefully this measure will add sufficient usefulness to compensate for the discontinuity which it causes. The reader, in brief, can utilize or ignore accessory material in accordance with his needs.

The book is divided into two primary parts. The first four chapters deal with introductory considerations. These chapters are not intended for the well-prepared reader, who has already gained most of this information from biological coursework, physical coursework, and many popular articles about space research. This section is included primarily for those individuals who have not previously availed themselves of all three sources. The remaining seven chapters consider specific problems.

As this subject is being approached as a basic rather than an applied science, the emphasis throughout is placed upon an elucidation of scientific principles rather than upon a description of the equipment or "hardware" necessary for carrying life beyond our planet. Elementary descriptions of some equipment are intended to introduce certain of the problems involved and in general to exemplify the approach to their solution.

A word of caution is necessary for any individual wishing to employ the biological data displayed in the figures or tables. It is well to bear in mind that biological material is much more variable and is more drastically influenced by the environment than is inanimate material. Data are provided primarily to indicate the nature of problems to be encountered, not to provide a basis for computing precise solutions to these problems. Moreover, the collection of needed information about the response to space conditions is a relatively new interest of most biological and medical scientists. For this reason, many values must be based upon scattered and poorly confirmed older work or more recent unfinished work. The reader is also cautioned that much of the astronomical data, particularly describing conditions on other planets, are frequently based upon indirect measurements rather than upon reliable, direct measurements.

The present rapid development of space sciences and technologies almost decrees that an undertaking such as this will become somewhat dated in the interval between manuscript preparation and publication. With this in mind, the author attempted to emphasize, in the body of the text, well-established concepts which should remain pertinent to space biology even after many of the descriptive facts and specific techniques have been revised. Thus, certain recent accomplishments, which only came to the author's attention after return of the galley proofs, are not discussed. This would involve such things as the later Gemini flights and discovery that the planet Mercury's rotation is not of a nature to perpetually shield one side from the Sun. Some attempt was made, however, to revise parts of the page proofs in consideration of the Mariner 4 findings for Mars.

The amateur status of essentially all space biologists has been acknowledged. The author himself is by training a biophysicist whose primary field of interest has been gravitational biology. Even before the recently enhanced emphasis upon space exploration he was concerned with the natural role that a planet's gravity plays in the control and guidance of biological growth. Unlike those individuals interested in space biology as a tool for space exploration, the author's enthusiasm stems from the desire that the space environment may serve as a scientific tool for the study of basic biological problems.

With the acknowledged peripheral interest of the author in problems not related to gravitational biology, suggestions were solicited from individuals whose interests were basic to other aspects of this text. Naturally, the author assumes full responsibility for all deficiencies or errors still present in this work. Without suggesting approval by the individuals, a sincere debt of gratitude is extended to the many persons who have made useful suggestions whereby many improvements were possible in the original text. Among many other people this would include: Dr. Karl Kammermeyer, Dr. Satoshi Matsushima, Dr. Herbert L. Jackson, Dr. J. W. Osborne, Mr. Brian Duling, Mr. Howard Bengele, Mr. Dean Eberly, and Mr. and Mrs. Seddie Cogswell.

Particular acknowledgment is made to the editor of this series, Dr. Jack H. U. Brown. I feel quite fortunate to have received from a man who is so well qualified in the area of space biology the encouragement, suggestions, and prompt but careful review of every stage of manuscript preparation.

Iowa City, Iowa   CHARLES C. WUNDER

Contents

Part 1

Introductory Considerations

1 | The Concept of Space Biology

The recent intensified interest in space exploration has opened new horizons to all the established scientific disciplines. Old sciences have hybridized or fused into new ones. New sciences have expanded and grown with remarkable speed. It is not surprising that the concept of *space biology* should arise, since the concern for studying conditions beyond our own planet is now coupled with the demand that this exploration be manned. This chapter will introduce briefly some of the biological considerations which space exploration can encompass.

For the purposes of this book, a working definition of the term *space biology* will be the *study of life, either of Terrestrial[1] or extra-Terrestrial origin, as it exists or could exist outside or beyond the atmosphere of the Earth,[2] with attendant consideration to biological problems arising as the atmosphere becomes rarefied.* Space biology could be more specifically defined as the study of those biological phenomena that exist or could exist in space. Unfortunately, there has never been a completely satisfactory definition for either *space* or *biology.* For the purposes of this book, the broadest definition of each term has been chosen. The author's concept of the scope of space biology is diagrammed in Figure 1-1.

A Criterion for Space

Space can be thought of as that realm which lies outside or beyond the atmosphere of the Earth, although space has been referred to as that part of the universe in which there is no matter. The latter criterion does not include the heavenly bodies beyond the Earth's atmosphere; it also overlooks the

---

[1] The adjective *terrestrial* (without capitalization) is recognized as denoting that which lives on land, above the water but below the higher reaches of the atmosphere. With capitalization, the adjective *Terrestrial* will have reference to the planet Earth and shall therefore designate that which exists on or has originated from this planet. For the sake of consistency, existence on or origin from some other planet will be designated by *extra-Terrestrial,* rather than the more commonly employed *extraterrestrial.*

[2] With capitalization, *Earth* will have reference to a specific geographical location, the third planet of the Solar System. In many published works, the uncapitalized *earth* is also used in this sense. For the purpose of this book, the latter will be used only to denote the soil found on the surface of this planet.

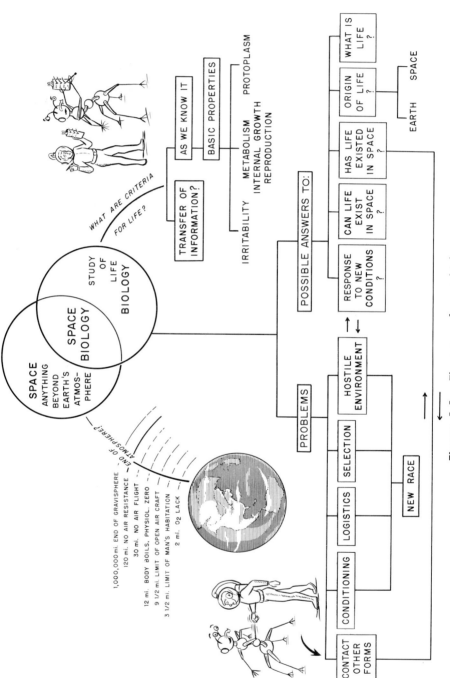

Figure 1-1. The scope of space biology.

fact that there is some matter throughout all parts of the known universe, though it may be of a very low concentration.

If space is to be considered as any area beyond the atmosphere of the Earth, it is necessary to first establish where the atmosphere ends. The gaseous envelope surrounding our planet starts at the surface of the Earth and thins out as it extends upward, with *no sharp line of demarcation* (Fig. 3-1). Insofar as our passageway to space is the atmosphere, we may consider the problems of space biology to start at that altitude where the rarefaction of the atmosphere begins to influence living material. With man, the effect of atmospheric rarefaction is noticed at a height of approximately 2 miles above sea level, where the symptoms of oxygen lack become obvious. This height is by no means a limit for Terrestrial life, since the highest human habitations (located in the Andes and Himalayan Mountains) are 3½ miles above sea level. One might consider this altitude the limit for most life on Earth and all higher altitudes as the beginning of space. When pure oxygen is employed, man can tolerate decreased ambient pressures up to heights as high as 9½ miles. At a height of 12 miles (Fig. 6-6), the atmospheric pressure drops to a level such that water will boil at the body temperature of man. As human tissue becomes rapidly desiccated at this pressure, the height of 12 miles has sometimes been considered the physiological limit and might well be called the absolute biological criterion for the beginning of space. At the height of 30 miles, the atmosphere is so thin that aerodynamic flight is no longer possible and higher altitudes require propulsion by means of rockets. For this reason, the height of 30 miles has been suggested as the international limit for the sovereignty of a nation in the air above it.

A height of 120 miles offers no measurable resistance to the movement of bodies. Here is the most commonly accepted boundary for the end of our atmosphere and the beginning of space. It is not, however, the boundary of our planet's influence upon bodies above the Earth's surface. The Earth's gravity has a readily measurable influence which extends for one million miles.[3]

Without a sharp demarcation between the domain of Earth and the domain of space, a broad definition of space biology must include some consideration of the biological phenomena occurring in the transition zone between Earth and space.

---

[3] In accordance with Newton's Law of Universal Gravitation, there is no end to the Earth's gravitational field g, though field intensity does drop off in an inverse-square manner with distance d, such that

$$g = G \frac{(\text{Earth's mass})}{d^2}$$

where G is the *universal gravitational constant*, with a value of 6.66×10^{-8} cm^3/gm-sec^2. At one million miles from this planet's center, the Earth's field is no greater than the Sun's (at the Earth's distance from the Sun).

Criteria for Life

The problem of defining life is even more difficult than that of defining the beginning of space. Biologists are unable to present a satisfactory definition or even satisfactory criteria for living material (see pp. 262-269). However, living material has certain fundamental properties which are recognized as common to all its forms: (1) It is irritable and will respond to stimuli. (2) It carries on processes of metabolism involving the building up and tearing down of constituents. (3) It executes internal growth (in contrast to the external growth of the type which is representative of crystal growth). (4) It will reproduce. (5) It is made up of a material referred to as *protoplasm*. This material, the basic substance in which all of the living Terrestrial reactions occur, is composed primarily of carbon, hydrogen, oxygen, and nitrogen, together with some sulfur, phosphorus, sodium, chlorine, magnesium, calcium, potassium, iron, and small traces of other elements. These elements have water as their primary solvent within protoplasm, and they are found in a number of compounds, of which proteins, carbohydrates, and fats are the most common. In some alien organism, protoplasm might be represented differently.

These classic properties of living material have been relatively satisfactory in describing life as we know it here on Earth. There is no assurance that all of these properties will necessarily apply to all extra-Terrestrial forms, should such forms exist. All types of life will probably exhibit some sort of irritability and metabolism. Whether they will contain what we think of as protoplasm or whether they will have a similar chemical composition is an open question. Our protoplasm depends upon water as a solvent and upon the carbon atom as a building block for complex molecules. Ammonia, glycerin, and some related type of compound have all been suggested as solvents to be found for life existing on planets of a much colder temperature than that of the Earth, with a silicon atom replacing carbon as the basic building block (Table 11-1).

Living material is known to be much more complex than non-living material found under the same conditions. Mathematicians have attempted to describe this type of complexity in terms of *information* content (pp. 259-262). Through yet to be understood processes of metabolism and growth, living molecules are able to communicate their information to previously inert molecules (which are then arranged into complex molecules of high information content), thus increasing the amount of living material. Perhaps the only practical criterion for life as it may be encountered throughout the universe is the state whereby self-replicating material does transfer information to produce more self-replicating material.

Problems of Space Biology

Space biology requires consideration of subjects which cannot be confined to any of the classical fields of biology, astronomy, physics, or technology. For the sake of organization, the biological topics have been divided into two basic categories: (1) the practical, life-support problems which must be solved in conquering space and (2) the yet unanswered questions of biology which might become partially answerable as a result of space studies.

There are four problems which must be solved if biological material is to travel into space: (1) the reaction of living material to a hostile environment, (2) the protection or preparation of living material so that it will be better able to survive this harsh environment, (3) the logistics of supplies adequate to aid life in resisting this environment, and (4) the selection of living individuals best able to tolerate the new environment.

A fifth problem is the contact with and the study of new forms of life, should they exist beyond our atmosphere (see pp. 283-286). Although no active life is believed to exist in the vacuum between the stars or planets, many scholars consider it conceivable if not probable that in our universe there is life in addition to that found on our planet. This new life must be contacted and its properties—including the dangers of interaction between Terrestrial and non-Terrestrial life—studied. There is reason to fear that if we are not contaminated by the new life to be encountered elsewhere there will be at least the danger of contaminating other planets with life from Earth.

As a result of meeting primary problems, a secondary racial problem arises. It is not inconceivable that individuals selected, conditioned, and finally enabled to survive the new environment may become so highly specialized that after a period of time there will develop as a result of space travel a new race of men or new races of other organisms. The environments to be encountered away from Earth are so different from our own that descendants of existing Terrestrial life might eventually evolve or adjust into new organisms which are no longer suited for life here on Earth (see Chapter 4).

The development of the short, squat, obese body of the Eskimo, which provides the minimum surface for loss of heat in a cold climate; of the tall, lanky, dark ethnic groups in the hot climates of central Africa; of the water-conserving metabolism of the Bushman; and of the ability of the natives of Tierra del Fuego to lie naked on bare ground in freezing weather without obvious discomfort; all are examples of adaptations which have occurred on our own planet within relatively moderate climatic extremes. Long exposure to climatic conditions on a planet with greater extremes may produce changes in man's makeup beyond our wildest dreams.

New Knowledge

New knowledge as the result of space travel is perhaps more important than the travel itself. Aspects of biology can be examined which would never be possible on the confines of a planet. Life can be studied under conditions which cannot be produced within the laboratory, including reduction or absence of gravitational field and the Earth's rotation, together with the various stimuli associated with these conditions. These new environments may be useful tools to the biological scientist.

The problem of contacting extra-Terrestrial life is a stimulating challenge for the biologist. From the new properties of such life, if contacted, and the differences from life as we know it, man might arrive at better criteria for life and a better understanding of the origin of life.

Problems of the Space Environment

Probably the greatest difficulty involved in carrying man into space is that all of his supplies must be carried into space with him. This new environment is so hostile and barren that none of the requirements for life may be found in a suitable form. A voyager will require sufficient gear to protect him from the extremes of temperature (see Chapter 5), from various dangerous chemical agents (Table 7-1), and from radiation. He will require energy sources not only for the maintenance of his vessel and his own micro-environment, but also energy for his own metabolism. During a space voyage, the average man will require an approximate total of 10 pounds per day of food, oxygen, and water (Figs. 7-2, 10-5). He will also require some equipment and materials whereby the waste products of metabolism can either be stored, inactivated, or removed. In this barren environment, there will be very little contact with reality, and the sensations ordinarily considered necessary for the proper

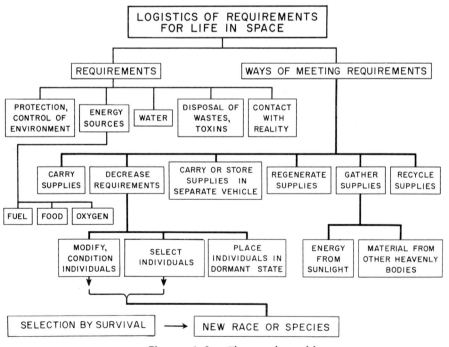

Figure 1-2. The supply problem.

orientation and sanity of the individual will be minimal. Sensory deprivation can result in severe psychological changes.

Different ways by which the space voyager might meet these requirements are outlined in Figure 1-2 and Chapter 10. If large enough rockets were available, the simple solution would be to carry in the vessel all supplies which are necessary for the voyage. Due to the cost of such a rocket, it would be preferable, if possible, to reduce the payload requirement. There are a number of ways by which this might be accomplished. One solution would be to carry or store supplies in a separate vehicle. Eventually, space stations will probably be placed in orbit about the Earth. Supplies carried to the space stations and transferred to another vessel which would travel directly from the space station to other parts of our Solar System may be a practical solution to the problems. Although this does not avoid the necessity for using vast amounts of energy in carrying supplies to the station, a lunar station might be able to produce some required materials from local minerals and this would lessen the energy demand.

Another proposal is to regenerate or recycle supplies. Oxygen gas could be generated, but chemicals and equipment would in turn have weight requirements. For long voyages, it would be preferable and probably necessary to cycle waste products back into potable water, edible food, and breathable oxygen. The space vessel would then become a closed ecological system. Plant life, probably a single-celled algae such as *Chlorella,* could utilize existing sunlight to recycle carbon dioxide back into oxygen and utilize waste materials to produce more food. Any type of recycling procedure would itself require an initial investment in the form of the weight requirements of the recycling machinery.

There also may be ways by which the material requirements could be reduced. The following may be considered: (1) Individuals having low metabolic requirements may be selected. A small astronaut might consume less food and oxygen than a large astronaut. This apparently insignificant factor can be important over a long period of time. (2) Individuals might undergo a program of conditioning enabling them to withstand prolonged periods of time with reduced food and oxygen intake. (3) Various operative procedures and appropriate application of drugs may alter the body temperature and metabolic rate. (4) The lungs may be replaced with some other type of respiratory device. It is quite likely, however, that before our surgical techniques and drugs have been developed to this level, sufficient advancements in engineering and related technology may be achieved, so that a larger payload of supplies could be carried.

It has been suggested that organisms could be placed in a dormant state. This would reduce the requirement for life during the major part of a long voyage. Some forms of life can be placed in a frozen state, during which there is little requirement for food, water, and oxygen (see pp. 79-85). Some animals can go into hibernation in such a way as to reduce their metabolic requirements drastically. It is not known whether this may be possible, after proper conditioning, with man.

Bibliography and References

As this chapter is in essence a prologue to the following portions of the book, all of the references cited in later chapters are appropriate and will not be repeated here. The reader is therefore referred to the bibliographies which accompany the remaining chapters.

2 | Biological and Cultural History

The Earth is believed to have been created approximately 5 billion years ago, the universe itself several billion years earlier. Many authorities feel that the newly created planet was surrounded by an atmosphere composed of hydrogen and hydrogen compounds (Urey, 1957; Oparin, 1964; Gilbert, 1965). As hydrogen with other light gases escaped into space, the atmosphere assumed an oxidizing character. It contained free nitrogen together with some carbon dioxide and/or water vapor. Before molecular oxygen became a major atmospheric constituent, primitive life appeared in the seas. We know that the oldest fossils of single-celled organisms are between 3½ and 1½ billion years old. As the exact date at which prehistoric events occurred is not known, many dates cited in this chapter and in Figure 2-1 may differ from the actual date by a factor of 2. The biological events which occurred in the interval between the Earth's creation and the laying down of these ancient fossils is not known. The conditions are believed to be quite similar to those under which the formation of various amino acids, the building blocks for proteins, can occur spontaneously. It is not unlikely that the appropriate complex of various amino acids might have combined to form proteins and later the first virus-like predecessor of higher forms of life (see pp. 265-274).

There are some who think that the history of space flight on this planet began with the arrival of the first organisms upon the Earth. Their suggestion is that life did not actually originate on Earth but appeared here as a result of spores from life forms which were either created on another planet or originated at the same time that the universe itself was created. Approximately 60 years ago, Arrhenius (1908), the originator of the theory of ionization of electrolytes, proposed such a theory, to which he gave the appellation *panspermia*. There now exists considerable doubt as to whether small particles, such as spores, could survive the radiation in space for a period of time adequate to permit the voyage of this living material from another planet or star. Within the last 3 or 4 years, evidence has been submitted that living material might have journeyed to this planet in meteors. Scientists have reported extraction of organic compounds from meteors, the existence of fossilized microorganisms, and the culture of bacteria-like organisms (see pp. 275-278). If these findings can be adequately confirmed

11

and substantiated, they would certainly add weight to the plausibility of theories suggesting that the life which is found on this planet descends from forms which originally arose in some other part of the universe.

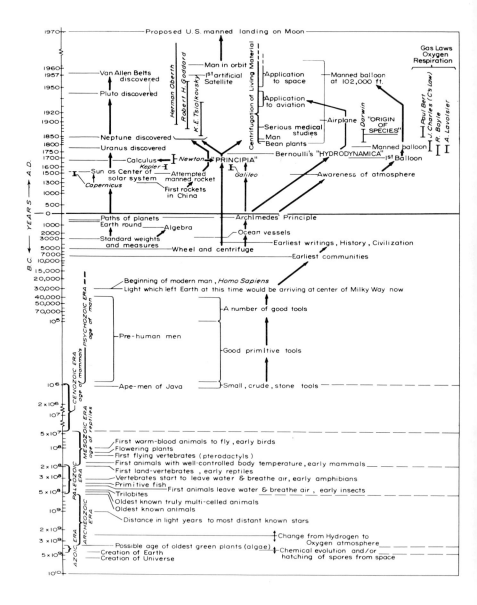

Figure 2-1. Time course of pertinent historical events.

The First Steps toward Space

The earliest life undoubtedly had only rudimentary control over its internal environment and was forced to conform very closely to the conditions of the external environment. The history of the preparation of life for a venture beyond the confines of this planet is to a large extent a continuation of the history of biological evolution and of technological developments whereby an organism can either tolerate or protect itself from the rigors of its environment. The better the preparation for environmental rigors, the better the preparation for hostile, vacuous space. This history has also involved an increasing opposition to gravity, which has held organisms and their material necessities on this planet and away from the vacuum which lies beyond the atmosphere.

Our universe is so extensive that light which left the Earth a billion years ago has traversed sufficient distance at 186,000 miles per second to arrive at the most distant known stars. Could rays of light which left the Earth one billion years ago be focused to adequate optical resolution, they no doubt would reveal nothing to an extra-Terrestrial astronomer except single-celled forms of life. The oldest known fossils of animals consisting of more than one cell are approximately 500 million years old.

Approximately 400 million years ago, relatively complex animals were abundant in our seas. These organisms contained neural and endocrine elements which permitted some control of the internal environment surrounding their cells and tissues. This ability to control the internal environment (Claude Bernard's *Interieur Milieu*), even on a limited scale, is one of the important properties of life as we know it.

Until 400 million years ago, all animals existed in an aquatic environment. Buoyancy protected them from the forces of gravity and the surrounding fluid protected them from desiccation. Insects which appeared about that time were probably the first animals to leave the protection of water and exist on land. A chitinous exoskeleton protected them from the rigors of the new environment.

During the next 100 million years of evolution, primitive fish appeared in the oceans. It was probably 300 million years ago that amphibians forsook the water's protective influence and began tentative ventures into a terrestrial environment. These were our earliest ancestors to stand at the edge of our threshold to space. Reptiles, the earliest of our ancestors to exist in a completely non-aquatic environment, appeared approximately 200 million years ago. Although dinosaurs and other reptiles were the predominant animals 150 million years ago, the earliest mammals had appeared. This marks the advent of warm-blooded animals and with it controlled body temperature.

The conservation of water was also a critical logistical problem for our remote ancestors as they left their aquatic environment (Smith, 1959). Aquatic vertebrates can rid themselves of the nitrogenous products of metabolism by diffusion across the gills; man, however, must excrete this material (primarily urea) in his urine. Land vertebrates (particularly the birds and mammals with the loop of Henle acting as a countercurrent system) have evolved a kidney which is a highly efficient recycling system for water. Of the 180 liters per day which are filtered in man's kidneys across the glomerular membranes from the blood, all, save the 1.0 to 1.5 liters (excreted as urine), is resorbed back into the blood. Space engineers involved with life-support systems are today searching for workable procedures whereby water can be recycled and reused.

Before the onset of plant life, oxygen in the atmosphere existed probably not in the free state but in the form of carbon dioxide. The type of animal life with which we are familiar could not have evolved in that atmosphere. The earliest of the green plant-life undoubtedly was responsible for the conversion of our atmosphere from one primarily devoid of free oxygen to one containing a sizeable portion of oxygen.[1] This was no doubt accomplished in a way quite similar to the present process of photosynthesis. In photosynthesis, sunlight (as absorbed by the respiratory pigment chlorophyll) is utilized as the energy source whereby green plants convert carbon dioxide and water into molecular oxygen and various carbohydrates. At the density at which it now exists, plant life would require an estimated five thousand years to produce the quantity of oxygen found in our atmosphere (Gilbert, 1965).

The existence of animal life on Earth has always been restricted to environments where adequate oxygen is present. As most regions in space will be devoid of a natural, adequate source of oxygen, methods of maintaining an artificial environment containing oxygen will be necessary for the existence of any conventional animals.

As is still true today, single-celled animals in the seas of the prehistoric Earth had no problem in obtaining the oxygen present in the environment. Simple diffusion was adequate for the transport of this gas. Diffusion alone, however, is not enough for maintenance of adequate oxygen tension within the body of a large multicellular animal. Animals of appreciable size could not develop until there first evolved a circulatory system and respiratory pigments capable of transporting and maintaining an adequate environment for the cells and tissues. With the more primitive multicellular animals, oxygenation of the blood or other circulatory fluid occurs at the animal's surface or skin. One can reason from simple geometrical considerations that the cell mass consuming oxygen would increase faster than the surface area of the organism and thus limit the animal's size. The development of complex organisms was thus limited until a special apparatus could be evolved which included respiratory surfaces and the means for ventilating these surfaces with oxygen. Gills are the most common ventilatory apparatus found in aquatic animals. The two primary types of animals which obtain oxygen directly from the atmosphere evolved two separate types of ventilatory apparatus.

---

[1] At one time scientists believed that previous to photosynthesis, a dense carbon dioxide atmosphere had evolved. Presently some believe that no such vast concentration existed. A high carbon dioxide concentration, as exists upon Venus, has been proposed to represent a "post-life" stage occurring when an abundance of the Terrestrial types of life would no longer be possible (Gilbert, 1965).

Insects developed a highly branched system of tubes and tiny tubules extending to all parts of the body, thus enabling gaseous free diffusion of the oxygen to within close proximity of all cells. This permitted the evolution of insects to a more complex form than any of the other invertebrates, although such a ventilatory apparatus is inadequate to permit the development of large animals. The land vertebrates, such as man, possess a ventilatory system which operates by forcibly pumping air back and forth into highly convoluted ventilatory surfaces, which we call *lungs*.

With the development of a controlled internal environment and air-breathing capacity, the evolution of man proceeded rapidly. Man, or at least various pre-human types of man, has existed for approximately one million years.

Ten thousand years ago, man is known to have lived in communities or villages and started the most primitive semblance of civilization. Before that time, man had already taken steps to moderate, if not actually control, his environment. He cultivated his own food and had domestic animals.

Gravity

Gravity has imprisoned man upon the planet's surface from the beginning of time. It has impeded and restricted his movements as he moved across the land. Seven thousand years ago there appeared man's greatest discovery, his most important invention. This was the wheel. Thus began man's first effective evasion of gravity. A modification of the wheel, the centrifuge, is to this day the only means by which a prolonged artificial gravity can be produced on the Earth's surface. This application of the wheel is probably as old as the application to travel. The potter's wheel was man's first useful centrifuge.

In the third century B.C., Archimedes' Principle set forth an explanation of the manner in which fluids provide buoyant forces to aid us in opposing gravity, although the flotation principle had been used since man first saw wood float on water. In 1300 A.D., the Chinese developed rockets and provided the first free flight under power. In 1500 A.D., Wan-Hoo, a Chinese official, is purported to have employed rockets in an attempted ascension and launched the first, although fatally unsuccessful, attempt to place a man (himself) into space.

By the beginning of the seventeenth century, Galileo had described the influence of gravity on the motion of falling bodies and had explained the way in which gravity restricts the maximum stable size which an organism can attain. Late in the same century, Sir Isaac Newton integrated Galileo's description of the motion of bodies on Earth with astronomical observations of the motion of the moon and planets into three basic laws of motion and the Law of Universal Gravitation. Newton suggested that his Third Law of Motion might someday enable man "to reach the stars." He was the first to offer a rational use of rocket ships in space travel and to propose methods whereby artificial satellites could be launched in orbit about this planet. Newton pointed out that satellites given adequate velocity would fall in a path beyond the curvature of the Earth, setting up an orbital trajectory, in which the centrifugal force, due to the circular path of the satellite, would counterbalance the force due to gravity.

Early in the nineteenth century, centrifuges were employed to demonstrate that the Earth's gravity plays a major role in influencing both the growth and orientation of living material. By 1818, the centrifuge had been employed in the observation of the effect of simulated high gravitational fields upon men.

During the early decades of the present century, the influence of intense centrifugal fields upon living cells and upon the sedimentation of large molecules was well documented. It was not until about 1930 that man became aware that one of the primary factors which would eventually limit the performance of high-speed manned vehicles would be human tolerance to intense fields of acceleration. Human centrifuges were constructed in America and Germany and other countries and were used throughout World War II in assessing the ability of man to survive the accelerations experienced during flight in airplanes. In the past 15 years, numerous applications of this equipment to space travel have been initiated.

Mathematics and Astronomy

By 3000 B.C., standard weights and measurements existed, and mathematics was well established. Algebra was invented by the ancient Babylonians sometime between 1500 and 1000 B.C. They knew the visible planets in the sky and distinguished them from the stars. By 500 B.C., they had accurate records of the paths which these bodies executed in the heavens. The Greek scholars demonstrated that the Earth was a sphere (Anaximander, 600 B.C.) and measured the distance between the Earth and the moon (Hipparchus, 150 B.C.).

Although Aristrachus proposed, as early as 300 B.C., that the Sun was the center of the Solar System, with the Earth and other planets revolving about it, most of the early Greek and Roman scholars considered this planet to be the center of the universe, with the Sun and all other heavenly bodies revolving about the Earth. It was not until the year 1593 that Copernicus established that the Sun was indeed the center of the Solar System. Employing the accurate astronomical measurements of Brache, the elliptical nature of the planetary orbits was established in 1610 by Kepler. The mechanical laws underlying the motion of these planets were then explained by Sir Isaac Newton in 1687.

Galileo was the first to employ a telescope in studying the heavens. It was not until 1781, however, that the nearest planet, Uranus, which is not normally visible to the naked eye, was discovered. Neptune was discovered in 1846 and Pluto, the most distant known planet in our Solar System, in 1930.

In recent years, the most spectacular astronomical study of biological significance has been that of the Earth's radiation belts, first detected by Van Allen and his co-workers in 1958 as a result of this country's earliest observations with artificial satellites. Van Allen pointed out that these belts contain particles of radiation in much greater density than would normally be encountered throughout the space above the Earth.

Ascents into the Earth's Atmosphere

Changes in the state of an organism as a result of travel into regions of high altitude have been recognized for many years. By the time of Galileo, scientists realized that there was substance to air and that the atmosphere had weight. In 1590, a Jesuit priest, José Acosta, described the afflictions resulting from his ascension of the Andes and attributed the effects to the thinning of the atmosphere with an increase in altitude. Shortly thereafter, one of Galileo's students, Torricelli, explained the relationship between hydrostatic pressure and the density of fluids. Employing this knowledge, he invented a barometer for the measurement of atmospheric pressure. In 1656, Otto von Guericke, mayor of the city of Magdeburg, Germany, provided a most spectacular demonstration of the force which results from atmospheric pressure. Later in the same century, Robert Boyle explained the relationship between the pressure and volume of a gas and then, together with Robert Hooke, came to the realization that a portion of the Earth's atmosphere was necessary for respiration. Approximately a century later, Joseph Priestley discovered oxygen, and Lavoisier then found that this gas was the constituent in air necessary for respiration and combustion. Lavoisier also realized that carbon dioxide and water were products of respiration.

In 1871, Paul Bert demonstrated that human subjects could avoid the altitude sickness to be encountered in rarefied atmospheres by use of additional oxygen. He also demonstrated that organisms could make various adjustments, such as increased hemoglobin concentration within the blood upon chronic exposure to a rarefied atmosphere.

Transportation to heights in our atmosphere may be accomplished by four methods. (1) Mountains may be climbed to several miles above sea level. (2) By taking advantage of the availability of gases which are lighter than air the buoyant force of a balloon may be utilized. (3) By the use of airfoils and power, the heavier-than-air airplane or glider may be launched. (4) Using the thrust provided by rapidly expanding materials in a closed space with directional opening, the rocket may be employed.

The first lighter-than-air balloon was developed by de Gusmao in Brazil in 1709; this balloon contained hot air. The first live cargo to be carried by a balloon rose to a height of 1500 feet in 1873, in a hot-air balloon developed by the Montgolfer brothers in France. In the same year and country, de Rozier made the first human ascent in a balloon, reaching a height slightly in excess of 300 feet. These two balloon flights demonstrated that that portion of the atmosphere which was beyond the immediate vicinity of the surface of land was safe for man to breathe. By 1932, balloons had ascended to a height of over 70,000 feet. The highest balloon ascent to date—to an altitude of 101,516 feet—is that made by Major David Simons of the U. S. Air Force in 1957.

The first airplane flight was performed by the Wright brothers in 1903. The theory basic to the design of their craft and all other successful winged airplanes dates back to the basic hydrodynamic principles first published by Daniel Bernoulli in 1738.

Rocketry

Early rocketry was discussed in the preceding section. Modern rocketry probably started in Russia in 1876 with the work of Tsiolkovsky concerning

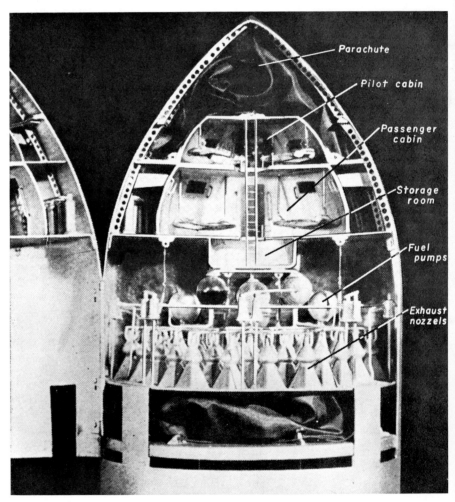

Figure 2-2. Early model of proposed space ship (Ley, 1961). This was based upon Oberth's designs and was employed for filming of the German motion picture, *Frau im Mond* (Girl in the Moon), in 1929.

the theoretical problems of rocketry as applied to space travel. Working independently in Germany, Oberth pursued comparable studies on the theoretical physics of rocketry (Fig. 2-2). Both men also devoted some consideration to the physiology and psychology of space flight. Modern work in experimental rocketry began in 1919 with the studies of Goddard in this country. Goddard developed the first rockets to be driven by liquid fuel (Fig. 2-3). Although largely neglected in this country, his work was continued by workers in Germany and Russia. No serious attention to the use of rocketry for space travel was evident in this country until the end of World War II.

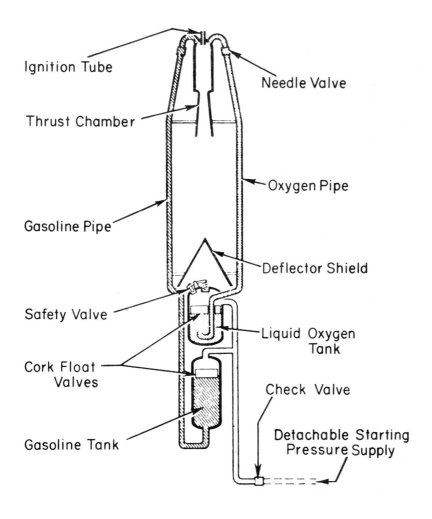

Figure 2-3. Goddard's liquid propellent rocket of 1926 (Maxwell, 1962).

TABLE 2-1. Abbreviated List of Animal Space Flights in Unmanned Suborbital and Orbital Flights, 1946-1962.*

Year	Investigator(s)	Animal Subject	Flight Profile
UNITED STATES			
1948	Henry et al.	Rhesus monkey— "Albert"	37-mile altitude in a captured V-2 rocket. Not recovered
1951	Henry et al.	Rhesus monkey, mice	236,000-ft. altitude in an Aerobee-2 rocket. Recovered
1950-54	Campbell et al.	Dogs, cats, hamsters, mice	Numerous balloon flights from 59,000 to 103,000 feet. Involved periods up to 22 hours at maximum altitude with successful recovery up to 6 days later
1955	Simons and Parks	Guinea pigs, mice	100,000 feet plus in balloons up to 24 hours. Recovered
1956-57	Simons, Haymaker et al.	Variety of animals	100,000 feet plus in several balloon flights. Some successful recoveries
1958	Van der Wal	Mice—"Wickie," "Laska" and "Benji"	1400 miles. None of the three flights were recovered
1958	Graybiel et al.	Squirrel monkey— "Old Reliable"	300-mile altitude over a 1300-mile distance via a Jupiter rocket. Not recovered
1959	Graybiel et al.	Rhesus monkeys— "Able" and "Baker"	300-mile altitude over a 1500-mile distance via a Jupiter rocket. Recovered
1959		Black mice	500 seconds of weightlessness via a Thor-Able rocket in Discoverer III. The Discoverer vehicle did not go into orbit and animals were lost
1959	Green et al.	Rhesus monkey— "Sam"	280,000-ft. altitude in Little Joe No 2. Recovered
1960	Green et al.	Rhesus monkey— "Miss Sam"	49,000 feet altitude in Little Joe No. 1-B. Recovered
1960	Clamann et al.	C-57 black mice	650-mile altitude over a 5000-mile range via Atlas RVX-2A. Recovered
1961	NASA, Aeromedical Lab Holloman AFB, NMex	Chimpanzee— "Ham"	156-mile altitude over a range of 414 miles via a Redstone booster, Mercury capsule. Recovered
1961	NASA, Aeromedical Lab Holloman AFB, NMex	Chimpanzee— "Enos"	2 earth orbits, 183-minute weightlessness at an apogee of 146 miles and a perigee of 99 miles. Atlas booster, Mercury capsule. Recovered

TABLE 2-1.   Continued

Year	Investigator(s)	Animal Subject	Flight Profile
SOVIET UNION			
1949-52	Galkin *et al.*	Nine dogs (three flown twice)	100-kilometer altitude in hermetically sealed cabins. Recovered
1953-56	Bugrov *et al.*	Twelve dogs (two at a time)	110-kilometer altitude in non-hermetic rocket compartments. Recovered
1957	Galkin *et al.*	Five dogs (some repeatedly)	200-212-kilometer altitude in hermetically sealed cabins. Recovered
1957	Chernov and Yakovlev	Dog—"Laika"	6 days of orbital flight at an apogee of 1038 miles and a perigee of 140 miles. Hermetically sealed cabin. Died on sixth day—Sputnik II disintegrated April 1958
1958		Dogs—"Belyanka" and "Pestraya"	450-kilometer altitude in hermetically sealed cabin. Recovered
1959		Dogs—"Otvazhnaya" and "- -" and a rabbit	Over 100 miles altitude. Recovered
1960		Dogs—"Belka" and "Strelka"— 21 black and 21 white mice	16 earth orbits (24 hours) via Sputnik V. First successful recovery of living creature from orbital flight
1960		Dogs—"Pchelka" and "Mushka"	16 earth orbits (24 hours). Spaceship destroyed during re-entry
1961		One dog, mice, guinea pigs and frogs	One earth orbit at an apogee of 249 kilometers and a perigee of 183 kilometers. Recovered
1961		Dog— "Lvetzdochka"	One earth orbit. Recovered
FRANCE			
1961		Rat—"Hector"	95-mile altitude in a capsule boosted by a Veronique rocket. Recovered
1963		Cat—"Felicette"	95-mile altitude in a capsule boosted by a Veronique rocket. Over 5-minute weightlessness. Recovered

* From Reynolds, H. H.: "Animals to Man in Space," as read November 18, 1964, at 3rd International Symposium on Bioastronautics and the Exploration of Space, at San Antonio, Texas, to be published by U. S. Air Force. The major source of information for this period was from Beischer and Fregley (1962).

Early Ventures into Space

Spectacular public and federal interest in rocketry and space travel began on October 4, 1957, when the first Soviet satellite, followed in short order by a second satellite, was launched. The latter vehicle carried a dog which remained alive for 6 days and which was the first Terrestrial animal to be subjected to prolonged exposure to little or no gravity. This constitutes the first biological study in the space environment unless we wish to consider the suborbital rocket studies in this country and Russia (Henry *et al.*, 1952, 1962; see Table 2-1). The first man to be placed in orbit was Yuri Gagarin in April of 1961. Since that time, several American and Soviet astronauts have orbited about the planet for flights lasting from hours to days.

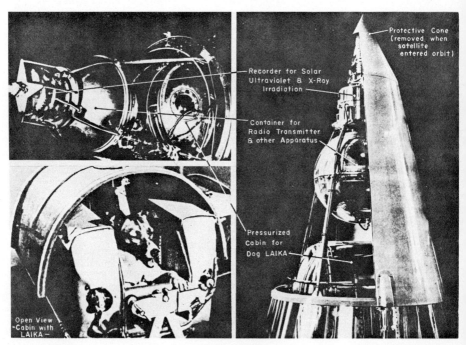

Figure 2-4. Russian Sputnik II, launched Nov. 3, 1957, with first living organism placed in orbit (*Soviet Union*, Dec. 1957, April 1958). The details of this experiment are available in a series of papers edited by Sisakyan. (Sisakyan and Yazdovskiy, 1962.)

The space trips thus far completed by man and other organisms represent triumphs for the engineers in delivering life into space and in protecting life from a harsh environment. Although various observations have been performed on man and other animals by both the Russians (Table 2-1; Sisakyan *et al.*, 1962; Sisakyan and Yazdovskiy, 1962) and the Americans (Table 2-3;

Cain, 1963; Mercury Summary Conference, 1963; White and Berry, 1964),
definitive, adequately controlled biological experiments have yet to be performed.[2] In essence, the only information established from biological experiments is that man (aided by existing methods of environmental control) can
survive in space for as long as 4 days (a dog for as long as 7 days) without
any obvious major detrimental effects which might hinder longer voyages.
Essentially all biological knowledge of use to what may be called "space biology" is based upon Earth-bound experiments which simulate some condition
anticipated in space.

Starting with Gagarin's historic flight of April 12, 1961, and concluding
with the first woman in space, Tereshkova, on June 16, 1963, Russia has
placed six one-man vehicles in orbit (Table 2-2). At this writing, the Soviets
have completed two flights with larger ships (Scanback, 1965). Launched
on October 17, 1964 to complete 16 orbits in 24.3 hours, Voskhod I carried
a three-man crew. They were Valdimir Komarov, the pilot; Konstantin
Feoktistov, the first trained scientist to visit space; and Boris Yegorov, the
first physician for such a voyage. The March 18, 1965, flight of Voskhod II
completed 17 orbits in 26 hours. Commanded by Pavel Belyayev, it carried
the first man, Alexi Lenov, protected only by his semi-rigid pressure suit,
to leave a space vehicle during flight for the famous "walk in space" (Fig. 2-5).
Physiological measurements were performed on all cosmonauts. Attempts
were made to perform experiments with other biological material. At the
present time, this series of experiments with the Russian vehicles obviously
represents the largest entry into and return from space of Terrestrial life.
Presumably, present Soviet vehicles contain a so-called "shirt-sleeve" environment with no need for space suits.

America initiated in 1961 and successfully concluded in 1963 its Mercury
Project (Table 2-3). This project involved four orbital flights by astronauts
confined in small, one-man capsules (Fig. 4-4) and the outlay of approximately $500,000,000. Although somewhat poorly controlled measurements
of the inflight electrocardiographs, blood pressure, body temperature, and
urine samples (together with pre- and post-flight medical examinations) were
performed, the primary purpose of the Mercury flights was not to collect
new scientific information; rather it was to pave the way for new manned
missions which might accomplish more scientific observations.

---

[2] There have been a number of exploratory experiments which might be interpreted
by a careless observer to imply that weightlessness can cause effects at the cellular
level. Space travel has been reported to cause mutations with fruit flies (Glembotskiy
and Parfenov, 1962). Arsen'yeva *et al.* (1962) report that histological disorders were
observed with mice in the bone marrow and spleen for 2 days following space flight;
there was sticking together of the chromosomes and possibly a disorder of the spindle
apparatus of certain cells. Petrukhin (1962) reported that histological observation of
the brain, liver, myocardium, spleen, and adrenal glands in mice and guinea pigs
yielded evidence of physiological stress. Katzberg (1963) reported faster growth for
human cancer cells and tissue culture. None of these publications described adequate
control conditions.

TABLE 2-2. Tabulation by Carlson (1964) of Soviet Manned Orbital Vostok Vehicles

Name	Vostok I	Vostok II	Vostok III	Vostok IV	Vostok V	Vostok VI
Launched	April 12, 1961	August 6, 1961	August 11, 1962	August 12, 1962	June 14, 1963	June 16, 1963
Payload weight	10,419 lbs.	10,408 lbs.	Possibly 15,000-20,000 lbs.	About 10,160 lbs.	About 10,160 lbs.	About 10,160 lbs.
Orbit time	89.1 min.	88.6 min.	88.3 min.	88.4 min.	88.4 min.	88.4 min.
Number of orbits	1	17	64	48	82	48+
Lifetime	Successful recovery 4-12-61	Successful recovery 8-7-61	Successful recovery 8-15-62	Successful recovery 8-15-62	Successful recovery 6-19-63	Successful recovery 6-19-63
Test subjects	Man (Gagarin)	Man (Titov) and other biological objects	Man (Nikolayev) and Drosophila, seeds, cancer cells	Man (Popovich) and Drosophila, seeds, cancer cells	Man (Bykovskiy) and flies	Woman (Tereshkova) and flies
Aims	1. Orbit first manned satellite	1. Study effects on human during prolonged space flight and return to Earth 2. Study man's ability to work during prolonged space flight	1. Study effects on man during prolonged flight 2. Study man's ability to work during space flight 3. Study effect of radiation on reproduction of Drosophila	1. Study effects on man during space flight 2. Study man's ability to work during space flight 3. Reproduction experiments on Drosophila	1. Study effects on man during space flight 2. Further biological investigations in sustained flight 3. Improve piloted spaceship systems	1. Compare effects of space flight on men and women 2. Continued study of effect of flight factors on human 3. New biomedical research

					4. Study possibility of space rendezvous	4. Improve systems of piloted spacecraft under conditions of simultaneous flight
Food and water	Ate only mashed food from tubes	Ate only mashed food from tubes	Ate food similar to regular meal. Had supplies sufficient for Moon trip	Ate food similar to regular meal. Had supplies sufficient for Moon trip	Ate individually prepared meals similar to regular meal. 1½ liters of water per day	Each day had 4 individually prepared, Earthlike meals and 1½ liters of water
Radiation instruments	1. Dosimeters 2. Thermoluminescent glasses	1. Dosimeters 2. Thermoluminescent glasses	1. Dosimeters 2. Nuclear photoemulsions 3. Scintillators	1. Dosimeters 2. Nuclear photoemulsions 3. Scintillators		
Radiation dosage	Average external dosage: .4–.6 mrad/orbit	Average external dosage: 8.4 mrad/day Inside dosage: .5 mrad/day (total inside dosage 60 mrad)	Total dosage: 62±5 tissue mrad (corrected from reading of 55 mrad)	Total dosage: 46±5 tissue mrad (corrected from actual reading of 41 mrad)	Total dosage: 35.40 mrad	Total dosage: 25 mrad
Physiological methods used for tests	1. Electrocardiography 2. Pneumography 3. Kinetocardiography	1. Electrocardiography 2. Pneumography 3. Kinetocardiography	1. Electrocardiography 2. Pneumography 3. Electro-oculography	1. Electrocardiography 2. Pneumography 3. Electro-oculography	1. Electrocardiography 2. Pneumography 3. Electro-oculography	1. Electrocardiography 2. Pneumography 3. Electro-oculography

TABLE 2-2. Continued

Name	Vostok I	Vostok II	Vostok III	Vostok IV	Vostok V	Vostok VI
			4. Electroencephalography 5. Cutaneous-galvanic responses 6. Kinetocardiography	4. Electroencephalography 5. Cutaneous-galvanic responses 6. Kinetocardiography	4. Seismography 5. Electroencephalography 6. Skin galvanic responses 7. Kinetocardiography	4. Seismography 5. Electroencephalography 6. Skin galvanic responses 7. Kinetocardiography
Cabin conditions	Pressure: 750-770 mmHg Humidity: 62-71% Temp: 19-20° C	Pressure: 740-760 mmHg Humidity: 30-70% Temp: 10-25° C	Pressure: 755-775 mmHg Humidity: 65-75% Temp: 13-26° C	Pressure: 755-775 mmHg Humidity: 65-75% Temp: 12-26° C %O_2 in air: 21%	Pressure: 775-780 mmHg Humidity: 40-65% Temp: 12-20° C %O_2 in air: 21%	Pressure: 754-770 mmHg Humidity: 34% Temp: 18-23.6° C %O_2 in air: 20%
Radiation protection	1. Carried anti-radiation medicine 2. Had protective shield	1. Carried anti-radiation medicine 2. Had protective shield	1. Carried anti-radiation medicine 2. Had protective radiation shielding	1. Carried anti-radiation medicine 2. Had protective radiation shielding	1. Carried anti-radiation medicine 2. Had protective shield	1. Carried anti-radiation medicine 2. Had protective shield
Exercise			Put head and feet on stationary object and flexed muscles	Put head and feet on stationary object and flexed muscles	1. Exercised to prepare for landing 2. Exercised with rubber stretcher 3. Controlled ship	1. Exercised to prepare for stress of landing

	1. No effect of specific factors endangering cellular structures and functions	1. Suspensions of *E. coli* 2. Lysogenic bacteria exposed to radiation	2. With Vostok 4, coordinated space flight 3. Nikolayev made medical observations	1. With Vostok 3, coordinated space flight 2. Popovich made medical observations 3. Drosophila reproduction experiments	1. Observations of Sun, Earth, Moon, constellations 2. Free from restraining straps for 1½ hrs per day	1. Reproductive system not damaged 2. Experiments on nervous system and cardiovascular system
Other experiments or results	1. Freed 1 hr. in weightless state; ate, wrote, steered spacecraft, retained working capacity 2. Some unusual sensations from weightlessness	[Drosophila re...]duction experiments	1. During weightlessness had good orientation, retained health and capacity to work 2. Drosophila reproduction occurred in weightless state 3. Freed from restraining straps for about 1 hr	1. Freed in weightless state for about 1 hr 2. Drosophila reproduction occurred in weightless state 3. Retained health, working capacity during weightlessness	1. Performed complex tasks while weightless 2. Slept 1½ hrs. while free from restraining straps 3. Study of human during prolonged weightlessness	1. Study of effect of weightlessness on woman 2. Comparison of weightlessness on man and woman 3. Slept well while free in weightless state
Respiration	16-26 cycles/min	4-28 cycles/min	10-18 cycles/min	10-20 cycles/min	15-24 cycles/min	16-22 cycles/min
Pulse	Awake 90-180 beats/min	Awake 80-156 beats/min Asleep 53-67 beats/min	Awake 60-120 beats/min Asleep 60-65 beats/min	Awake 60-130 beats/min Asleep 60 beats/min	Awake 60-106 beats/min Asleep 45-56 beats/min	Awake 64-82 beats/min Asleep 52-60 beats/min

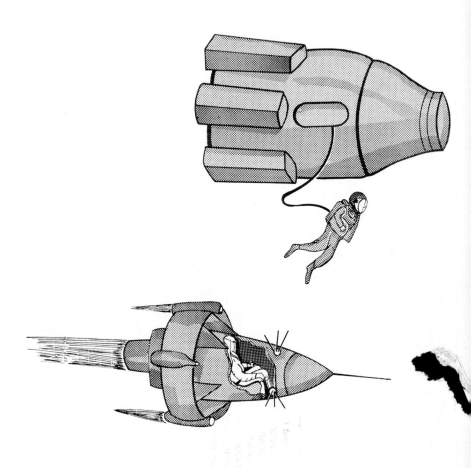

Figure 2-5. Probable appearance of Soviet space ship Vokhod II, with cosmonaut outside of ship, and a one-man Vostok space ship. (Modified from *Soviet Life*, June, 1965.)

The next American manned project was NASA's Gemini program (Fig. 4-4), which first carried men in a two-passenger capsule (on March 23, 1965). Piloted by Virgil Grissom, the first man to be rocketed twice into space, and co-piloted by John Young, this ship completed three orbits and was popularly known as the "Molly Brown." This was the first ship to have a manually controlled orbit. Future flights will last as long as 2 weeks and will be

TABLE 2-3. Flights of the Mercury Project

Approximate Duration	Passenger	Vehicle	Date
5 min (suborbital)	Unmanned	MR-1A	Dec. 19, 1960
5 min (suborbital)	Chimpanzee	MR-2	Jan. 31, 1961
5 min (suborbital)	A. B. Shepard	MR-3	May 5, 1961
5 min (suborbital)	V. I. Grissom	MR-4	July 21, 1961
3 hr (orbital)	Chimpanzee	MA-5	Nov. 29, 1961
4 hr, 15 min (orbital)	J. H. Glenn	MA-6	Feb. 20, 1962
4 hr, 39 min (orbital)	S. Carpenter	MA-7	May 24, 1962
9 hr (orbital)	W. Schirra	MA-8	Oct. 7, 1962
34 hr (orbital)	L. G. Cooper	MA-9	May 5-6, 1963

Modified from Cain, 1963.

intended to investigate rendezvous, and carry out other procedures necessary for lunar exploration. By 1968, the Air Force plans to use this capsule as a taxi vehicle to the Manned Orbiting Laboratory (MOL; see Fig. 2-6), which will be America's first space capsule intended specifically as a manned laboratory. With the Apollo vehicle, NASA plans to orbit the Moon by 1968 and place a man on its surface by 1970. Later, Apollo voyages will carry a scientist, probably a geologist, to the Moon. The Apollo project will cost an estimated $20,000,000,000.

Of less spectacular public interest but of perhaps more immediate significance to the biologist will be NASA's Bios (or Biosatellite) program. It will be this country's first extensive[3] space study intended specifically for biological investigation. Flights will be at 3-month intervals and will last for as long as 30 days. Satellites will carry a myriad of different organisms, including primates. The program is intended for the study of the effects of weightlessness, altered biological rhythms (in the absence of the Earth's 24-hour cycle), and altered susceptibility to radiation.

Before man actually sets foot on another planet, he will undoubtedly be preceded by automated capsules which will search for any conceivable extra-Terrestrial life (which might interact unfavorably with Terrestrial life). It has been predicted (Dryden, 1964b) that by 1980 man will have completed round trips to Mars (requiring 1.5 years of manned travel) and to Venus (requiring one year of manned travel). Dr. Dryden (Deputy Administrator, National Aeronautics and Space Administration) further predicts that "before the year 2000 unmanned probes will have scouted all the planets of the solar system."

---

[3] Although extensive, this program must, at the present time, be considered primarily an exploratory rather than a definitive study. The proposed flights will not have adequate controls (such as might be placed at 1 G in sufficiently large centrifuges [see pp. 156-171]) which will permit differentiation between weightlessness and the many other conditions to be encountered.

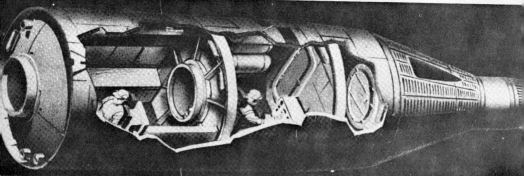

Figure 2-6. Preliminary concepts of Air Force's manned orbital laboratory. *(Astronautics and Aeronautics, June 1964.) (Missiles and Rockets, June 1964.)*

Bibliography and References

ARRHENIUS, S. (1908): "Worlds in the Making." Harper, New York.

ARSEN'YEVA, M. A., ANTIPOV, V. V., PETRUKHIN, V. G., L'VOVA, T. S., ORLOVA, N. N., IL'INA, S., KABANOVA, L. A., AND KALYAYEVA, E. S. (1962): Cytological and histological changes in the hematopoietic organs of mice under the influence of space flight on spaceships. *In* "Problemy Kosmicheskoy Biologii" [Problems of Space Biology] (N. M. Sisakyan and V. I. Yazdovskiy, eds.), *Vol. 2*, pp. 123-135. As translated from Russian in OTS:63-21437. U. S. Dept. of Commerce, Washington, D. C.

BALAKHOVSKIY, I. S., GAZENKO, O. G., GYURDZHIAN, A. A., GENIN, A. M., KOTOVSKAYA, A. R., SERYAPIN, A. D., AND YAZDOVSKIY, V. I. (1962): Results of experiments carried out in satellites. *In* "Problemy kosmicheskoy biologii" [Problems of Space Biology] (N. M. Sisakyan, ed.). *Vol. 1*, pp. 393-404. As translated from Russian in NASA TT F-174, National Aeronautics and Space Administration, Washington, D. C.

BEISCHER, D. E., AND FREGLY, A. R. (1962): "Animals and Man in Space. A Chronology and Annotated Bibliography through the Year 1960." 5 ONR Report No. ACR-64; USNSAM Monograph 5, Dept. of the Navy, Washington, D. C.

BERT, P. (1878): "Barometric Pressure." (As translated in 1943 by Hitchcock and Hitchcock.) College Book Co., Columbus, Ohio.

BRIGGS, M. H., AND MAMIKUNIAN, G. (1963): Venus: a summary of present knowledge. *J. Brit. Interplanetary Soc., Vol. 19,* No. 2, 45-52.

CAIN, C. C. (1963): Predictions on the biological effects of weightlessness. *In* "Physical and Biological Phenomena in a Weightless State" (Proceedings of the Second AAS Symposium on Physical and Biological Phenomena under Zero Gravity Conditions, January 18, 1963, Los Angeles) (E. T. Benedikt and R. W. Halliburton, eds.), pp. 318-349. *Vol. 14* of *Advances in the Astronautical Sciences.* American Astronautical Society, New York.

CALVIN, M. (1962): Communication from molecules to Mars. *AIBS Bulletin 7,* 29-43.

CAMPBELL, P. A. (1962): History and background of astronauts. *In* "Lectures in Aerospace Medicine," pp. 7-20. School of Aerospace Medicine, Brooks AFB, Texas.

CARLSON, L. D. (1964): The necessity for biological experimentation in space. *Advances in the Astronautical Sciences, Vol. 17,* pp. 1-20. Amer. Astronautical Society, New York.

DRYDEN, H. L. (1964a): NASA progress in life sciences. *In* "Lectures in Aerospace Medicine," pp. 13-25. Brooks AFB, Texas.

DRYDEN, H. L. (1964b): Footprints on the moon. *J. Natl. Geogr. Soc. 125,* No. 3, 356-401.

GAMOW, G. (1962): "Gravity." Doubleday and Co., Inc., Garden City, N. Y.

GAUER, O. H., AND ZUIDEMA, G. D. (1961): "Gravitational Stress in Aerospace Medicine." Little, Brown and Co., Boston.

GENERALES, C. D. J., JR. (1960): Space medicine and the physician. *N. Y. State J. of Med. 60,* 1741-61.

GENERALES, C. D. J., JR. (1963): Weightlessness: its physical, biological, and medical aspects. *In* "Medical and Biological Problems of Space Flight" (G. H. Bourne, ed.), pp. 123-187. Academic Press, New York.

GILBERT, D. L. (1965): Atmosphere and Oxygen. *The Physiologists 8,* 9-34.

GLEMBOTSKIY, YA. L., AND PARFENOV, G. P. (1962): The effect of space flight factors on some biological indices in insects. *In* "Problemy Kosmicheskoy Biologii" [Problems of Space Biology] (N. M. Sisakyan and V. I. Yazdovskiy, eds.), *Vol. 2*, pp. 104-122. As translated from Russian in OTS: 63-21437. U. S. Dept. of Commerce, Washington, D. C.

HANRAHAN, J. S., AND BUSHNELL, D. (1960): "Space Biology: The Human Factors in Space Flight." Basic Books, Inc., New York.

HENRY, J. P., BALLINGER, E. R., MAHER, P. J., AND SIMONS, D. G. (1952); Animal studies of the subgravity state during rocket flight. *J. Aviat. Med. 23,* 421-432.

HENRY, J. B., AUGERSON, W. S., BELLEVILLE, R. E., DOUGLAS, W. K., GRUNZKE, M. K., JOHNSTON, R. S., LAUGHLIN, P. C., MOSELY, J. D., ROHLES, F. H., VOAS, R. B., AND WHITE, S. C. (1962): Effects of weightlessness in ballistic and orbital flight. Aerospace Med. 33, 1056-1068.

"A History of Technology" (1954): Vol. I. (C. Singer, E. J. Holmyard and A. R. Hall, eds.). Oxford University Press, London.

KATZBERG, A. (1963): Observations on the possible effect of zero gravity on the mitotic process of human cells. Anat. Rec. 145, 248.

LEY, W. (1961): "Rockets, Missiles and Space Travel." The Viking Press, New York.

MAXWELL, W. R. (1962): Some aspects of the origins and early development of astronautics. J. Brit. Interplanetary Soc., Vol. 18, 415-425.

"Mercury Project Summary Including Results of the Fourth Manned Orbital Flight, May 15 and 16, 1963" (1963): NASA SP-45, National Aeronautics and Space Administration, Washington, D. C.

OPARIN, A. I. (1964): "The Chemical Origin of Life." Charles C Thomas, Springfield, Ill.

PARIN, V. V. (ed.) (1963): Aviatsionnaya i kosmicheskaya meditsina: materialy konferentsii 1963 goda [Aviation and Space Medicine: materials of the 1963 conference]. Moscow. (As abstracted in A. T. D. Press 3 [10] 1964, Library of Congress, Washington, D. C.)

PETRUKHIN, V. G. (1962): Pathological changes in the internal organs of animals under the influence of flight in spaceships. In "Problemy Kosmicheskoy Biologii" [Problems of Space Biology] (N. M. Sisakyan and V. I. Yazdovskiy, eds.), Vol. 2, pp. 136-147. As translated from Russian in OTS:63-21437. U. S. Dept. of Commerce, Washington, D. C.

"Scanback of the Soviet Manned Space Flight Program" (1965): anonymous ATD Report P-65-19, Library of Congress, Washington, D. C.

SINGER, C. (1959): "A Short History of Scientific Ideas to 1900." Oxford University Press, New York and London.

SISAKYAN, N. M., GAZENKO, O. G., AND GENIN, A. M. (1962): Problems of space biology. In "Problemy kosmicheskoy biologii" [Problems of Space Biology] (N. M. Sisakyan, ed.), Vol. 1, pp. 17-27. As translated from Russian in NASA TT F-174, National Aeronautics and Space Administration, Washington, D. C.

SISAKYAN, N. M., AND YAZDOVSKIY, V. I. (eds.) (1962): "Problemy Kosmicheskoy Biologii [Problems of Space Biology]," Vol. 2. Translated from Russian in OTS:63-21437. U. S. Dept. of Commerce, Washington, D. C.

SMITH, H. W. (1959): "From Fish to Philosopher." CIBA Pharmaceutical Products Inc., Summit, N. J.

UREY, H. C. (1959): Primitive planetary atmospheres and the origin of life. In "The Origin of Life on the Earth" (Oparin, A. I., Pasynskii, A. G., Braunshtein, A. E., and Paulouskaya, T. E., eds.), pp. 16-22. Pergamon Press, New York.

WHITE, S. C., AND BERRY, C. A. (1964): Résumé of present knowledge of man's ability to meet the space environment. Aerospace Med. 35, 43-48.

3

Entering Space

In Chapter 1, attention was called to the fact that there is no sharp line of demarcation between the atmosphere of the Earth and space itself. As we ascend higher and higher into the atmosphere, we move closer to the environment of space and further from the environment of the Earth. A number of gradual changes occur in the environment as ascension is made to a higher altitude (Fig. 3-1): (1) density and pressure of the atmosphere decrease, (2) intensity of radiation and the number of high-speed particles increase, (3) temperature alters radically, and (4) gravitational intensity decreases.

Atmospheric Pressure, Atmospheric Density, and Radiation

The atmosphere becomes more rarefied at higher and higher altitudes. Some of the effects of these reduced pressures are indicated in Figure 3-1 and will be discussed in Chapters 6 and 7. The pressure decrease is described by an exponential relationship which predicts that the pressure of the atmosphere halves with each increase in altitude of approximately 16,000 feet. Precise change in the pressure of a planet's atmosphere depends not only upon altitude h but also upon the molecular weight M of the gases in the atmosphere, the planet's gravitational field g, and the absolute temperature of the atmosphere.[1] On Mars, the atmospheric pressure at ground level is approximately one fiftieth the atmospheric pressure of Earth. Due to a gravity which is four tenths that of the Earth's, however, a more gradual drop in the pressure occurs on Mars than on the Earth (Fig. 3-1). Thus the pres-

---

[1] From the Maxwell-Boltzman distribution, one can show that the change of gaseous pressure can be predicted by the following equation:

$$\text{Log}_{10}\left(\frac{P_1}{P_0}\right) = \frac{Mgh}{2.3\,RT}$$

where R is the ideal gas constant, which is equal to 8.32×10^7 ergs per mole-degree. Temperature is expressed in degrees Kelvin and P_0 is the pressure at sea level. It is obvious from this relationship that pressure changes will depend heavily upon a planet's gravity and the temperature of the gas.

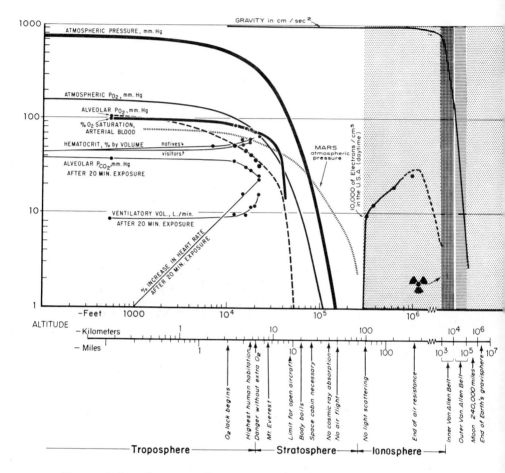

Figure 3-1. Changes with increasing altitude. Reports indicate lower values for pressure on Mars (Kaplan *et al.*, 1964, and Mariner 4).

sures at 50 miles above ground level would be approximately the same upon both Earth and Mars. At higher altitudes, pressure would be greater in the Martian atmosphere than at corresponding altitudes on Earth. This inability of smaller planets to hold atmospheric gases tightly against their surfaces explains why the smaller planets have lost a greater proportion of atmosphere into space.

At higher altitudes, the atmosphere becomes so thin[2] that it no longer

---

[2] Assuming constant composition and temperature, the density of a gas per unit of volume varies directly with pressure. This relationship is more accurately described in the following equation, which can be derived from the Ideal Gas Law:

$$D = \frac{MP}{RT}$$

Plate 3-1. Photograph from Mercury Capsule, MA-5, showing transition from the daylight haze at the horizon (as produced by atmospheric light scattering) to the darkness of space. (O'Keefe *et al.*, 1963.) (Official NASA photograph S-63-22497.)

absorbs radiations which are potentially dangerous to life. At heights in excess of 12 miles, the shorter wavelengths of ultraviolet light are abundant. Only the less active longer wavelengths of ultraviolet light are found on the Earth's surface. Beyond 25 miles of altitude, the intensity of primary cosmic ray particles increases markedly.

At altitudes in excess of 60 miles, the atmosphere becomes too sparse to accomplish light scattering and "darkness of space" exists (Plate 3-1). The daylight sky loses its bluish hue and is black like the nighttime sky. All objects are exposed either to the direct illumination of the Sun or are in the complete blackness of the heavy shadows which exist in the absence of scattered light.

The sparse atmosphere which exists at altitudes between 50 and 500 miles absorbs ultraviolet light of short wavelengths. This energy absorption by the particles of gas yields positive ions and free, negatively charged electrons. For that reason, this portion of the atmosphere is referred to as the "ionosphere."

Relatively light covering should prove adequate in protecting life from radiations found below altitudes of 400 miles. The radiations encountered at altitudes between 500 and 6,000 miles prove more formidable. This is the region of the inner Van Allen belt of trapped radiation. It contains electrons and penetrating, high-energy (10-100 Mev) protons. An extended stay in this area would require 4 centimeters of lead shielding. The intensity of radiation in this region is from 5 to 10 Roentgens per hour, which is a relatively intense radiation. Five Roentgens per year is considered the maximum safe radiation for a human being. It has been suggested that passage into space would require either a rapid flight through the inner belt or passage into space at either the North or South Pole, above which the Van Allen belts do not exist.

Although the outer Van Allen belt also consists of charged particles producing approximately 5 or 10 Roentgens per hour, these are lower energy (1 Mev protons) particles, which are less penetrating and therefore of less potential hazard for space travel. This belt extends from approximately 10,000 to 60,000 miles above the Earth.

The radiation belts will be discussed in more detail in Chapter 9. Both of these belts contain trapped electrons and protons. Those in the inner belt are believed to originate from the Earth's atmosphere as a result of interaction of the Sun's energy with the atmosphere. Those in the outer belt are believed to have originated directly from the Sun's radiation.

Some though not all of the other planets are believed to possess radiation belts. Both Earth and Jupiter are known to have such belts. They are believed to be absent from the Moon, from Venus, and from Mars.

The atmosphere shields the Earth's inhabitants from the radiations which are found in outer space. It removes 40 per cent of the visible light as well as practically all of the more dangerous radiations, which include the shortwave ultraviolet light and cosmic rays, together with the particulate radiations, such as electrons, protons, and ionized atoms. Beyond the radiation belts, the only radiation which is consistently of sufficient intensity to pose a problem is ultraviolet light. However, a space-suit covering should prove an adequate shield for this radiation. During solar flares, dangerous quantities of high-energy radiation are present. Solar flares are sudden, temporary, and intense outbursts of energy arising from small areas on the Sun's surface. The energy of the solar flares is so intense that, if maintained for a sufficiently long period of time, dangerous radiation could penetrate to within 50,000 feet of the Earth's surface. Further discussion of the radiations to be found in space and of their biological implications will be found in Chapter 9.

Temperature Changes and Frictional Heat

The temperature of the atmosphere gradually drops until an altitude of 8 miles is attained. From heights of 8 to 20 miles, the atmospheric temperature is almost constant for a given time and latitude. Although there is an increase in temperature beyond 20 miles, these changes are of little or no biological significance.

Temperature is defined in terms of the average kinetic energy of molecules. Although a few molecules of gas in the higher reaches of the atmosphere have high average kinetic energy, there are too few of them to take part in heat exchange between stationary objects. At sea level, air plays an important role in temperature exchange with other objects. This is accomplished by means of conduction and/or convection. But at the lower pressures found 20 miles above sea level, molecules are too sparse for these mechanisms to play an important role. At these heights, as in space itself, essentially all heat exchange occurs by radiation. For any given distance from the Sun, the temperature of a space vehicle could be increased by increasing the amount of dark, absorbent surface orientated toward the Sun's rays. Temperature could be decreased either by increasing the proportion of surface reflecting the Sun's rays or by increasing the proportion of dark, heat-radiating surface in the vehicle's shadow facing away from the Sun.

At speeds which will be necessary for space travel, frictional heat will be generated as a vessel passes through the atmosphere (see Figs. 5-1, 5-2). It is by this mechanism that the atmosphere protects the Earth's surface from all save the largest meteors. Most meteors are incinerated as they start to fall through the atmosphere. The same fate would befall a space vehicle not adequately decelerated before it penetrated deep into the atmosphere. For this reason, it is not possible to accelerate vehicles or missiles to speeds necessary for orbiting or escaping the planet until they have passed through the major part of the atmosphere. Most rockets possess several stages of acceleration, so that the velocity attained within the atmosphere will not permit frictional heat to destroy the rocket.

Some investigators believe that various organisms might have traveled to this planet from some other planet within a meteor. If so, such an organism had either a high tolerance to temperature or was imbedded deep within a meteor large enough to insulate it from intense frictional heat.

Gravitational Changes

The gravitational field between masses decreases inversely with the square of the distance from their centers of gravity. If the distance from the Earth's center is doubled by rising to an altitude of 4000 miles (8000 miles from the Earth's center), the gravity will have dropped to one quarter of its normal intensity. Rising to 8000 miles (12,000 miles from the center of the Earth) causes gravity to drop to one ninth of its normal value. After traveling a great distance from any mass, there will be little or no gravity present, and objects in these positions will be almost *weightless*.

Throughout the last several million years, the Earth's gravity has been almost constant. In leaving the Earth, man and other organisms will for the first time be placed in a truly different gravitational state. This altered gravitational state, plus the effective changes in gravity which operate during the accelerations necessary for moving a rocket, will have a pronounced influence upon various organisms. Biological implications of gravity and inertial forces are discussed in Chapter 8.

In leaving any planet, work must be done to counteract the force of gravity. The amount of work required will depend upon the mass of the object, the mass or gravity of a planet, the diameter of the planet, and the distance to which an object is removed from the planet. For planets of the same diameter, the amount of work required increases directly with the body's mass and the surface gravity of the planet.

In order to escape completely from a planet's gravity, an object must be lifted to such a distance that it is so far from the planet's center that the intensity of gravity at that location may be considered equal to zero (see pp. 225-230, eqs. 10-4 and 10-5). The velocity which an object must attain so that it will possess kinetic energy sufficient for escaping from a planet's gravity is referred to as the "escape velocity." The velocities and energies required for escape from various planets are shown in the nomogram of Figure 3-2. For the Earth, a velocity of 7 miles per second, with an energy expenditure of approximately 15,000 kilocalories for every kilogram of escaping payload, would be required. The nomogram indicates that in order to achieve this escape a total of approximately 5.5 kilograms of hydrogen and oxygen fuel would be required for every kilogram which escapes. The energy figures shown in the nomogram are somewhat misleading. They include only the requirements necessary for lifting the payload itself and do not include the requirements for lifting the fuel which is burned as the payload is accelerated upward, for lifting the earlier stages of the rocket casings, for maintaining static thrust, or for overcoming atmospheric friction. The total energy requirement would probably be more than one hundred-fold in excess of those listed (Clarke, 1960; see Fig. 10-2).

To be placed in orbit, an object must be moving at a velocity such that the centrifugal force of its rotation about the planet just equals the planet's gravitational field. The energy requirement for an orbit in the immediate vicinity of a planetary surface would ideally be one half of that required for escape;

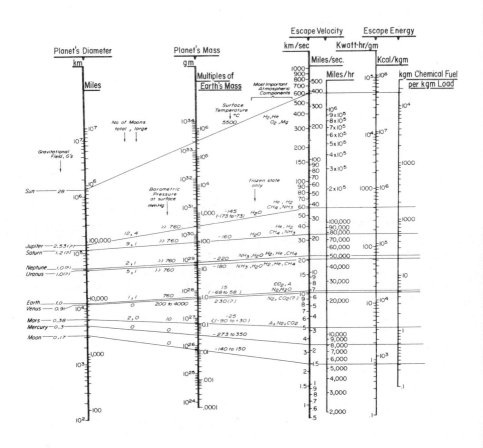

Figure 3-2. Physical properties of the planets. The first three vertical lines from left to right comprise a nomogram whereby escape velocities from planets of varying diameter and mass can be computed. The equivalent amount of energy required in accelerating payloads to these velocities is shown. Such values do not include the energy expenditures involved in accelerating the fuel itself. With Jupiter, Saturn, Neptune, and Uranus determinations of diameter and surface gravity must be qualified. Dense atmospheres prevent measurement of diameters for these bodies. Likewise temperatures for these planets might well be higher at the surface. Recent work (Kaplan et al., 1964) cites a lower barometric pressure for Mars.

and the orbital velocity itself would be less than the escape velocity by the square root of 2, so that the orbital velocity of a satellite orbiting quite close to the Earth would be approximately 5 miles per second. Tremendous rocket loads and energy expenditures are required to lift the smallest payload into space. The direct energy requirements for lifting a kilogram of material from the Moon are about one twentieth those for the Earth (Fig. 3-2). For this reason, a much smaller and simpler rocket would prove adequate in escaping from the Moon. The National Aeronautics and Space Administration plans in the first visit to our Moon (Project Apollo) to include such a rocket (Fig. 4-4). If the material for space travel can be manufactured from minerals found on the Moon, extensive exploration in the rest of the Solar System would undoubtedly involve the establishment of a large lunar colony. The Moon would serve as a principal terminal for travel to and from the various parts of the Solar System.

The energy requirements for escape from some of the larger planets are many-fold greater than those for the Earth. Thus, a round trip to the surface of such bodies is presently not under consideration.

Other Planets and the Moon

None of the other bodies in our Solar System is believed to possess surface conditions favorable to the type of life with which we are familiar.[3] None is believed to have adequate concentrations of oxygen. For this reason, containers in the form either of large pressurized chambers or space suits would be necessary in providing an adequate gaseous environment when man visits another part of the Solar System. Certain properties of these bodies are indicated in Figures 3-2 and 3-3.

Before successful manned landings can be attempted on any heavenly body, it is first necessary to have more detailed information concerning the surface conditions of these bodies. For planets possessing vast atmospheres (Jupiter, Saturn, Uranus, Neptune), extensive cloud covers (Venus), and/or remoteness (Pluto), surface conditions can only be surmised. For other bodies possessing no atmosphere (the Moon and Mercury) or a transparent atmosphere (Mars), certain information regarding the temperature and gross topography is available. Adequate information concerning the exact nature and texture of the surface or crust of these bodies will probably be first relayed to us by unmanned probes (such as Ranger 7 and Mariner 4).

The Moon is too small to hold a significant atmosphere. Although the interior composition of the Moon and the planets of the Solar System is unknown, it is generally agreed that the Moon possesses a barren surface which experiences temperatures varying from $-140°$ C (at the height of lunar darkness at the Equator) to $+150°$ C (at the height of lunar illumination at the Equator). To escape these extremes of surface temperatures, space

---

[3] This does not eliminate the possibility, however, that some organism may dwell beneath the surface, where conditions of oxygen supply, moisture, and temperature might be more favorable.

stations, if they are to be built on the Moon, will probably be buried beneath the surface in tunnels or caves.

When viewed through a telescope, the lunar surface is pockmarked with

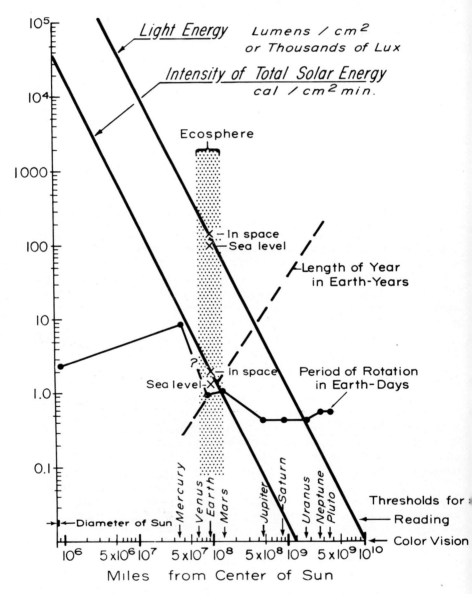

Figure 3-3. Changes with increasing distances from the Sun.

craters. There are also black areas called "seas" or "maria," and mountain ranges. The craters, which are believed to have been caused either by volcanic activity or by meteor bombardment, have diameters ranging from a few feet up to 150 miles, with rims as high as 20,000 feet. The mountains reach altitudes of 30,000 feet and are not accompanied by the valleys (formed by the action of running water) characteristic of Terrestrial formations. The "maria" (which, centuries ago, due to misinterpretation by astronomers, were

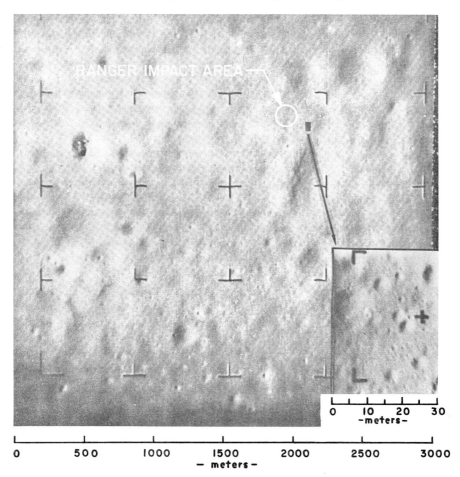

Figure 3-4. Pictures of lunar surface photographed by Ranger 7 immediately before impact 6:25 A.M., P. D. T., July 31, 1964. (Courtesy Jet Propulsion Laboratory, Calif. Inst. Tech.) Larger photo is from 6000 meters above surface and shows craters as small as 10 meters in diameter. Smaller photo is from 300 meters showing craters as small as one meter. Area shown in these photographs lies in a small mare lying between the craters Tyco and Copernicus.

believed to be true seas) are relatively flat surfaces and are generally thought to be beds of lava, though some observers regard them as organic matter laid down by ancient seas which might actually have existed during earlier geologic history.

Until the summer of 1964, there was some concern that the Moon might be covered by thousands of feet of dust which would bury any expedition attempting to land on its surface. The exact nature of the lunar crust is not known. Astronomical observations (of the temporal pattern of heat or infra-red emission, light scattering, radio emission, and radar reflection) suggest a consistency either of dust or porous rock (Gold, 1964a). Gold contends that, due to outgassing (in the near vacuum of the Moon's surface) and due to condensation of residual heat, any dust would be fused into a "crunchy" material. Pictures transmitted from Ranger 7 (as it descended to the lunar surface in the summer of 1964; Fig. 3-4) indicate that there is no thick layer of loose dust (which would have otherwise obscured those craters no wider than 2 or 3 feet) and that there are no large boulders which might endanger a soft rocket landing (Bozajian, 1965).

Mercury is so close to the Sun that its weak gravity has been unable to retain an atmosphere. The same side of the planet always faces the Sun. The dark side of Mercury has a temperature of nearly absolute zero, while the sunlight side has a temperature of approximately 350° C at the Equator. Any manned landing would probably be attempted in the areas of transition between light and darkness, where more favorable temperatures are anticipated. Astronomers summarize what is known of this planet's topography by stating that in appearance it is quite similar to the Moon.

Venus is still a planet of mystery. Its atmospheric pressure has been estimated at from 0.3 to 5 times that of the Earth. Although oxygen is probably not a major atmospheric gas, we do not know if gases other than carbon dioxide are major constituents (Briggs and Manikurian, 1963). This planet hides beneath a layer of clouds or dust of unknown composition, which does not permit measurement of period of rotation or surface temperature. At one time, Venus was believed to be the Earth's sister planet, with vast oceans of water under a covering of mist. Now many scientists believe that the planet is a hot (300° C at the surface and −20° C in the upper atmosphere), dry, barren, dust-shrouded body. If life comparable to our green plants existed on Venus, the carbon dioxide found in appreciable amounts in its atmosphere would have been converted into oxygen and carbon compounds. It has been suggested that Venus might be convertible to a habitable planet (see page 286) by placing green plants high in the atmosphere (where the temperature is less extreme), thereby producing oxygen and removing carbon dioxide which is believed by some scientists to be responsible for the "greenhouse" effect that retains so much of the planet's radiant heat.

Though far from hospitable, Mars presents what is likely to be the environment which most nearly resembles the Earth's. To the naked eye, Mars presents an orange color; when viewed through a telescope, the planet is seen to be composed primarily of large, red areas, with some dark areas. Although it is now recognized that there are no open bodies of water, these dark areas were once regarded as seas. Seasonal color variation of these dark areas (proceeding as the summer progresses not from equator to pole, as on the Earth, but from pole to equator) has supported the conjecture that life exists there. The red areas are thought to be vast deserts composed, possibly, of iron compounds, such as limonite ($Fe_2O_3 \cdot 3H_2O$) or rhyolite (a mixture of various silicon compounds including SiO_2 and $NaAlSi_3O_8$; Smoluchowski, 1965; Kuiper, 1952).

Polar caps apparently contain most of the free water which exists upon the surface of the planet. The release of some of this water during the summer is believed to cause the seasonal changes observed in the dark areas. The existence of ice or water beneath a frozen topsoil has been suggested (Strughold, 1963). Another potential source for water might be the *bound* water in limonite.

For a number of years, many faint lines across this planet had been reported, but most could not be documented photographically. Inability to photograph these "canals" is not surprising.[4] Turbulence within our own atmosphere will not permit adequate resolution of an image for a long enough time to be photographed with the amount of light from Mars and the speed of existing photograph emulsions.

The atmosphere of Mars has a surface density of approximately one fiftieth that of the Earth.[4] Nitrogen is the primary constituent, and there is little or no oxygen. The pressure is sufficiently low that a full-pressure suit would be required of any human visitor (see Chapter 6). Nonetheless, experiments have been performed which demonstrate that bacterial cells will grow in the temperatures and atmospheric conditions believed to occur on Mars.

As a planet becomes more distant from the Sun, the intensity of light and other radiation from the Sun decreases[5] (Fig. 3-3). In the region from Venus to Mars, the intensity of light is such that appreciable photosynthesis would be possible, and radiant heat is of sufficient intensity to permit the existence of liquid water (the primary solvent for Terrestrial life). As a result, this region of the Solar System, which lies between 60 and 150 million miles from the Sun, is sometimes referred to as the "ecosphere." The use of systems which contain algae for the purpose of recycling oxygen and food from the

---

[4] During preparation of this manuscript, estimates of pressure on Mars changed from 75 mm Hg to 19 mm Hg (Kaplan *et al.,* 1964) and then to 10 mm Hg (Mariner 4 results as released by news media and Leighton *et al.,* 1965). Mariner 4 results were not obscured by the Earth's atmosphere but did not confirm the presence of "canals." It showed a crater-scarred surface devoid of any evidence of erosion effects which might have indicated that bodies of water or a denser atmosphere once existed there.

[5] When intensity is expressed in energy per unit of area but not if expressed in energy per unit of area per unit solid angle.

carbon dioxide expired from animals should prove feasible in space stations or in colonies within the ecosphere. The energy for this purpose will be available from sunlight. The three planets—Venus, Earth, and Mars—are said to have oxidizing atmospheres. They contain oxygen in either a free or combined form. They also contain sufficient quantities of carbon dioxide for the growth of green plants. This should simplify the logistics of supplying food to individuals stationed in this region of the Solar System.

The planets beyond Mars are colder and, with the exception of Pluto, larger than the inner ones. The lower temperatures cause the molecules of atmospheric gas to possess slower thermal motion. Due to the planetary masses, greater energy would be necessary for molecules to escape from the planets' gravity. As a result, these planets have been able to retain atmospheres, the density and pressure of which are tremendous as compared to those on the Earth's surface. Lighter gases also remain in the atmospheres. Oxygen is believed to exist within these atmospheres only in the frozen state. The predominate gas is hydrogen. These dense atmospheres, consisting of hydrogen, helium, methane, and ammonia, are of the type which must have existed upon the Earth before the major portion of the lighter elements were lost to space. Organisms which might conceivably exist and multiply on these planets would by necessity be greatly different from those found on Earth.

Other Solar Systems

In order to find a planet which is wholly hospitable to man, a voyage beyond our solar system is necessary. There are countless billions of stars in our heavens. Although there is no direct evidence of Earth-like planets orbiting about other stars, astronomers believe that many stars have their own system of planets. Estimates have been made that 6 per cent or approximately 10^{18} stars possess planets comparable to the Earth (see Chapter 11).

The present state of our sciences and technology is such that a voyage beyond the reaches of our Solar System appears to be out of the question. The nearest star is a distance of 4 light-years. In other words, a vehicle traveling at the speed of light (which is presently a theoretical limit for the velocity of any body) would require 4 years to arrive at the star and another 4 years for a return trip. Most of the stars are much further away. Some of the technical difficulties to be encountered in approaching the speed of light have been recently reviewed by von Hoerner (1962). Limitations are imposed both by man's ability to withstand the prolonged acceleration necessary in arriving at these high velocities and also by the weight limitations of adequate rockets (see page 228). Trips to most parts of the galaxy would require a period of generations.

Intriguing distortions of elapsed time are predicted for the occupants of star ships. It can be shown from Einstein's Theory of Special Relativity that time is shorter for objects moving at nearly the speed of light than it is for an observer who remains stationary. Von Hoerner[6] has computed that an individual could leave the Earth, travel to a star which is a distance of 16 light years away, and then return after experiencing a total time lapse and aging of 12 years. If an astronaut were a very young man when he left on the voyage, he would still be relatively young when he returned. The same would not be true for the friends and relatives whom he left behind. For them, a period of 42 years would have elapsed. If this astronaut decided on a more distant voyage to a star 750 light years distant, he would return 27 years later to a civilization which might be vastly different, for a period of 1600 years would have elapsed on Earth. The reader will note that elapsed time is greater than that required for travel of light; the voyage would require time for acceleration toward the speed of light in addition to that for actual travel near the speed of light.

In order to visit the distant stars, one of three alternatives is necessary: (1) a vehicle capable of maintaining a civilization over a number of generations, (2) a practical condensed time scale, or (3) some sort of suspended animation. Techniques have been developed whereby various single-celled organisms as well as the mammalian eggs and sperm can be preserved for long periods of time by storage at extremely low temperatures (see page 82). Although the dream exists that living men can be similarly preserved during extensive voyages, science has not yet reached the point where the theoretical possibility of such an achievement can be evaluated.

Unless unexpected discoveries occur in physics and biology, the dates of such interstellar journeys become too remote to justify consideration. Visits to neighboring planets may offer a more than adequate challenge to the men and resources of the next century.

Bibliography and References

ALTMAN, P. L., GIBSON, J. F., JR., AND WANG, C. C., compilers. (1958): "Handbook of Respiration" (D. S. Dittmer and R. M. Grebe, eds.). WADC Technical Report 58-352. ASTIA Document No. AD-155823. Wright Air Development Center, Wright-Patterson AFB, Ohio.

ARMSTRONG, H. G. (1961): "Aerospace Medicine." Williams and Wilkins Co., Baltimore.

BAKER, R. H. (1947): "Introduction to Astronomy." 3rd ed. rev. D. Van Nostrand Co., Inc., New York.

BOZAJIAN, J. (1965): Simulation and structural dynamics of spacecraft during lunar landing. *In* "Proc. of Conf. on Role of Simulation in Space Technology," *Engineering Extension Series Circular No. 4, Part D,* Va. Poly. Inst., Blacksburg.

BRIGGS, M. H., AND MAMIKUNIAN, G. (1963): Venus: a summary of present knowledge. *J. Brit. Interplanetary Soc. 19,* 45-52.

---

[6] Von Hoerner has made two basic assumptions in his calculations. First, he has assumed that for long trips the amount of acceleration the astronaut could tolerate would be 980 cm per sec^2, which would have the same effect upon an individual as the Earth's gravity. Von Hoerner's second assumption is that the Special Theory of Relativity is applicable to conditions which do not involve constant acceleration. Visiting and returning from a distant star involve a changing acceleration. Physicists have thus far been unable to rule upon the validity of this second assumption.

BUCKHEIM, R. W., and THE STAFF OF THE RAND CORP. (1959): "Space Handbook: Astronautics and Its Applications." Modern Library Paperbacks, Random House, New York.

CLARKE, A. C. (1960): "Interplanetary Flight." Harper & Brothers, New York.

GOLD, T. (1964a): Structure of the lunar surface. *In* "Lectures in Aerospace Medicine," pp. 240-271. USAF School of Aerospace Medicine, Brooks AFB, Texas.

GOLD, T. (1964b): Ranger moon pictures: implications. *Science 145,* 1046-1048.

KAPLAN, L. D., MÜNCH, G., AND SPINRAD, H. (1964): An analysis of the spectrum of Mars. *Astrophys. J. 139,* 1-15.

KELLOGG, W. W. (1961): The upper atmosphere as observed with rockets and satellites. *In* "Lectures in Aerospace Medicine" (Paper No. 6). School of Aviation Medicine, Brooks AFB, Texas.

KOELLE, H. H., ed. (1961): "Handbook of Astronautical Engineering." McGraw-Hill Book Co., Inc., New York.

KUIPER, G. P. (1952): "The Atmosphere of the Earth and Planets." Univ. of Chicago Press, Chicago.

LEIGHTON, R. B., MURRAY, B. C., SHARP, R. P., ALLEN, J. D., AND SLOAN, R. K. (1965): Mariner IV photography of Mars: initial results. *Science 149,* 627-630.

O'KEEFE, J. A., DUNKELMAN, L., SOULES, S. O., HUCH, W. F., AND LOWMAN, P. D., JR. (1963): Observations of space phenomena. *In* "Mercury Project Summary Including Results of the Fourth Manned Orbital Flight May 15 and 16, 1963," pp. 327-347. NASA SP-45. National Aeronautics and Space Administration, Washington, D. C.

RUDAUX, L., AND DE VAUCOULEURS, G. (1959): "Larousse Encyclopedia of Astronomy." Prometheus Press, New York.

SHOEMAKER, E. M. (1964): The geology of the moon. *Scientific American 211*(6), 38-47.

SMOLUCHOWSKI, R. (1965): Is there life on Mars? *Science 148,* 946-947.

STRUGHOLD, H. (1960a): Biophysics of the space environment. *In* "Lectures in Aerospace Medicine" (Paper No. 2). School of Aviation Medicine, Brooks AFB, Texas.

STRUGHOLD, H. (1960b): Celestial bodies—II. Planetary ecology (astrobiology). *In* "Lectures in Aerospace Medicine" (Paper No. 5). School of Aviation Medicine, Brooks AFB, Texas.

STRUGHOLD, H. (1963): The ecological profile of Mars: bioastronautical aspect. *In* "Lectures in Aerospace Medicine," pp. 433-447. School of Aerospace Medicine, Brooks AFB, Texas.

TOMBAUGH, C. W. (1960): Celestial bodies—III. Moon, Mars, Venus. *In* "Lectures in Aerospace Medicine" (Paper No. 6). School of Aviation Medicine, Brooks AFB, Texas.

TOMBAUGH, C. W. (1961): Celestial bodies—II. The Moon. *In* "Lectures in Aerospace Medicine" (Paper No. 4). School of Aviation Medicine, Brooks AFB, Texas.

VON HOERNER, S. (1962): The general limits of space travel. *Science 137,* 18-23.

4

Overcoming the Problems of the Space Environment

Life on Earth exists and adapts to a myriad of environmental conditions. The extremes within which the adaptations occur must be regarded as very narrow in comparison to the conditions to be expected in other parts of the Solar System (Figs. 4-1 and 3-2). The ability of man to adjust to a new situation depends upon three factors: (1) the environment itself, (2) the adjustments which can be made to modify the environment to make it more endurable, and (3) the adjustments which can be made by the organism to enable it to withstand the environment (Fig. 4-2). The nature, source,

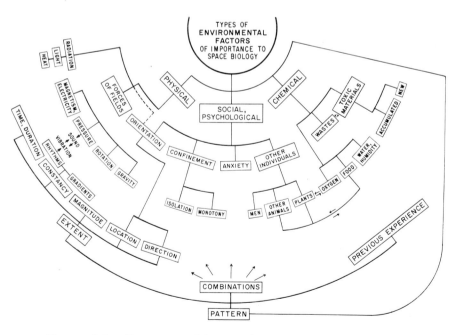

Figure 4-1. Environmental factors of importance to space biology.

consequences, and possible technical or physiological modifications of effects for a few of the more significant adversities of the space environment are outlined in Table 4-1.

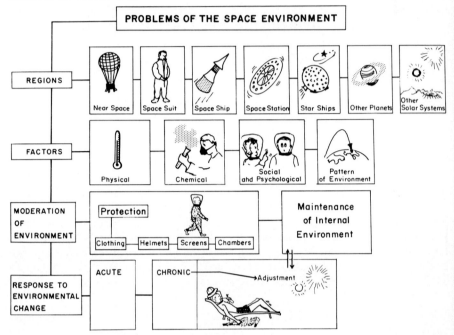

Figure 4-2. Categories of problems associated with the space environment.

Regions and Factors of the Space Environment

Certain environmental changes occur as we approach space (Fig. 3-1). The most familiar is the decrease in ambient temperature at higher altitudes (see Chapter 5; Table 4-1-B). Man has successfully adjusted to this situation by wearing heavier clothing. Oxygen lack at higher altitudes is also well known (see Chapter 7). For 50 years, man has had available for his use equipment whereby supplies of oxygen permit activity at altitudes where the ambient oxygen concentration is below that necessary to maintain activity (Table 4-1-A). Man has also utilized the pressure suit (Fig. 4-3) for altitudes above 9½ miles, where the pressure becomes too low to sustain life (see Chapter 6).

The space ships which are in use today are little more than such pressurized chambers mounted on rocket engines (Fig. 4-4). Indirectly, they serve another function. The metals which form the chamber also protect man to some extent from the hostile environment of radiation in space (Table 4-1-G; see Chapter 9). Heat shields are also utilized to protect him from the intense heat generated as the ship leaves and returns to the atmosphere. A particular aspect of the environment is still beyond ready control.

Figure 4-3. Prototype of pressure suit proposed for lunar landing during project Apollo. Not shown is a 23-kg life-sustaining unit (Fig. 10-6) which attaches as a back-pack. That unit will supply pure oxygen from a pressure tank at ¼ atmosphere, and will remove carbon dioxide and metabolic heat over a 4-hour period. Gas exits to the unit from the right side of the helmet under the ear. Finished suit will be covered with aluminized material to reflect radiant heat. (Eckman and Helvey in *Astronautics and Aerospace Eng.* Nov. 1963, p. 21.)

TABLE 4-1.   Some of the Potential Hazards to Man in the Hostile Environment of Space*

Hazard	Source or Cause of Hazard	Possible Effect
A. Low pressure	1. Vacuum of space 2. High cost of carrying supplies for artificial atmosphere in a space ship 3. Explosive decompression as a result of accident or meteor puncture	1. *Direct Effects:* A sudden decrease can cause bends due to partial pressure of inert gases (particularly nitrogen) in body fluids and tissues, earache (due to uncompensated air pressure within middle ear acting on ear drum), abdominal pain (due to uncompensated pressures of intestinal gases). Sufficiently low pressures will cause desiccation or boiling of body tissues (due to uncompensated vapor pressure of water)
		2. *Oxygen lack* eventually results in inadequate quantities of this gas being delivered to the metabolizing cells. When anoxia is mild but chronic all body tissues are affected with impaired ability for physical activity together with general fatigue or tiredness, nausea, and possible headaches. Acute anoxia profoundly influences cells of the central nervous system with visual impairment and a behavior characteristic of alcohol intoxication (giddiness, poor judgment, and poor neuromuscular coordination). Sufficient oxygen lack results in unconsciousness or even arresting of breathing and of heart action

* This information has been gathered from a number of sources; however, the primary source for action of and adjustment to these conditions as they naturally exist on Earth has been "Handbook of Physiology," 1964. The reader should also be aware of two pertinent publications which became available after this table was prepared: Schmidt and Lambertsen (1965) presented a review of various speculative drug administrations which might prove useful in attenuating the adversities of these hazards; Sisakyan (1965) reviewed recent Soviet studies of adaption to the space environment.

Methods of Artificial Protection or of Temporary Physiological Adjustment	*Possible Conditioning or Procedure for Long-Term Protection*	*Examples of Conditioning or Adjustment Which Occur to Organisms on Earth*
a. Pressure suits and space cabin b. Self-sealing material lining the walls of a space cabin to correct meteor puncture	a. Maintain pressure within cabin at a lower than sea level condition (with normal oxygen partial pressure but devoid of nitrogen) so that in event of decompression the uncompensated pressures with the body would not be so drastic b. Permit only gradual changes in ambient pressure when leaving or entering a chamber c. Surgical puncture of ear drum	Workers experienced in working at high pressures (such as deep-sea divers and caisson workers) develop greater tolerance to decompression but the mechanism of this adjustment is unknown

a. Emergency supplies of O_2 in the event of accident to space cabin or regular O_2 source
b. Reflexes initiated by low O_2 or high CO_2 partial pressures in the blood will result in:
  1) More release of epinephrine and norepinephrine from the adrenal medulla, enhancing heart action and blood pressure (permitting more efficient distribution of available O_2 by the blood)
  2) Faster and deeper respiration
  3) Increased heart activity due to neural control
	a. Carrying O_2 sources in space vehicle
	b. Reduced activity (which could result in deconditioning in long flights)
	c. Acclimate astronauts to low oxygen tension by chronic exposure to same. This has also been suggested as a procedure to prevent the adverse effect of reduced activity (Lamb, 1965)
		a. After a few days, men exposed to high altitude demonstrate a higher concentration of red blood cells and hemoglobin. This (together with the adjustment of circulating concentration of CO_2 toward a lower level) permits a greater oxygen-carrying capacity of the blood
		b. Tissues from some experimental animals exposed to low oxygen pressures demonstrated ability to utilize lower concentrations of oxygen, greater myoglobin concentration (for the storage of oxygen) and enhanced anaerobic metabolism. (Barbashova, in *Handbook of Physiology,* 1964.) Certain other characteristics appear to be of a genetic nature

TABLE 4-1. Continued

Hazard	Source or Cause of Hazard	Possible Effect
B. Temperature extremes		
1. High temp.	Sunlight, body heat, machinery and rocket operation, air friction (particularly during re-entry)	a. Decreased cardiovascular tolerance (orthostatic hypotension) to gravity presumably as a result of lowered blood volume (plasma fraction) attributable to water loss and as a result of peripheral vasodilatation
		b. Muscular cramps (heat cramps) believed attributable to the electrolyte imbalance associated with salt loss
		c. If tissue temperatures rise drastically, a progressive chemical destruction of cellular constituents pursues with death occurring after irreversible destruction of neural and cardiac tissue

Methods of Artificial Protection or of Temporary Physiological Adjustment	Possible Conditioning or Procedure for Long-Term Protection	Examples of Conditioning or Adjustment Which Occur to Organisms on Earth
		c. Natives to high altitudes, such as Indians of the Peruvian Andes, also display larger chests with greater lung capacity; some high altitude animals, such as the llama, also possess hemoglobin with a greater oxygen-binding capacity than is found with most low-altitude animals.
a. Adequate remoteness from Sun's rays by means of distance or shadows b. Thermal insulation from such hot surfaces as the forward portion of a space vehicle during re-entry with the use of heat shields c. Pumping of cool gases through a space suit d. Dilation of arteries leading to the body surface with a constriction of deeper arteries so that more heat can be transferred from the body	a. High fluid intakes (a potential difficulty in small space vehicles with low pay loads) b. Consumption of salt tablets c. General good physical conditioning. Some physical conditioning should be necessary during flight as problem of weightlessness and confinement are thought capable of contributing to orthostatic hypotension d. Inactivity would reduce production of body heat but could cause dangerous deconditioning e. Increasing the ratio of radiating to absorbing surfaces f. Chronic exposure to heat preceding unavoidable conditions of high temperature	a. Greater fluid and salt retention by the kidney coupled with lower salt concentration in the sweat of heat-conditioned men b. Tropical men have a slower metabolism primarily because of intentionally slower voluntary movements c. There is a tendency for tropical men to possess a greater surface to volume ratio thus permitting better heat dissipation. (The average native African Negro is supposedly lankier and less obese than the average Eskimo)

TABLE 4-1. Continued

Hazard	Source or Cause of Hazard	Possible Effect
2. Low temp.	Remoteness from Sun	a. Freezing of extremities
		b. If body temperature drops, the rate of breathing drops more drastically than metabolic rates with a resulting anoxia to the tissues
C. Gravitational extremes		
1. High gravity	Short bouts of simulated high gravity during acceleration and deceleration (at re-entry) of rockets. Visits to regions of actual high gravity are not likely in the near future but return from weightlessness might have a similar effect	Acute exposure if not so intense as to cause direct mechanical damage will cause impairment of circulation (particularly venous return) and of breathing

Methods of Artificial Protection or of Temporary Physiological Adjustment	*Possible Conditioning or Procedure for Long-Term Protection*	*Examples of Conditioning or Adjustment Which Occur to Organisms on Earth*
a. Appropriate heating of cabin or satisfactory garments b. Shivering and other movements to increase metabolism c. Constriction of blood vessels leading to body surface	a. Adequate temperature control of the space capsule is the only presently available solution b. The eventual use of artificial hibernation (which at the present time is not adequately understood) has been suggested c. Increasing ratio of absorbing to radiating surface	a. Some primitive people, such as the Eskimos, are able to tolerate greater cold. However, this is largely due to heavy clothing and a diet (high protein) which permits a greater basal output of body heat. The control of peripheral circulation is more localized thus permitting heat (which would otherwise be conserved by the body) to reach particular parts of the body surface when necessary b. Some insects possess glycerin in the body fluids to act as an "antifreeze-like" substance
a. Corset-like devices ("Anti-G-Suits") to prevent venous pooling b. Assuming supine position to reduce height of blood columns c. Water immersion has been suggested for buoyant support against gravity but would add too much to the required size for a payload d. Voluntary muscular contraction to enhance "muscular pumping" and return of venous blood e. Release of norepinephrine to increase vascular constriction combined with faster pumping by the heart thus maintaining high pressure	a. Physical exercise particularly during weightlessness b. Conditioning cardiovascular system during weightlessness by means of pressure-cuff occlusion of veins c. Centrifugation of subjects to prevent deconditioning while weightless d. Injection of norepinephrine to deconditioned individuals upon re-exposure to high gravity e. Intake of large quantities of water (which might be in short supply) would be a good preventative measure against kidney stones anticipated during weightlessness	a. The cardiovascular system of erect men can perform better against the Earth's normal gravity after several hours of standing or sitting than after bed rest. Prolonged bed rest can even result in fainting shortly after arising from bed b. Added weight support causes animals to develop thicker bones

TABLE 4-1.   Continued

Hazard	Source or Cause of Hazard	Possible Effect
2. Low gravity or weightlessness	Remoteness from large heavenly bodies or counterbalancing natural gravity by oppositely directed artificial gravity (as is the case in orbital flight)	Although this has not been adequately investigated in any well-controlled experiment, indirect evidence would strongly suggest a general deconditioning of the vascular system (with lower norepinephrine levels and smaller blood volume), muscular, and skeletal systems. This is not likely to cause difficulty until returning to gravity or acceleration save for the possibility of kidney stones after two or more weeks of skeletal deconditioning
D. Immobilization	Confinement in space vehicles	Many of the suggested effects of weightlessness are known to occur with immobilization
E. Nutritional and fluid lack	Payload limitations of existing rocketing	
1. Water lack		When coupled with immobilization and weightlessness, decreased water would enhance a decreased plasma volume (and thus hydrostatic hypotension); with a decreased flow but increased calcium concentration in urine, these factors would also encourage kidney-stone formation

Methods of Artificial Protection or of Temporary Physiological Adjustment	Possible Conditioning or Procedure for Long-Term Protection	Examples of Conditioning or Adjustment Which Occur to Organisms on Earth
	f. Weightlessness would be one instance where the adjustments are more likely to be harmful than beneficial	

a. Develop larger rockets and space vehicles
b. Pursue physical exercise during space travel
c. A low oxygen tension has been suggested (Lamb, 1965)

Larger space vehicles	a. Recycling and recovery of supplies b. The eventual development of artificial hibernation so as to conserve supplies	
a. Carry adequate quantities of stored water	c. Some sources of water in adequate quantities seems the only safe procedure possible with existing biomedical methods	Terrestrial animals (particularly mammals, birds, and insects) have evolved kidney structures which can permit the kidney to excrete a highly concentrated urine. With mammals and some birds, the existence of the loop of Henle permits the concentration by means of a *counter-current* system. Some desert rodents, such as the kangaroo rat, that consume no water and only dry food (obtaining body water from metabolism of foods) excrete a urine which is approximately 20 times as concentrated as the plasma. This animal also exhibits a very low evaporative loss of water.

TABLE 4-1. Continued

Hazard	Source or Cause of Hazard	Possible Effect
2. Reduced caloric intake		a. Decrease in available carbohydrates and fats with eventual depletion of body proteins and death b. A general slowing of body process.
F. Toxic chemicals	1. Constant recycling of trace amounts of toxic materials in food, water, and gases 2. Exhaust fuels 3. Fires 4. Volatile solvents in such things as paints	
G. Ionizing radiation	1. Solar emission 2. Cosmic rays originating from other stars 3. Bands such as the *Van Allen belts* of magnetically-trapped charged particles 4. Power sources for the space ship	Essentially all tissue can be damaged to some extent. Massive doses can cause "radiation burns" associated with release of toxic materials from injured cells. Destruction of the highly sensitive bone marrow results in leukemia and decreased susceptibility to infection. Due to interference with cell division, growing tissue exhibits an apparent high susceptibility

Meth Protecᵢ Physiol	*Methods of Artificial Protection or of Temporary Physiological Adjustment*	*Possible Conditioning or Procedure for Long-Term Protection*	*Examples of Conditioning or Adjustment Which Occur to Organisms on Earth*
1. Requ ber oi tasks 2. Close groun	a. Carry supplies of "quick-energy" foods such as sugar for short trips	a. Although previous periods of fasting can reduce caloric requirements and to some extent enhance tolerance to starvation, this might generally reduce the over-all physical condition and tolerance to other hazards b. To assure physical conditioning and exercise, attempts should be made to provide an adequate supply of food. If adequate sources of water are existent, dried foods will probably be employed until food recycling procedures are available. However, some feel that an exclusive diet of dried food enhances the incidence of cancer (Generales, 1963)	a. Although reduced food intake can reduce metabolic rate this is partially related to loss of actual body mass (particularly with the liver) b. Moderate caloric restriction can sometimes merely reduce the rate of body processes without any deleterious effects as exemplified by the slower growth but longer life span of experimental mice
1. Care withiı 2. With so drᵢ gener an evᵢ Howᵢ "exhᵢ vigor			
	1. General care to remove potential hazards in design of space cabin 2. Flushing with or permitting some escape of air from the cabin 3. Filtering and treatment (with such agents as activated charcoal) of recycled air and water 4. Previous exposure to some toxic agents might increase later tolerance to the same or related agents		Tolerance of animals to carbon monoxide has been observed as a result of an increased level of hemoglobin in the blood Increased tolerance of insects to insecticides and of microbes to antibiotics is believed to be merely a result of Darwinian selection
distaı techn Cli to be be nᵢ space offer phere trave envir Th envir	Avoiding the time (solar flares) and place (radiation belts) of high intensity radiation	Extensive shielding (another factor which will impose an added requirement for more powerful rockets)	
	Although hibernation, very low temperatures, anoxia, and certain drugs could reduce the indirect effect (short-lived toxic substances such as free radicals produced by radiation) only avoidance of exposure can insure true protection		

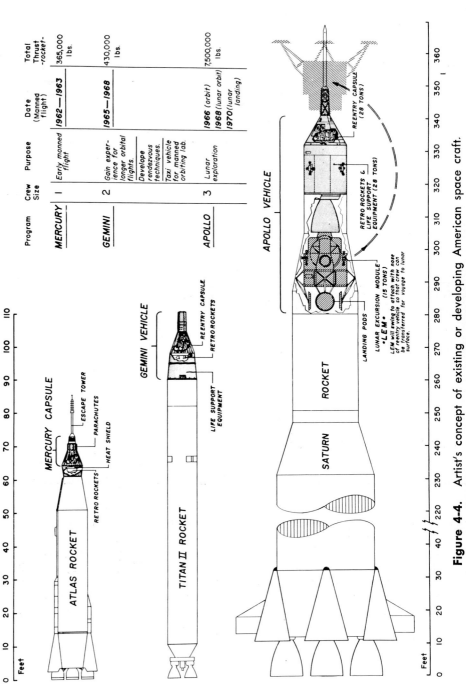

Program	Crew Size	Purpose	Date (Manned flight)	Total Thrust -rocket-
MERCURY	1	Early manned flight	1962—1963	365,000 lbs.
GEMINI	2	Gain experience for longer orbital flights. Develope rendezvous techniques. Taxi vehicle for manned orbiting lab.	1965—1968	430,000 lbs.
APOLLO	3	Lunar exploration	1966 (orbit) 1968 (lunar orbit) 1970 (lunar landing)	7,500,000 lbs.

MERCURY CAPSULE

ESCAPE TOWER

PARACHUTES

HEAT SHIELD

RETRO ROCKETS

ATLAS ROCKET

GEMINI VEHICLE

REENTRY CAPSULE

RETRO ROCKETS

LIFE SUPPORT EQUIPMENT

TITAN II ROCKET

APOLLO VEHICLE

REENTRY CAPSULE (28 TONS)

RETRO ROCKETS & LIFE SUPPORT EQUIPMENT (28 TONS)

LUNAR EXCURSION MODULE •LEM• (15 TONS)

LEM will swing to attach with nose of reentry vehicle so that crew can be transferred for voyage to lunar surface.

LANDING PODS

SATURN ROCKET

Figure 4-4. Artist's concept of existing or developing American space craft.

OVERC

by themselves
ature or low
upon the pre
man's ability
to cardiovascu
effective gravit
sitting, or star
ture and prev
temperature di
increase in pc
adequate to n
in the individu
immersion.

Living
modules

Figure 4-5.
possess a diame
ready for assem
rocket. A Saturi
vous of ferry ve
house laborator
organisms could
first manned spc
not be rotating.

	Methods of Artificial Protection or of Temporary Physiological Adjustment	*Possible Conditioning or Procedure for Long-Term Protection*	*Examples of Conditioning or Adjustment Which Occur to Organisms on Earth*
P₁ Ph			
1. I t t 2. (g	a. Carry supplies of "quick-energy" foods such as sugar for short trips	a. Although previous periods of fasting can reduce caloric requirements and to some extent enhance tolerance to starvation, this might generally reduce the over-all physical condition and tolerance to other hazards b. To assure physical conditioning and exercise, attempts should be made to provide an adequate supply of food. If adequate sources of water are existent, dried foods will probably be employed until food recycling procedures are available. However, some feel that an exclusive diet of dried food enhances the incidence of cancer (Generales, 1963)	a. Although reduced food intake can reduce metabolic rate this is partially related to loss of actual body mass (particularly with the liver) b. Moderate caloric restriction can sometimes merely reduce the rate of body processes without any deleterious effects as exemplified by the slower growth but longer life span of experimental mice
1. C w 2. V s g a H "' v	1. General care to remove potential hazards in design of space cabin 2. Flushing with or permitting some escape of air from the cabin 3. Filtering and treatment (with such agents as activated charcoal) of recycled air and water 4. Previous exposure to some toxic agents might increase later tolerance to the same or related agents		Tolerance of animals to carbon monoxide has been observed as a result of an increased level of hemoglobin in the blood Increased tolerance of insects to insecticides and of microbes to antibiotics is believed to be merely a result of Darwinian selection
di te			
to be sp of ph tra en en	Avoiding the time (solar flares) and place (radiation belts) of high intensity radiation	Extensive shielding (another factor which will impose an added requirement for more powerful rockets)	
	Although hibernation, very low temperatures, anoxia, and certain drugs could reduce the indirect effect (short-lived toxic substances such as free radicals produced by radiation) only avoidance of exposure can insure true protection		

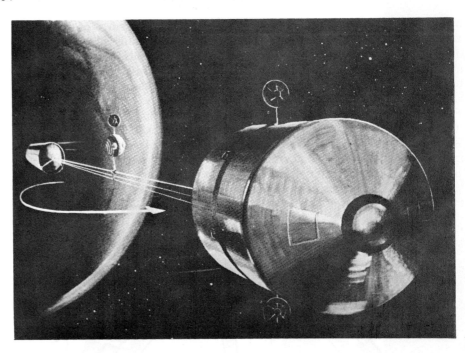

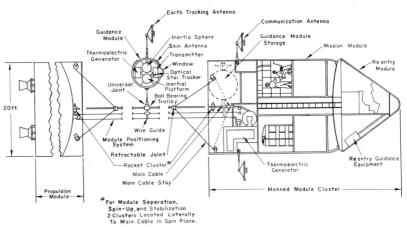

Figure 4-6. Proposed manned interplanetary spacecraft
designed for rotation (Lally, 1962).

When an astronaut leaves the Earth, his physical condition should be such that he could tolerate not only exposure to the acceleration of rocket departure or the deceleration of reentry but perhaps the gravity of a larger planet. After a sufficiently long period of weightlessness, he might lose

adjusts
period
carryin
4-8);
the en
may b

This
ferred
intensi
return
Certair
times t
growth
to high
just as

increased resp
the initial peri
sure, faintness

Patterns of R

Most of the
voyage will be
of the bodily n
This highly dy
in the external
ment occurs ir

the capacity to tolerate these gravitational conditions. In fact, he might not even be able to endure the previously modest rigors of the Earth's own environment.

Limitations with respect to the amount of cargo which can be carried by a space craft from Earth (without tremendous rockets exceeding in size those presently in use) will force the adoption of new and untried sources for oxygen, water, and food. Long flights will require some method whereby oxygen and water can be recycled and reused (see Chapter 10). This constant reuse could result in the accumulation of various toxic materials (Table 4-1-F), with previously unsuspected actions. Even for those chemicals of recognized potential hazard, tolerable concentrations in a space craft are not known. Tolerable concentrations have been determined primarily for industrial situations involving a 40-hour week (not constant exposure) and the normal Terrestrial gravity (not zero G). If not removed from the air by filtration, various powders and dusts, in the absence of any gravity to cause their settling, could remain as a constant source of danger or irritation in the air which an astronaut breathes. If food cannot also be recycled from body wastes, it will undoubtedly be transported in a dehydrated form. Some concern has been expressed that a prolonged diet consisting entirely of dried food could have adverse effects (Generales, 1963).

Although this book is concerned primarily with the biological problems of space travel, the social and psychological problems should not be overlooked. Extended exposure to unique environmental stimuli is known to have pronounced emotional influences upon man. Long and close contact in a confined capsule may result in serious sociological repercussions. Extended periods of space travel may require a new set of mores and social values.

The availability of land and supplies in most parts of this country, in comparison to the limitations imposed in a space craft, is sufficient to permit the luxury of highly civilized manners and customs. In the harsher confines of a space craft, it might become necessary to eliminate the presence of people who, in spite of rigid selection, would impose an undue tax upon the precious supplies and morale of other more useful occupants.

Any of the many factors in a new environment may produce a characteristic *stress* response in the astronaut (Table 4-1-I).[1] The initial response (in man and in other higher animals) is characterized by the release of epinephrine into the blood stream, resulting in increased heart rate,

1.8
1.6
1.4
1.2
1.0
.8

Fraction of Original Mass

AC
IRREVERSIBLE
DEATH DEGREES OF DEBILITATION
DELIBERATE SELE
CONDITI
DELIBERATE MODIFIC

Figure

Figur
by chror
of the e)
procedu
longed
manned
and dev
the lowe
will caus

² Unfortunately,
organism's respons
Adaptation sometin
after a long period
is used to designat
period of seconds u
to the adjustment w
a new environment.
made within the lifet
and generally applit
within its own lifeti
³ In the older li
maintenance of an
of a larger number
maintain a *steady-st*

[1] Confusion exists with regard to the word *stress*. The term, as originally employed by engineers, referred to the passive restoring action exerted by a body following displacement or deformation by a *strain*. In biological terms, stress is the restoring action exerted by the organism following the imposition of a strain. However, it is an active rather than a passive process, calling upon the homeokinetic mechanisms of the body to maintain the internal environment in a steady state (Table 4-2). This may involve a series of responses of the central nervous system, the endocrine system, and the cells and tissues of the body. Confusion has been further compounded by the failure of some biologists even to distinguish between the actual distorting action (more appropriately referred to as the *stressor*) and the opposing action or *stress*.

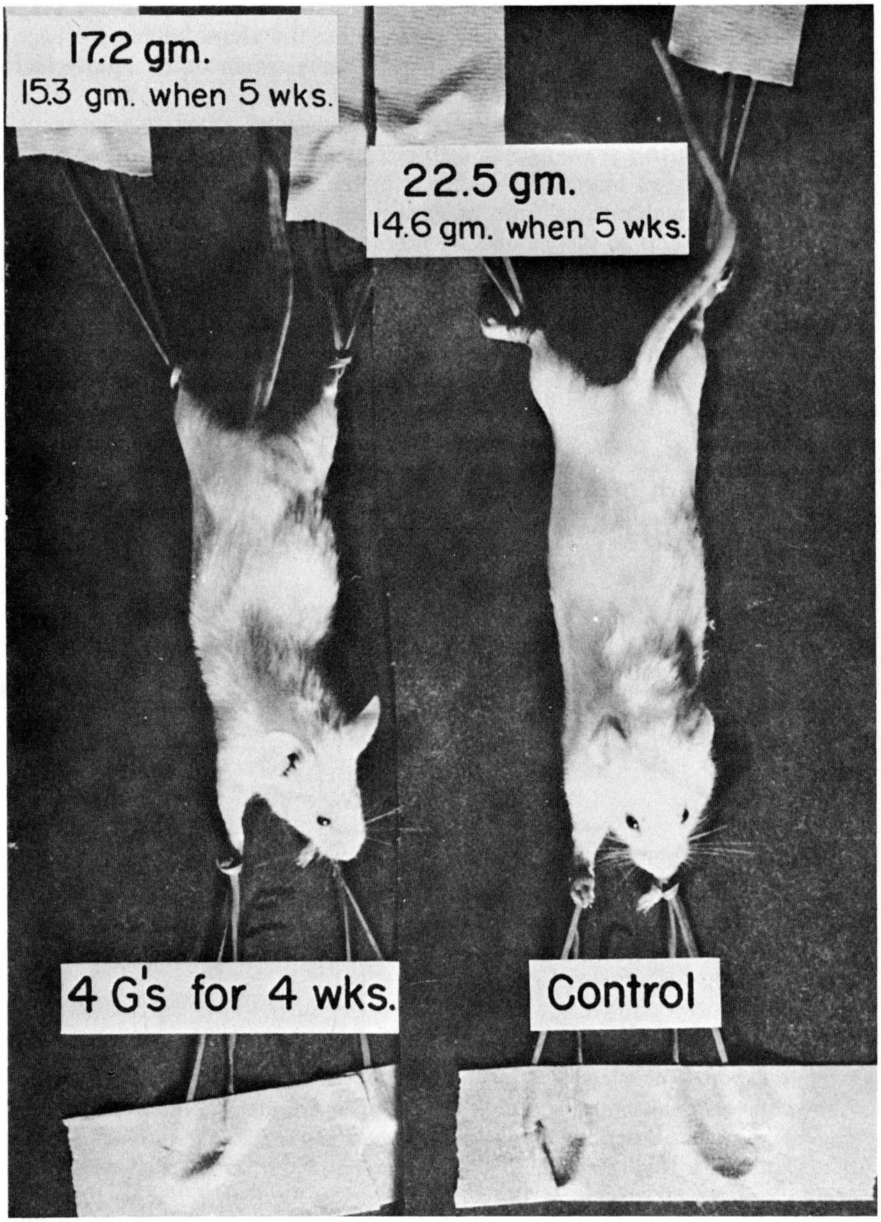

Figure 4-10. Mice described in Figure 4-9. Note the smaller size of the experimental animals (Wunder *et al.*, 1963).

TABLE 4-2. Comparison of the Response of Passive and Living Bodies to Distortion

Spring or Hookeian Body   Control System or Governor   Living System

increased respiration, and increased blood pressure. Within a few minutes, the initial period may deteriorate into "shock," with decreased blood pressure, faintness from circulatory failure, and eventual unconsciousness.

Patterns of Response to Environmental Changes

Most of the adverse environmental changes to be found during a space voyage will be the chronic type. This will require a long-term adjustment[2] of the bodily mechanisms which maintain the constant internal environment. This highly dynamic activity which must adjust to all changing conditions in the external world is known as *homeokinesis*.[3] The process of adjustment occurs in several phases (Figs. 4-7, 4-8): (1) a period of shock,

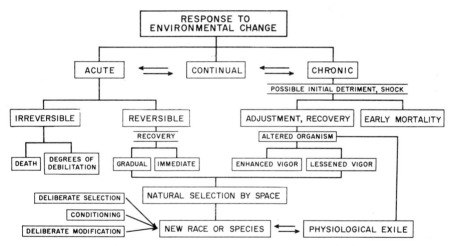

Figure 4-7. Types of response to environmental change.

---

[2] Unfortunately, the terminology describing unfavorable environments and the organism's response to such environments is somewhat confused (Egan, 1963). *Adaptation* sometimes refers to the adjustment which is made by a race or species only after a long period of natural selection and evolution. At other times, the same term is used to designate the immediate response which a cell or organ makes within a period of seconds upon exposure to a new condition. *Acclimatization* sometimes refers to the adjustment which is shown by a species over several generations of response to a new environment. In other situations, however, it is used to refer to the adjustment made within the lifetime of one individual. The term *acclimate* is somewhat less confused and generally applies only to the adjustments or adaptations made by an individual within its own lifetime, without any reference to hereditary adaptations.

[3] In the older literature, this was referred to as *homeostasis*, emphasizing the maintenance of an equilibrium condition. The newer term emphasizes the existence of a larger number of dynamic adjustments, which, by their net action, strive to maintain a *steady-state condition*.

during which the condition of the organism is altered from the normal homeokinetic state, (2) a period of adjustment, during which there is a gradual return toward a normal condition (Fig. 4-9), (3) a long-term adjustment of the animal, so that it can continue to meet the adversity, and (4) a very long-term adjustment of the animal characterized by a permanent alteration in function or by a genetic alteration. These may well be illustrated by the responses of man to high altitude. Man may faint in shock on first exposure to the low oxygen concentration of a mountain top; he then

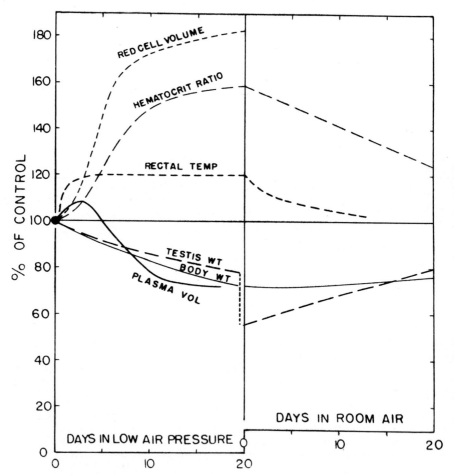

Figure 4-8. Some of the adjustments by man during exposure to high altitude (left) and return to normal conditions (right). (Adolph in "Handbook of Physiology," 1964.)

adjusts by a more rapid breathing and by deeper respirations. Over a longer period of time, he adjusts still further by permanently altering the oxygen-carrying capacity of the blood to deliver more oxygen to the tissues (Fig. 4-8); finally, he may be able to genetically alter the shape of his rib cage, the enzyme catalyzing oxygen transfer, or other permanent changes which may be transmitted to other generations.

This pattern of response is illustrated by the case of growing mice transferred from the Earth's gravity to an artificial gravity of four times the normal intensity. There is an immediate decrease in the growth rate, followed by a return to the normal rate as time of exposure increases (Figs. 4-9, 4-10). Certain animals, such as turtles and fly larvae, are reported to exceed sometimes the normal growth rate under enhanced artificial gravity. The total growth of mice ceases at an earlier time under increased gravity. Exposure to high gravity would be expected to cause stouter, denser bones (Fig. 4-11) just as weightlessness may evoke bone demineralization.

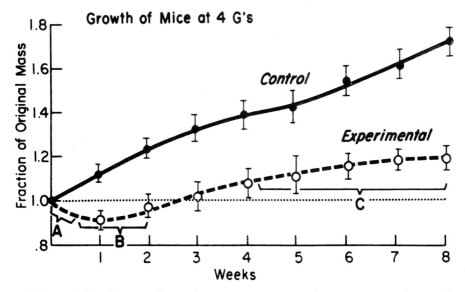

Figure 4-9. Pattern of growth in response to an adverse agent as illustrated by chronic exposure of mice to 4 G. Mice were 5 weeks of age at the beginning of the experiment. This figure is further described in Chapter 8. The experimental procedure has been described elsewhere (Wunder et al., 1963). Although prolonged exposure to high gravity is not contemplated during the early years of manned space travel (see page 144), this does show that an organism's growth and development vary with the magnitude of a gravitational field. Undoubtedly the lower gravitational intensities to be encountered in space or on the Moon will cause an altered development of organisms. Standard errors are shown.

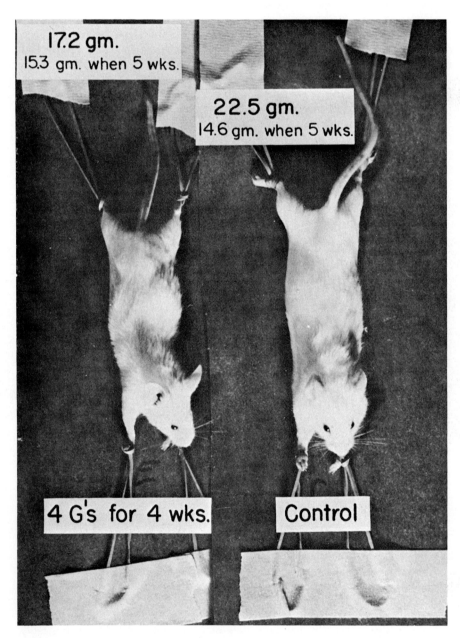

Figure 4-10. Mice described in Figure 4-9. Note the smaller size of the experimental animals (Wunder *et al.*, 1963).

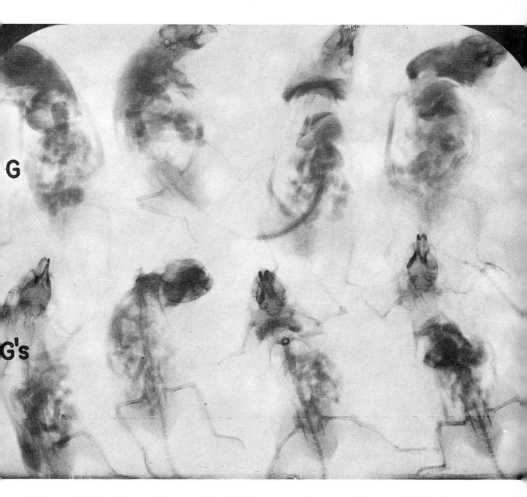

Figure 4-11. X-ray photographs of mice grown in a centrifuge at 2 G's (courtesy of Maj. Duane E. Graveline, USAF, presently a member of the NASA Scientist-Astronaut Program, from previously unpublished results). Photograph would suggest greater radiographic density of mice grown at high gravity. This would complement the finding that young mice centrifuged for several weeks at 4 G develop larger, rounder femur bones (Wunder *et al.*, 1960). Photograph is for mice centrifuged continuously from the third to the sixth week of age. Note that essentially all bones rather than merely those expected to support greater gravitational loaas appear denser. Denser bones for experimental animals might reflect the effects of altered rate of development rather than a direct gravitational effect upon bone density.

A period of readjustment upon return to an original environment also occurs (Fig. 4-8). Once an organism has successfully adapted or acclimatized to a new environment, it is entirely possible that it may not be able to return to its original environment. It has become a different organism physiologically. If genetic processes intervene, it may become a different organism anatomically. This might be exemplified by Caucasians who, after many generations in a region of the Earth which receives less intense rays of sunlight than those to which their ancestors had been accustomed and which therefore requires less protection from ultraviolet rays, have lost most of their protective pigmentation. (Presumably man evolved as a tropical animal with dark pigmentation.) Long exposure to weightlessness may result in an individual so conditioned to a weightless state that he is unable to return to the rigors of the Earth's gravitational environment.

Bibliography and References

APPLEZWEIG, M. H. (1961): Neuroendocrine aspects of stress. *In* "Psychophysiological Aspects of Space Flight" (B. F. Flaherty, ed.), pp. 139-157. Columbia University Press, New York.

BERGLUND, R. A. (1962): AEMT space-station design. *Astronautics, Vol. 7, No. 9,* 19-24.

BROWN, J. H. U., AND BARKER, S. B. (1962): "Basic Endocrinology for Students of Biology and Medicine." F. A. Davis Co., Philadelphia, Pa.

EGAN, C. J. (1963): Introduction and terminology. *Federation Proceedings 22,* 930-932.

GENERALES, D. J., JR. (1963): Weightlessness: its physical, biological, and medical aspects. *In* "Medical and Biological Problems of Space Flight" (G. H. Bourne, ed.), pp. 123-187. Academic Press, New York and London.

"Handbook of Physiology" (1964): Section 4: Adaptation to the Environment (D. B. Dill, E. F. Adolph, and C. G. Wilber, eds.). American Physiological Society, Washington, D. C.

LALLY, E. F. (1962): To spin or not to spin. *Astronautics, Vol. 7, No. 9,* 56-58.

LAMB, L. E. (1965): Hypoxia—An anti-deconditioning factor for manned space flight. *Aerospace Med. 36,* 97-100.

SCHMIDT, C. F., AND LAMBERTSEN, C. J. (1965): Pharmacology in space medicine. *Ann. Rev. Pharmacol. 5,* 383-401.

SELYE, H. (1950): "The Physiology and Pathology of Exposure to Stress: A Treatise Based on the Concepts of the General-Adaptation Syndrome and the Diseases of Adaptation." Acta, Inc., Montreal.

SISAKAYAN, N. M. (1965): "Nekotoryye Problemy Ekofiziologii (Some problems of ecophysiology). Akad. nauk SSSR, Moskva (as presented at 2nd Int. Symp. Basic Environmental Problems of Man in Space, Unesco House, Paris, June 14, 1965; as translated by Boris Mandrovsky in *A.T.D. Press 3* (243), 1-8.

WUNDER, C. C., BRINEY, S. R., KRAL, M., AND SKAUGSTAD (1960): Growth of mouse femurs during continual centrifugation. *Nature, 188,* 151-152.

WUNDER, C. C., LUTHERER, L. O., AND DODGE, C. H. (1963): Survival and growth of organisms during life-long exposure to high gravity. *Aerospace Med. 34,* 5-11.

Part 2

Specific Considerations

5 | Temperature and Heat

Of the environmental conditions to be encountered in outer space, the best known and understood are the effects of temperature. The high sensitivity of living material to temperature change is well known. Almost all Terrestrial biological reactions occur between 273°K (0° C, freezing point of water) and 373° K (100° C, boiling point of water). Although some living organisms are known to have survived at a temperature of 205° K and although certain algae live in hot springs at about 350° K, most biological reactions occur between the range of 283° K and 323° K.

Altered Temperature Conditions

The reader is already aware that at moderate altitudes there is a reduced atmospheric temperature. He has been reminded, moreover, that at extremely high altitudes there exists a measurable but biologically meaningless rise in atmospheric temperature (due to reduced conduction and convection of heat by atmospheric air).[1] At these high altitudes, as in space, heat exchange between one body (such as a space capsule or planet) and other bodies (particularly the Sun) occurs primarily by radiation, at a rate which depends

---

[1] The absolute temperature T of a system is defined in terms of the average molecular kinetic energy due to translational motion. When expressed in degrees Kelvin, the absolute temperature can be described by the following equation, which defines temperature:

$$T = \frac{2}{3} \frac{(\text{average kinetic energy per mole})}{R}$$

$$= \frac{2}{3} \frac{(\text{average kinetic energy per molecule})}{k}$$

where R is the ideal gas constant, which is equal to 1.99 calories per degree-mole, and k is the Maxwell-Boltzman constant, which is equal to 1.38×10^{-16} ergs $\times$ degree^{-1}.

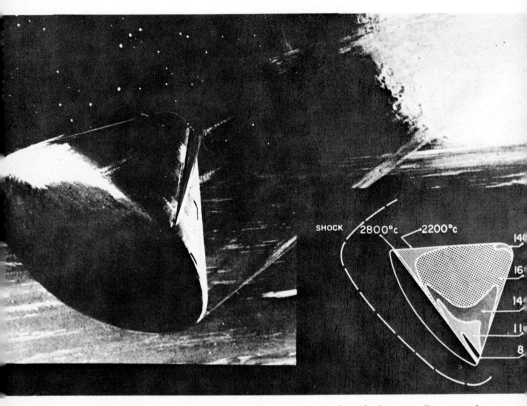

Figure 5-1. Equilibrium temperatures predicted for Apollo capsule should it execute a 20-G emergency reentry (Kotanchik, 1964).

upon the radiating and absorptive surfaces, as well as the fourth power of absolute temperature, in accordance with the Stefan-Boltzman Law.[2]

Extremes of temperature might be expected to arise from one of three sources: (1) malfunction of a space craft's temperature control system (causing either improper distribution or radiation and absorption of heat), (2) high frictional heat generated during reentry, or (3) different climatic conditions on some non-Terrestrial body (as a result of distance from the Sun, rate of rotation, degree of atmospheric convection, or varying ability to absorb or emit radiant heat (see Fig. 3-2). Moreover, low temperatures might eventually be deliberately employed during space travel as a method for reducing metabolic requirements during long voyages (which would otherwise demand large, expensive payloads of consumable supplies).

Astronauts could be exposed to intense bouts of acute heating if not adequately protected from the frictional heating of reentry. During a 20-G

---

[2] Footnote on page 77.

emergency reentry of the Apollo capsule (Fig. 5-1), parts of the capsule may be heated to 2800°C or 5000° F (Fig. 5-2). Heat shields (Fig. 5-3) which utilize some ablating materials (such as phenolic-nylon or phenolic-asbestos, that will consume or radiate the heat as the materials are converted into a carbonaceous char [Brooks, 1965]) are currently under development.

The study of temperature and heat as they act upon organisms divides itself into two primary considerations: (1) changes brought about at the molecular and cellular level as a direct result of the actual temperature of the reacting material, and (2) changes which occur to the entire organism as a result either of the direct molecular and cellular effects (of temperature) or of attempts to maintain a satisfactory internal thermal state in the face of an adverse, external, thermal environment.

Direct Action of Temperature upon Reacting Material

All of the life which we know on Earth, together with most suggested extra-Terrestrial life, involves highly organized chemical activity. The temperature dependence of biological activity can be elucidated from an understanding of the energetics of the chemical processes underlying the biological processes. Increasing temperature causes more molecules to

---

[2] In accordance with the Stefan-Boltzman Law,

Heat radiation from a body = k (surface area) δT^4

where δ is equal to 1.36×10^{-12} cal cm^{-2} degrees^{-4} and k is a coefficient which depends upon the nature of the radiating surface (approaching unity for a black surface and zero for a reflecting surface).

The amount of heat absorbed from the Sun would depend upon solar intensity I, as indicated in Figure 3-3, so that

Radiant solar heat absorbed = k (area facing Sun) I

An equilibrium temperature would be arrived at when

Radiant solar heat + heat produced by body = heat radiated by body

The heat produced by a body would include such things as the astronaut's body heat and output from equipment. If we can ignore this quantity, the equilibrium temperature of a sphere (of uniform temperature and of uniform k over its surface) would (as discussed by Clarke, 1960) be equal to

$$T = \left(\frac{I}{4\,\delta}\right)^{1/4}$$

which at the Earth's distance from the Sun would be equal to 4° C (277° K).

By a judicious differentiation of k for surfaces of differing orientation, various equilibrium temperatures can be obtained. For instance, if the night or shadowed side of the sphere were silvered (k = 0) and the sunward side blackened (k = 1), the temperature at the Earth's distance from the Sun would be 56° C.

Another example of this differential k would be the "greenhouse" effect, which apparently is responsible for the high surface temperatures of the planet Venus. For the Sun's rays, the covering cloud surfaces would present a high value for k (as a result of the temperature-dependent nature of rays emitted from the Sun and Venus) but a lower value for the rays from the plant's surface.

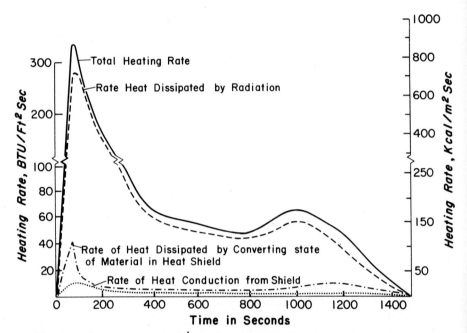

Figure 5-2. Hearing rate $\dot{Q}$ predicted for Apollo capsule during 20-G reentry (Kotanchik, 1964). Note that most heat is dissipated by radiation ($\dot{Q}_{rad}$) with smaller rates for dissipation by blowing and pyrolysis ($\dot{Q}_{blow + pyro}$) or by conduction into material of the shield or into the capsule ($\dot{Q}_{cond}$).

possess sufficient energy (*Energy of Activation* or μ^*) to enter into the chemical processes which underlie not only the basic processes of life but also the processes of death and decay (Fig. 5-4). In general, only a slight temperature rise (relative to the absolute temperature) produces drastically faster rates of reaction in a manner which depends upon the specific μ^* of a reaction in question (Fig. 5-5).[3]

---

[3] Although the amount of energy present might vary directly with temperature, the availability of energy for the rearrangement of bonds between atoms and molecules is not directly proportional to temperature. This availability is described by the Maxwell-Boltzman equation, the same equation which (when μ^* is considered equivalent to Mgh; see page 33, footnote 1) describes the changing density of an atmosphere with temperature and altitude. The equation describes the fraction of molecules which have a particular amount (μ^*) of potential energy as follows:

or
$$N\mu/N_{total} = e^{-\mu^*/RT}$$
$$\log_{10}(N\mu/N_{total}) = {}^-\mu^*/(2.3RT)$$

Thus, assuming that the rate of reaction is proportional to the fraction of reacting particles, the logarithm of the rate of some biological processes (provided the process is to be regulated by the rate of a single molecular "master process") would be proportional to $-\mu^*/(RT)$.

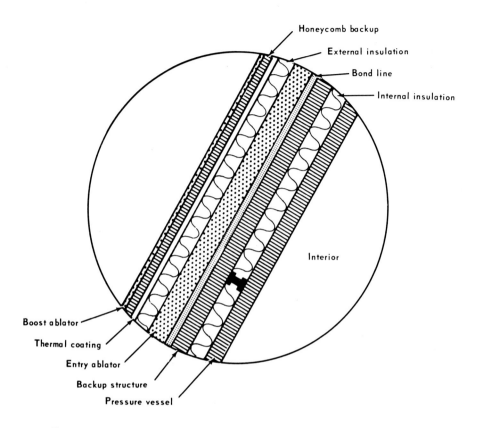

Figure 5-3. Layers of material for proposed Apollo heat shield (Kotanchik, 1964).

As temperature increases, most biological processes proceed at faster and faster rates until an optimal temperature is reached (Fig. 5-6). The decreasing rates at extreme temperatures are usually indicative of irreversible tissue damage (Fig. 5-7). Survival of some tissue or cells is conceivable at the very low temperatures (this would involve techniques which have not yet been perfected for man). Life-support equipment, however, which prevents marked temperature rises of an astronaut's tissues beyond the normal body level of 37° C, will undoubtedly always be necessary.

Survival at Very Low Temperatures

Although reactions can proceed at the surface of a solid, a solvent will usually speed the process. Water (as a plentiful polar compound which permits ionization of electrolyte compounds) is the universal solvent on Earth for all biological processes. Perhaps if there is a warm enough temperature somewhere on one of the large, colder planets (Uranus, Jupiter, Neptune) ammonia, which is also a polar compound permitting ionization of dissolved electrolytes, might act as a solvent for a different and probably slower life (the freezing temperature of ammonia is $-78°$ C). Under certain conditions, glycerin can replace water. Insects can have a certain portion of the water in their cells replaced with glycerin and then can tolerate extremely low temperatures. Some algae have antifreeze-like compounds in the cells.

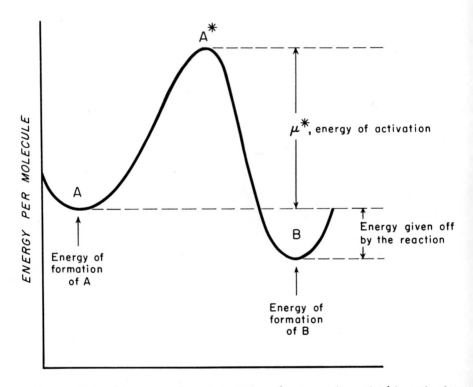

Figure 5-4. Diagrammatic representation of energy μ^* required in activation of chemical reactions. When a molecule or complex, here designated by A, receives sufficient potential energy, it will arrive at an activated state of this molecule, as designated by A*. This activated complex can then proceed to yield a new molecule with a different arrangement of bonds, which is designated by B.

$$A \rightarrow A^* \rightarrow B$$

In a growing system, A might correspond to a molecule of some food material, A* to a complex of the food material and an enzyme molecule, and B the food material converted into some part of a biologically active molecule of protoplasm.

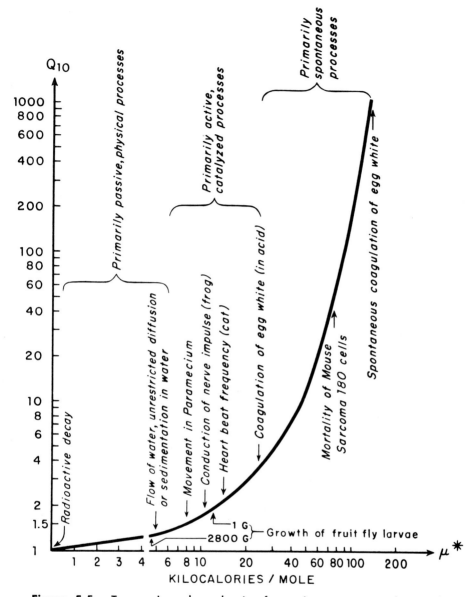

Figure 5-5. Temperature dependencies for various processes. Low activation energies of 5000 calories per mole are typical of passive viscosity dependent processes such as fluid flow. Activation energies of 8000 to 25,000 calories/mole are typical of most catalyzed chemical reactions. These values are typical also of the chemical processes of life which are catalyzed by the biological catalysts, enzymes. Activation energies of up to 100,000 calories/mole are characteristic of processes which are spontaneous such as destruction of enzymes by heat.

The curve shows the values of Q_{10} (for the range of 30-40° C) as a function of theoretical activation energy μ^*. Although modern chemical nomenclature refers to the activation energy of a process, the older biological literature used the term "Q_{10}" indicating the increase in rate (actually the ratio of rates) of a reaction for a 10-degree change in temperature. This method (use of Q_{10}) was imprecise as Q_{10} values for various 10-degree ranges varied widely.

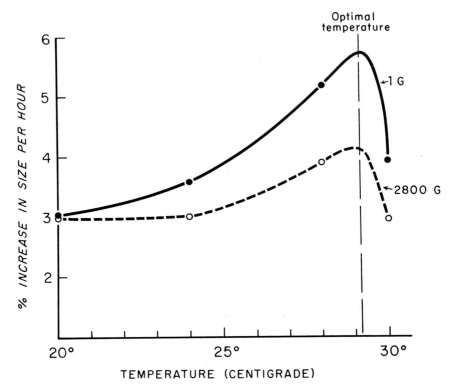

Figure 5-6. Influence of temperature and gravity upon growth of fruit-fly larvae. Note that the response to one environmental factor cannot be predicted unless other environmental factors are also known (After Wunder *et al.*, 1959).

Human sperm and other tissues treated with glycerin can survive low temperatures for long periods of time.[4]

Procedures have not yet been developed to the extent that any vertebrate is capable of surviving freezing of the entire body. Should such procedures be developed, an astronaut placed in the frozen state would undergo

---

[4] Freezing can cause the destruction of cells due to the formation of large ice crystals, which rupture the various parts of a cell. Glycerin binds the water molecules in such a manner that the freezing point is lowered, so that when solidification finally occurs the large destructive crystals of ice are not formed. Were it not for the eventual destruction by the small amount of radioactive material which is found everywhere in all material, freezing, it is believed, would render possible the indefinite preservation of the biological activity of sperm and other materials. Cooling of biological material to very low temperatures will, however, result in some protection from radiation, presumably because solidification hinders the movement of the toxic particles produced by radiation.

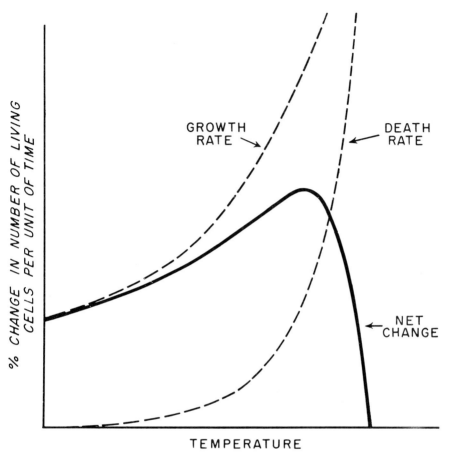

Figure 5-7. Change in the nature of temperature dependence. A hypothetical situation is graphed for which the total change in vigor (in this case the number of living cells) depends upon two opposing processes. The total rate will be equal to the differences between the height of the two broken lines. At the lower temperature, only the enzymatically catalyzed process (growth) plays a major role in determining the rate of change. With rising temperatures, there is initially an increasing availability of activated complexes for enzymatically controlled reactions. Ultimately, there is the so-called "optimal" temperature at which a process proceeds at its fastest rate. Still higher temperatures can result in a highly temperature dependent decrease in biological activity due to the spontaneous destruction of such materials as the enzymes themselves. The spontaneous process (in this case, death) has a greater temperature dependence and with increasing temperatures, therefore, it plays an increasingly important role in determining the vigor of a living system.

suspended animation and, as a result, decreased metabolic requirements during an extended voyage. This would in part simplify the logistical problems associated with manned trips to the outer planets or perhaps even to the stars. Moreover, on the basis of experiments with lower animals (Black-Schaffer, 1962), body cooling should permit an increased tolerance to inertial fields. Hibernation is purported to increase tolerance to radiation.

Some warm-blooded animals can reduce their body temperature (together with heart rate, blood pressure, and other parameters) to induce torpor in which the metabolic needs may drop to as low as 0.7 percent of the normal level. Hibernation is the best example of such a torpor.[5] It is conceivable that a maintained dormancy of this nature could preserve the crews of manned vessels for voyages which would normally exceed a human lifetime. Hock (1960), in reviewing Rubner's contention that longevity is a function of energy expenditure per unit of mass, compared the longevity of two animals of comparable size. The bat, *Myotis lucifugus*, is a hibernator which lives to more than 20 years. The shrew, *Sorex cinereus*, lives for less than a year and one half and metabolizes at a rate over ten times as fast. Both, however, consume a total of approximately 3000 Kcal in a lifetime.

A number of processes (such as cardiac contraction, respiratory metabolism, and tissue metabolism) can be slowed by local cooling. The temperature dependency of these and other processes differ, but their rates mesh to compatible levels at normal body temperature (37° C). Many birds and mammals (including man) have evolved a control system which maintains a constant temperature and are unable to tolerate the asynchrony which can occur when tissue temperatures drop. Although there is with man a general decrease in all activity, breathing drops faster than metabolic needs, so that tissue anoxia would occur without artificial respiration. Although human beings whose rectal temperatures have dropped to as low as 18° C have recovered, cardiac fibrillation can occur at temperatures below 30° C.

In preparing for hibernation, the physiological activities of an animal must assume temperature dependencies which will permit synchronous operation at low temperatures. This involves a number of changes (such as fat storage, altered endocrine activities, and perhaps even enzymatic changes). The μ^* for hibernating hamsters is reported to be lower than in nonhibernating hamsters (Hoffman, 1964, in reviewing the work of Smith). Hock (1960), in discussing the feasibility of placing man in conditions approximating deep hibernation, lists four presently unsolved problems: (1)

---

[5] The word *hibernation*, as presently employed by scientists concerned with that phenomenon, refers only to the seasonal torpor associated with winter temperatures, during which body temperatures drop almost to ambient temperature. This is exemplified by ground squirrels, hamsters, and bats but not by the winter state of bears, which is commonly regarded by the layman as hibernation. Like other large mammals which undergo some sort of winter dormancy, there is a reported 50 per cent drop in metabolism with a drop of only a few degrees in body temperature. Torpor or dormancy need not be brought on by cold temperatures. A condition of summer torpor called *aestivation* can be brought on by lack of food and water. It, too, is characterized by lowered body temperature and a general decrease in the rate of body processes.

the ability to lower body temperature to 10° C without ventricular fibrillation; (2) maintenance of man for prolonged periods in the above condition; (3) understanding the manner of energy turnover (presumably working in known hibernators), which will permit producing these conditions in man; and (4) the mechanism for periodic arousal to permit rebuilding of energy levels.

Influence of Environmental Temperature

In those animals which maintain constant body temperature, tolerance to the extremes of temperature in the environment may be modified by prior conditioning. Man's ability to adjust to extremes of temperature is regulated by many factors, including the rate of heat transfer, the duration of exposure (Fig. 5-8), and the humidity (Fig. 5-9).

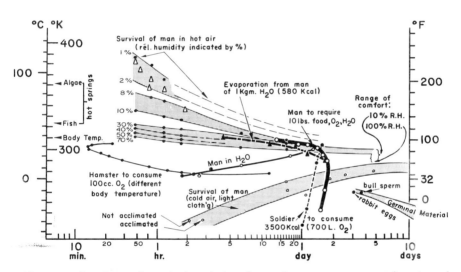

Figure 5-8. Time of survival and time for various processes as a function of temperature. Values have been collected from several sources including Handbook, 1949; Altman et al., 1958; Winslow et al., 1937; and Buckheim et al., 1959.

The heat production by an individual depends upon the constant oxidation of material (foodstuffs) within the body. The rate of heat production is dependent upon the rate of processes of the body and this in turn depends upon activity. The sleeping individual consumes 10 per cent less oxygen and produces 10 per cent less heat than does the man who is awake. It is conceivable that, relative to similar activity under gravity, the weightless state will require a decreased expenditure of energy and therefore a decreased utilization of oxygen.

Heat is lost from the body to the atmosphere by the processes of conduction, convection, and radiation (Fig. 5-10). The proportion of heat lost

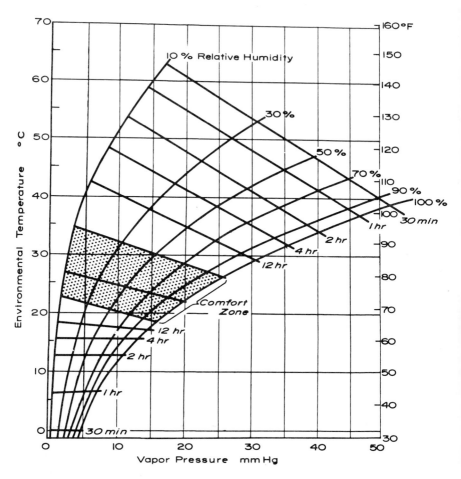

Figure 5-9. Influence of man sitting in light clothing (1.0 clo) to tolerate extremes of temperature as influenced by humidity (after Kaufman, 1963, as modified from MR No. TSEAL-3-695-55). In revising this chart, Kaufman reported that tolerance time at 45° and 55° C would be approximately twice that shown on previous charts.

Relative humidity of man's *immediate* (i.e., between clothing and skin) external environment has very little effect upon ability to tolerate lower temperature. It was once believed that high humidities increased the thermal conductivity of the skin and therefore decreased ability for heat retention. Actually the humidity has more of an effect upon the thermal conductivity of man's clothing. Therefore, tolerance to low temperatures would be influenced somewhat by the humidity of the remote external environment and by the permeability of clothing.

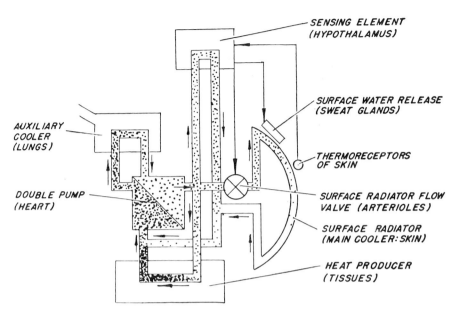

Figure 5-10. Mechanisms for heat exchange in mammals (Stacy et al., 1955). In mammals the primary "physiological thermostat" is the hypothalamus. (The hypothalamus is a center in the brain for the integration of visceral function. It comprises the ventral part of the diencephalon. The diencephalon is philogenetically the second segment of the brain.) The anterior part of the hypothalamus is primarily concerned with heat loss while the posterior part is concerned with heat production and conservation. When this anterior portion is directly heated or receives stimuli from peripheral temperature receptors there follows sweating, panting (to increase heat loss across the lung surface), and an increase in parasympathetic activity. The heart slows down to slow the supply of blood to and from heat-producing tissue. At the same time, there is vasodilatation of the blood vessels to the skin so that the blood can carry more heat for conduction to the surface. It is believed that when the anterior hypothalamus is stimulated, there also occurs an inhibition of metabolic processes and an inhibition of the sympathetic nervous system.

Upon cold stimulation of an animal with a functioning posterior hypothalamus, there is constriction of skin vessels, raising of the hair (pilo-erection—this tends to decrease the conduction by increasing the extent of air pockets), shivering, elevation of blood sugar, increased metabolic rate and an over-all increase in the activity of the sympathetic nervous system.

When the skin temperature is between 19 and 31° C, the body temperature can, as a rule, be controlled by the amount of blood which is permitted to circulate to the skin. Above this temperature the body must be controlled by evaporative heat loss.

by each process is dependent upon a variety of factors (Fig. 5-11). Heat can be lost by convection only when air is moving. In a weightless state, it is possible that convective losses will be minimal unless some means of circulation is provided. Heat is lost by body evaporation, and when environmental temperatures exceed the temperature of the body, evaporation becomes the only significant means of heat loss. This process can place serious restraints on the temperature limits of a space craft. Desiccation either by evaporative loss or by other processes results in decreased blood volume (plasma fraction) and thus in a lessened tolerance of the circulatory system

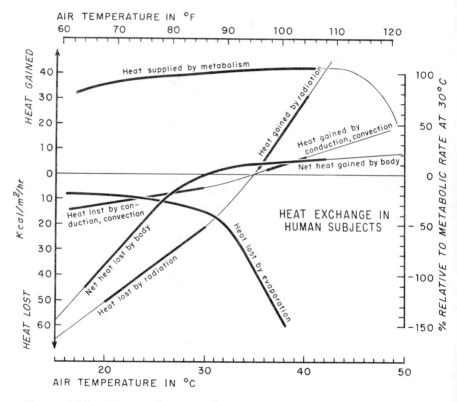

Figure 5-11. Heat exchange in human subject. Curves are modified from an analysis by Stacy *et al.*, 1955, p. 167 of data originally reported by Winslow *et al.*, 1937, for nude subjects exposed to air at various temperatures with air moving at 17 ft./sec. and with a relative humidity of 40 percent. Narrow lines are used to indicate values based upon speculation or upon fragmentary data. As it is experimentally difficult to differentiate between heat exchange due to radiation, convection, and conduction, it is assumed that of the total heat lost by these three processes 81 percent of the exchange can be attributed to radiation.

to the intense accelerations to be encountered during reentry. Heat accompanying an acceleration would further reduce the effective blood volume due to additional flow to the periphery for the purpose of heat dissipation.

In acute pulses of intense heat, such as might occur during an emergency reentry, ability to control body temperature is exceeded. Under such conditions, heat must be stored. Survival would depend upon tolerance of critical tissues (cardiac and nervous). In experiments inside ovens (with walls heated to a peak of 200° C and air to 140° C), Kaufman (1963) reported that human subjects could tolerate the storage of approximately 2.3 kcal of heat per kilogram of body mass. Essentially the same quantity of heat was tolerated whether absorbed during the intense 13-minute bout (intended to simulate conditions of emergency reentry) or a less intense exposure lasting 8 to 12 hours (at 45 to 55° C). During intense pulses, heat rate and body temperature rose (by 30 beats/min and by 40° C, respectively); burns occurred wherever metal touched the skin; subjects displayed giddiness at the end of the experiment.

Bibliography and References

ALTMAN, P. L., GIBSON, J. F., JR., AND WANG, C. C. (compilers) (1958): "Handbook of Respiration" (D. S. Dittmer and R. M. Grebe, eds.). WADC Technical Report 58-352. ASTIA Document No. AD-155823. Wright Air Development Center, Wright-Patterson AFB, Ohio.

BLACK-SCHAFFER, B. (1962): Protection by deep hypothermia and immersion against 2300 "G" acceleration of a nonhibernator (rat) and hibernator (hamster). *Aerospace Med. 33*, 286-296.

BROOKS, W. A. (1965): Evolution of materials and structural responses in entry heating simulators. Paper No. 8. *In* "Proc. of Conf. on Role of Simulation in Space Technology," *Engineering Extension Series Circular No. 4, Part B*, Va. Poly. Inst., Blacksburg.

BUCKHEIM, R. W., and the STAFF OF THE RAND CORPORATION (1959): "Space Handbook: Astronautics and Its Application." Modern Library Paperbacks, Random House, New York.

BURTON, A. C., AND EDHOLM, O. G. (1954): "Man in a Cold Environment; Physiological and Pathological Effects of Exposure to Low Temperatures." Williams and Wilkins Co., Baltimore.

CLARKE, A. C. (1960): "Interplanetary Flight: An Introduction to Astronautics," 2nd ed. Harper and Brothers, New York.

CLOUDSLEY-THOMPSON, J. L. (1964): Terrestrial animals in dry heat: introduction. *In* "Handbook of Physiology," Sec. 4 (E. F. Adolph and C. G. Wilber, eds.), pp. 447-465.

COCKETT, A. T. K., AND BEEHLER, C. C. (1963): Total body hypothermia for prolonged space travel. *Aerospace Med. 34*, 504-506.

EDHOLM, O. G., AND LEWIS, H. E. (1964): Terrestrial animals in cold: man in polar regions. *In* "Handbook of Physiology," Sec. 4 (E. F. Adolph and C. G. Wilbur, eds.), pp. 435-446.

HAMMEL, H. T. (1964): Terrestrial animals in cold: recent studies of primitive man. *In* "Handbook of Physiology," Sec. 4 (E. F. Adolph and C. G. Wilber, eds.), pp. 413-434.

HANDBOOK STAFF OF TUFTS COLLEGE (1949): "Handbook of Human Engineering Data for Design Engineers." Technical Report SDC 199-1-1. NavExosP-643. Tufts College Institute for Applied Experimental Psychology, Medford, Mass.

HEILBRUNN, L. V. (1952): "An Outline of General Physiology," pp. 349-356. W. B. Saunders Co., Philadelphia.

HICKS, C. S. (1964): Terrestrial animals in cold: exploratory studies of primitive man. *In* "Handbook of Physiology," Sec. 4 (E. F. Adolph and C. G. Wilber, eds.), pp. 405-412.

HOCK, R. J. (1960): The potential application of hibernation to space travel. *Aerospace Med. 31*, 485-489.

HOFFMAN, R. A. (1964): Terrestrial animals in cold: hibernators. *In* "Handbook of Physiology," Sec. 4 (E. F. Adolph and C. G. Wilber, eds.), pp. 379-403.

HUDSON, J. W., AND BARTHOLOMEW, G. A. (1964): Terrestrial animals in dry heat: estivators. *In* "Handbook of Physiology," Sec. 4 (E. F. Adolph and C. G. Wilber, eds.), pp. 541-550.

IRVING, L. (1964): Terrestrial animals in cold: birds and mammals. *In* "Handbook of Physiology," Sec. 4 (E. F. Adolph and C. G. Wilber, eds.), pp. 361-377.

JOHNSON, F. H., EYRING, H., AND POLISSAR, M J. (1954): "The Kinetic Basis of Molecular Energy," pp. 187-285. John Wiley and Sons, Inc., New York.

KAUFMAN, W. C. (1963): Human tolerance limits for some thermal environments of aerospace. *Aerospace Med. 34*, 889-896.

KOTANCHIK, J. N. (1964): Manned spacecraft material problems. *Astronautics & Aeronautics, July,* 12-17.

LADELL, W. S. S. (1964): Terrestrial animals in humid heat: man. *In* "Handbook of Physiology," Sec. 4 (E. F. Adolph and C. G. Wilber, eds.), pp. 625-659.

LEE, D. H. K. (1964): Terrestrial animals in humid heat: man. *In* "Handbook of Physiology," Sec. 4 (E. F. Adolph and C. G. Wilber, eds.), pp. 551-582.

PROSSER, C. L., AND BROWN, F. A., JR. (1961): "Comparative Animal Physiology," 2nd ed., pp. 153-197. W. B. Saunders Co., Philadelphia.

SMITH, A. U. (1961): "Biological Effects of Freezing and Supercooling." Edward Arnold, London.

STACY, R. W., *et al.* (1955): "Essentials of Biological and Medical Physics," pp. 147-190. McGraw-Hill Book Co., Inc., New York.

WINSLOW, C. E. A., AND HERRINGTON, L. P. (1949): "Temperature and Human Life." Princeton University Press, Princeton.

WINSLOW, C. E. A., HERRINGTON, L. P., AND GAGGE, A. P. (1937): Physiological reactions of the human body to various atmospheric humidities. *Amer. J. Physiol. 120*, 288-299.

WUNDER, C. C., HERRIN, W. F., AND CRAWFORD, C. R. (1959): Combined influence of gravity and temperature upon growth of fruit fly larvae. *Growth 23*, 349-357.

6 | Pressures and Vacuums

There are two primary, immediate concerns of altered environmental pressures: (1) man's equipment must withstand the vacuum of outer space, and (2) man himself will encounter unnatural atmospheres within the space cabin. Pressure decreases progressively toward an almost complete vacuum (10^{-19} atmospheres in outer space) as one leaves the Earth (Figs. 6-1, 3-1).[1]

---

[1] Unfortunately, considerable confusion exists in the description of the magnitude of pressures. The reader will remember that pressure is defined in terms of force per unit of area acting *normal* (at right angles) *to some surface*. It should not be thought of as a height, since the actual head to which pressure can raise a fluid will vary with the existing g field and is expressed in units which, if carelessly handled, are not compatible with force/area (see the equation below). Moreover, there is an unfortunate tendency among many individuals who are naive about the nature of physical quantities to confuse gravity (which exerts a force in proportion to its field intensity g and the *mass* of a body being acted upon; see Chapter 8) and pressure (which exerts a force in proportion to the magnitude of pressure and the *area of a surface* being acted upon).

At sea level, the pressure resulting from the atmospheric gases is equal to 15 pounds per square inch (76 cm Hg, 760 torr [after Torricelli], 34 feet of water, 1.01 million dynes/cm², 1.01 bar). This magnitude of pressure is frequently referred to as "standard pressure." Thus, pressures are frequently expressed in terms of "atmospheres" (multiples of 15 lbs. per square inch). As one atmosphere of pressure is considered the reference, engineers and medical scientists frequently arbitrarily define one atmosphere as zero pressure. The pressure values would differ from the actual or absolute pressure by one atmosphere, so that a pressure of less than one atmosphere would be defined as a negative pressure.

Pressure differences are frequently expressed in terms of a *head,* which is actually the height of a fluid column that will result in a hydrostatic pressure just adequate to counterbalance a given pressure difference. From the equation in footnote 2, one can see that although this head h is indeed proportional to pressure P, it also depends upon the density δ of the manometer fluid and the existing inertial or gravitational field g.

$$h = \frac{P}{\delta g}$$

As head can change with gravitational field, the acceptance of absolute units such as bar or millibar (mb) by biologists and others concerned with space science will probably become a necessity in precise descriptions.

With properly functioning life-support equipment, this vacuum will have little direct effect upon man. However, it will cause outgassing of the exterior coating of a pressurized cabin, converting the surface materials into substances of a relatively untested nature; and it will expose the coating

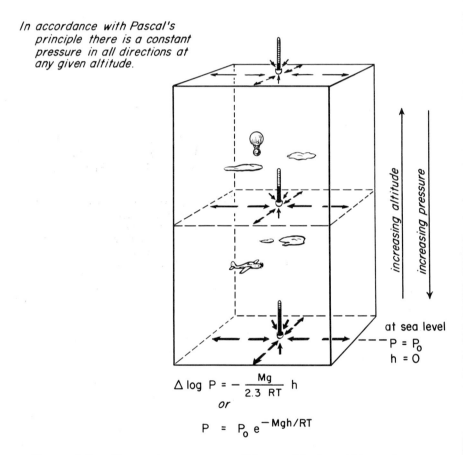

In accordance with Pascal's principle there is a constant pressure in all directions at any given altitude.

$$\Delta \log P = - \frac{Mg}{2.3\ RT}\ h$$

or

$$P = P_0\ e^{-Mgh/RT}$$

Figure 6-1. Change in pressure at different altitudes within a planetary atmosphere. With fluids of uniform density, such as water, pressure would rise in a direct proportion to the depth. As gases do not display a uniform pressure with depth, an exponential relationship exists. Values for atmospheric pressures at various altitudes on Earth and Mars are given in Figure 3-1.

There are two principal categories of pressure: hydrostatic pressure and collision pressure. Hydrostatic pressure was defined by Pascal as a pressure which is transmitted equally throughout all parts (which are at a constant gravitational potential or, roughly speaking, the same distance from the center of a planet) of a stationary liquid.

to erosion by dust-like micrometeors, to pitting and denting by small meteors, to puncture by large meteors, and to penetration by high-energy radiation (see Chapter 9).

Some of these effects are currently being investigated in large vacuum chambers called "space simulators" (Fig. 6-2). Expediency may demand (as is presently the case with American projects; see pp. 234-252) that this atmosphere possess a barometric pressure and a composition which are unnatural to man.

The internal pressure environment will be altered for yet another reason. Acceleration and altered gravitational fields will change the hydrostatic pres-

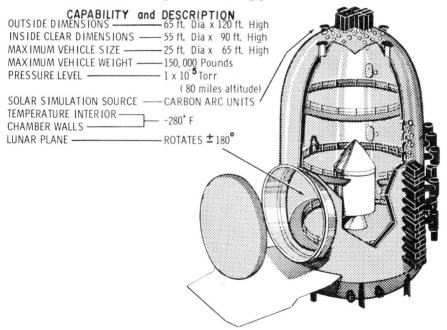

Space Environment Simulation Laboratory Chamber A

CAPABILITY and DESCRIPTION

OUTSIDE DIMENSIONS ———— 65 ft. Dia x 120 ft. High
INSIDE CLEAR DIMENSIONS ——— 55 ft. Dia x 90 ft. High
MAXIMUM VEHICLE SIZE ———— 25 ft. Dia x 65 ft. High
MAXIMUM VEHICLE WEIGHT ——— 150,000 Pounds
PRESSURE LEVEL ———————— 1 x 10^{-5} Torr
                                (80 miles altitude)
SOLAR SIMULATION SOURCE ——— CARBON ARC UNITS
TEMPERATURE INTERIOR ———┐
CHAMBER WALLS ——————————┘ -280° F
LUNAR PLANE ———————————— ROTATES ± 180°

Figure 6-2. Space simulator presently under construction at NASA Manned Space Flight Center, Houston, Texas (Official NASA drawing). At this writing the largest known vacuum chamber in operation belongs to General Electric Company. Although existing vacuum chambers are unable to achieve a vacuum as complete as outer space (10^{-19} atm) it is believed that the conditions for various effects can be approached with less complete vacuums (mechanical, 10^{-2} atm, thermal conduction, 10^{-8} atm; electrical discharge, 10^{-9}; on surfaces of bearings, 10^{-13} atm, Stantler, 1965).

sure contribution from fluid columns (such as blood vessels) within the body, in accordance with the same principle which causes greater pressures to exist at progressively greater depths of the ocean.[2]

Of eventual significance will be the differing pressures on other planetary bodies. Some planets are too small (and thus require a smaller escape velocity than that velocity afforded by a gas molecule's thermal motion, as is the case for the Moon and for Mercury) to retain an atmosphere. On some such bodies (Mars, Fig. 6-6), the existing atmospheric pressure is too low to permit an adequate supply of oxygen, even when inspired from an oxygen mask, without a full-pressure suit. Although the pressures at the surfaces of the larger planets (Jupiter, Saturn, Uranus, and Neptune, which are obscured by dense atmosphere) are not precisely known, they are believed to exceed that on this planet by many fold.

There are several ways in which pressure can influence an organism (Fig. 6-3). The total, or gross absolute, pressure (if equal throughout a system) does not so readily exert a mechanical effect as do pressure differences across two parts of an object or the pressure changes which occur with time. The absolute magnitude of the pressure does have marked influences upon the solubility of biologically significant gases, the state (such as solid, liquid, or gas) of material, and with sufficiently high magnitude, the chemical rates of reaction.

Distortions Caused by Pressure Gradients

The most readily observed result of pressure is the distortion caused from pressure differences.[3] The rate at which blood and other fluids pass through a channel is proportional to the pressure difference across the two ends of the channel rather than the absolute ambient pressure.

The distortion of extensible containers of gases and fluids is determined by pressure difference across the two sides of a container. Distortion can proceed until rupture occurs or until the force resulting from the pressure

---

[2] Total weight of a fluid (whether it be atmospheric gas, whose density changes with pressure and altitude, or a fluid of constant density) is proportional to its mass and the gravitational field intensity. Mass in turn is proportional to the height h and density δ of a fluid column:

$$\text{hydrostatic pressure attributable to a fluid column} = \delta hg$$

[3] In speaking of pressures, we should distinguish between pressure differences and pressure gradients. Gradients refer not to the actual differences in amount or quantity across distance but rather to the pressure differences divided by the distance separating the two points possessing a pressure difference. More precisely, a gradient is the rate of change in a quantity per unit of distance. In a blood vessel 100 cm long with a driving pressure of two atmospheres at one end and a pressure of one atmosphere at the other end, the pressure difference would be one atmosphere while the pressure gradient would be 1/100 of an atmosphere per centimeter. Knowledge of pressure gradients can provide a more precise prediction of flow patterns than the knowledge of pressure difference alone. The flow of fluid for constant viscosity and constant cross-section of channel is directly proportional to the pressure difference and inversely proportional to the channel length.

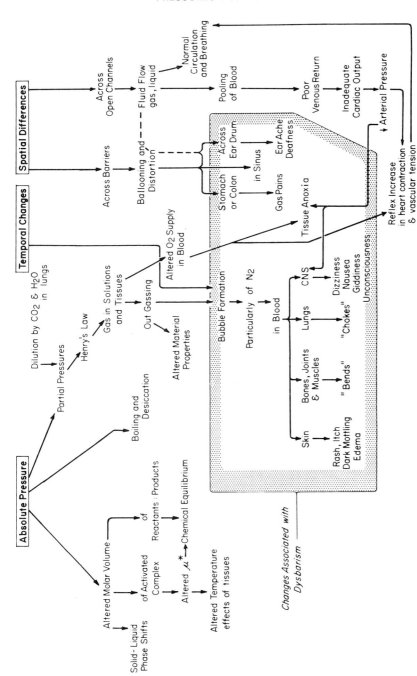

Figure 6-3. Some of the possible effects of altered pressure. Those portions referring to dysbarism are based primarily upon the discussion by Adler, 1964.

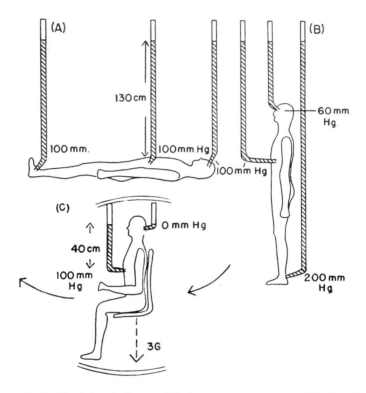

Figure 6-4. Hydrostatic factor δgh in operation on arterial blood pressure (Burton, 1960). Cannulae inserted into aorta and arteries of brain and foot would support columns of blood to heights shown. The head of 100 mm Hg indicated for an individual exposed to 3 G's is not the actual head that would be measured by a mercury manometer. Rather it is the reading in proportion to pressure from a recording device calibrated by a mercury column at 1.0 G. Actually a mercury column would rise to only 33 1/3 mm under these conditions (3 G's). Note that the piezometric pressure (total static pressure) would be at a constant level even though the hydrostatic and reference levels would change with posture or with gravitational field. There would be a small loss in total pressure due to the energy lost overcoming resistance to flow. That is ignored in the figure.

In Part A the individual has been resting in a supine position for at least 30 seconds. Pressures shown in Parts B and C are for the very first moment of exposure to these conditions. Within 5 or 10 seconds, arterial pressure at the level of the heart and head would drop to a lower level due to pooling of blood in the veins of the legs and abdomen and the resulting decreased amount of blood which can be pumped from the heart. Within a few more seconds, compensatory reflexes would cause these lowered pressures to rise back up toward more desirable levels.

differences on the two sides of the containers is just equal to that resulting from the tension along the walls of the stretched container. This can be described by the Law of LaPlace.[4] Examples of such hollow structures might be the stomach, intestines, blood vessels, bubbles, and vacuoles (tiny vessels which are found inside of cells). Tension along the walls of these structures is caused either by the stretching of tissues or by molecular attractions which give rise to surface tensions and interfacial tensions.

To partially negate the potential hazard of explosive decompression, the space capsules employed in the Mercury and Gemini Projects and those contemplated for the Apollo Project contain a gaseous mixture which is at a pressure of one third of an atmosphere. In the event of a meteor puncturing the capsule, the pressure change would not be quite so abrupt as with full atmospheric pressure and might permit survival of a space chamber's occupants for sufficient time to apply an oxygen mask or space helmet.

Any abrupt change in barometric pressure (such as the explosive decompression which would accompany the meteor-puncture of a pressure chamber) can cause a number of medical disorders related to the unbalanced pressures between the inside and the outside of an individual (Fig. 6-3). *Dysbarism* is the term used to describe any of these disorders (Adler, 1964).[5] Among the most familiar symptoms to almost anyone who has made rapid ascents or descents (by airplane, high speed elevators, or even mountain roads) are those resulting from gases which, if not trapped, would expand in accordance with Boyle's Law (Fig. 6-5). These symptoms include the discomfort (barotalgia) and impaired hearing associated with pressure differences across the ear drum, the pain and headaches due to unbalanced pressure within the sinuses of the head, and the gas pains from within the abdomen.

Of far greater consequence are the bubbles of gas which, in accordance with Henry's Law, evolve to obstruct circulation. Circulation can be obstructed in the bone joints and in the muscles to cause pains known as "bends." Impaired circulation to the skin can result in rash, itch, and discoloration. When the central nervous system (CNS) is affected, dizziness and giddiness can occur. Respiratory discomfort is referred to as "chokes."

---

[4] In accordance with the Law of LaPlace, the net pressure difference $\triangle P$ across the walls of a vessel just necessary to balance that generated by the tension of the walls would be

$$\triangle P \text{ (cylindrical vessels)} = \frac{\text{Tension}}{\text{radius}}$$

$$\triangle P \text{ (spherical vessels)} = \frac{2 \text{ Tension}}{\text{radius}}$$

[5] When the changes occur across ranges which do not include any pressures in excess of one atmosphere, the resulting disorder is referred to as *altitude dysbarism*. *Caisson disease* refers to those changes associated with absolute pressures which are in turn associated with changes in excess of one atmosphere (such as might be encountered by deep sea divers or tunnel workers).

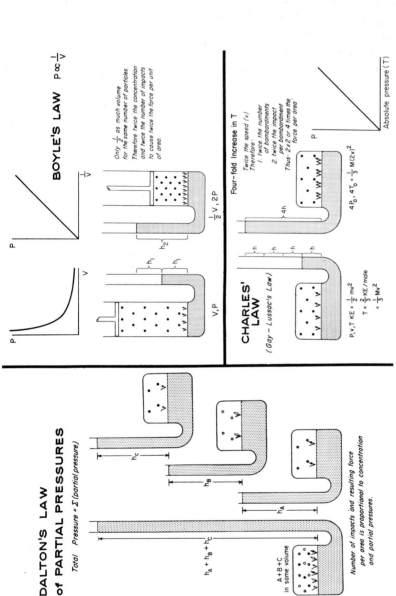

Figure 6-5. Gas laws as visualized in terms of molecular kinetic impact. Boyle's Law and Charles' Law can be combined to give the *Ideal Gas Law*

$$PV = NRT = nkT$$

where N is the number of moles of gas, R is the Ideal Gas Constant which is equal to 1.99 calories per (mole-degree K) or 0.082 liter-atmospheres, n is the number of molecules and k is the Boltzman constant, which is equal to 1.4×10^{-16} ergs per degree K. More elaborate relationships, such as the van der Waals' equation, are necessary when one wishes to account for the volume of molecules and the attraction between them.

The effects of changes in absolute pressure within an individual subjected to acceleration or high gravity (Fig. 6-3) can be largely overcome if gradients do not occur. When an individual stands erect in a high G field, the column of blood effected by the force will result in an outward ballooning of the blood vessels in the abdomen and legs. Pooling of blood occurs in these regions and circulation is impaired. This distortion occurs because the pressure outside the blood vessels is much lower than that inside the vessels. Human skin is an integument with inadequate tension to generate sufficient pressure to oppose the pressure resulting from an increased weight (gravitational force) of the blood. The same effect occurs when standing in the Earth's g field, but the effects are much less pronounced. Two measures may be used to prevent this distortion: one method is to increase the tension, either of the vessel walls or of the effective integument; the other method is to decrease the pressure difference across the walls. Another way of effecting greater tension is by means of an exoskeleton, as is the case with such arthropods as lobsters and grasshoppers, or with most turtles. In these instances, the integument undergoes little or no distortion. The body tissue cannot be pushed outward and therefore develops an opposing pressure which is almost equal to that inside of the blood vessel. This permits little or no distortion.

Men have achieved the effect of a tougher integument by using the so-called "anti-g suit." Basically, the anti-g suit is a corset which is placed about the abdomen and legs of a pilot or astronaut. By compression of the blood vessels, a greater tolerance to increased gravity can be achieved. Occasionally anti-g suits are used clinically with individuals possessing poor vascular tension who would not otherwise be able to perform tasks which require erect posture.

Submersion in water can utilize buoyancy to eliminate high-pressure gradients which could otherwise be produced by g fields. As water possesses potentially the same density as blood, the same pressure gradients exist with respect to depth in the fluid surrounding the body as exists within the blood vessels and other fluids of the body. Save for pressures generated by the muscular action of the heart, there is no major pressure difference across either the blood vessels or the external body walls.

Various reflex-induced adjustments occur when pressure differences across the vascular bed are inadequate to provide sufficiently fast circulation either as a result of gravitationally induced pooling (which reduces the venous return and thus the heart's volume output of blood) or for other reasons. Low arterial pressure (causing subnormal stimuli to the special nerve endings called *baroreceptors* in the arch of the aorta and in the carotid sinus) is followed by increased heart rate and constriction of certain arteries (particularly those leading to regions like the gut, which are relatively unnecessary during emergency situations).

Gaseous Pressures

The pressure which a gas exerts against a surface can be considered a type of collision pressure, which is generated by the bombardment of the individual molecules of gas. The force generated by this bombardment can be shown to be equal to the force attributable to a gas's weight in the atmosphere. Thus, in considering the interaction of gases under pressures with material, it is convenient to think of gaseous pressure as a collision pressure; however, from the point of view of computing pressures on the basis of the weight of columns of gases, this pressure can just as conveniently be considered a hydrostatic pressure. The biological influence of gaseous pressure is quite obvious if one remembers certain fundamental laws. These are: *Boyle's Law,* which describes the relationship between volume and pressure; *Charles' Law,* which describes the relationship between temperature and pressure; *Dalton's Law,* which describes the relationship of pressures in a mixture of various gaseous components; and *Henry's Law,* which describes the solubility of gases in liquid. The justification of these laws can be visualized in terms of the frequency of molecular impact against a surface (for the first three of these laws see Fig. 6-5) or frequency of molecular passage across a liquid-gas interphase for Henry's Law.[6]

Let us consider the dilution of air which occurs as a result of the partial pressure of carbon dioxide and of water vapor in the lungs (Fig. 6-6). Atmospheric air contains 21 per cent oxygen and is approximately in equilibrium with the gaseous pressure in the lungs.

$$P_{\text{Barometric}} \simeq P_{\text{Air in atmosphere}} = P_{\text{Lungs}}$$

However, the total gaseous pressure in the lungs is equal to the partial pressure of the air plus the partial pressure of carbon dioxide released into the lungs from the venous blood, plus the partial pressure of water at body temperature.

$$P_{\text{Lungs}} = P_{\text{Air in lungs}} + P_{\text{CO}_2} + P_{\text{H}_2\text{O}}$$

Thus, the partial pressure of the air in the lungs is less than the barometric pressure:

$$P_{\text{Air in lungs}} = P_{\text{Air in atmosphere}} - P_{\text{CO}_2} - P_{\text{H}_2\text{O}}$$

$$P_{\text{O}_2 \text{ in lungs}} = (P_{\text{Air in atmosphere}} - P_{\text{CO}_2} - P_{\text{H}_2\text{O}}) \times 21\%$$

---

[6] In accordance with Henry's Law for the Concentration of Dissolved Gases in Liquid, the concentration C by volume of a given gas in solution is proportional to its partial pressure P.P. (which at equilibrium will be the same in the gas mixture and in the liquid):

$$C = s \times P.P.$$

where s is the coefficient of solubility which will be specific for a given gas and liquid.

Athough the ratio of exposed area to volume will influence the rate at which a gas can be dissolved or evolved, it will not influence the equilibrium concentration. This relationship applies only to the concentration of gas dissolved in solution and not to that which may be bound chemically (such as that fraction of oxygen in blood which is chemically bound by the hemoglobin).

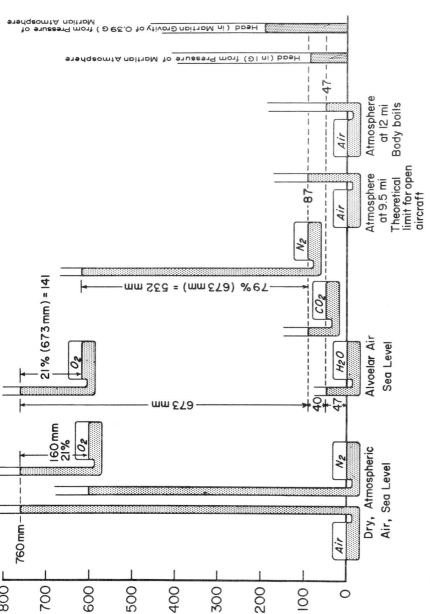

Figure 6-6. Application of Dalton's Law for predicting availability of oxygen within the lungs at various ambient pressures. Note that on Mars the barometric pressure, believed to exist when this figure was prepared, is so low that a full pressure suit would be necessary in presenting oxygen to human lungs. Also note that heads of barometric fluids would be higher for the same pressure in that planet's lower gravity. (Recent work cites a still lower pressure, 10 mm Hg, for Mars.)

and the resulting partial pressure of oxygen is also less. At an atmospheric pressure of 760 mm of mercury, the partial pressure of carbon dioxide in the lungs of the average, resting, healthy man at sea level is equal to 40 mm of mercury, and the partial pressure of water at 37° C is equal to 47 mm of mercury. Oxygen pressure after dilution by internally produced gases in the lungs is then equal to:

$$(760 \text{ mm} - 40 \text{ mm} - 47 \text{ mm}) \times 21\% = 673 \times .21 = 143 \text{ mm}$$

(Even less would be present after some is absorbed by the blood in the capillaries of the lungs.[7])

As we rise higher and higher into the atmosphere, the partial pressure of oxygen in the atmosphere drops. The partial pressures of water vapor and carbon dioxide in the lungs, however, which are functions of temperature and respiration respectively, do not greatly change; and the fraction of oxygen in the air of the lungs progressively decreases until it has dropped to zero at 9.5 miles (the height at which the barometric pressure is equal to the sum of the partial pressures of carbon dioxide and water vapor in the lungs). Until this altitude is reached, the oxygen in the lungs can be partially enhanced by inhaling pure oxygen rather than atmospheric air. Once the height of 9.5 miles is attained, however, the ambient pressure will be in equilibrium with carbon dioxide plus water vapor produced internally, so that no inhalation can occur. For this and higher altitudes, a pressurized chamber, or at least a pressurized helmet, is necessary, so that the immediate ambient pressure can be in excess of that attributable to carbon dioxide and water.

From Henry's Law, one can predict the amount of oxygen which would be carried in solution by the blood. However, this is a relatively small fraction of the amount of oxygen *actually* carried by the blood. The remainder is carried by hemoglobin. The amount of oxygen bound by the hemoglobin increases with the concentration in solution and thus with oxygen partial pressure, but the nature of the oxygen-hemoglobin dissociation curve is not linear with pressure. Saturation is approached near 80 mm of oxygen tension (see Fig. 7-6). The ability of the blood to carry oxygen is thus primarily a matter of chemical binding rather than a direct consequence of pressure-induced forces. The changes in oxygen binding with partial pressure will therefore be discussed more fully in the subsequent chapter.

---

[7] The equations listed in the text refer to the oxygen tension presented to the lungs. After sufficient absorption of oxygen and release of carbon dioxide across the alveolar walls to equilibrate with the blood in the alveolar capillaries, the oxygen tension would be more accurately approximated by:

$$P_{O_2 \text{ in lungs}} = 0.21 \ [P_{\text{Air in atm}} - P_{H_2O} - P_{CO_2} (1 - \frac{1}{0.82})] - \frac{P_{CO_2}}{0.82}$$

where 0.21 is the assumed volume concentration of oxygen in the atmospheric air and 0.82 is the assumed respiratory quotient (volume rate of CO_2 release to the volume rate of O_2 absorption).

Henry's Law also explains the formation of air bubbles associated with dysbarism to cause bends, chokes, etc. At higher pressures, the gases in air, particularly nitrogen (which has a large solubility coefficient), will be driven into tissues and liquids as a result of the greater partial pressure. When there is a sudden decrease in the ambient pressure of a gas, the maximum amount of the gas which can be dissolved in the tissues and fluids of the body decreases, and the gas is released in the form of bubbles. These bubbles in the blood vessels of the body cause circulatory disturbances and pains.

When nitrogen has not been present in an individual's tissues, those symptoms of dysbarism associated with bubble formation are either eliminated or drastically reduced. Nitrogen can be flushed from the tissues by prolonged breathing of pure oxygen prior to decompression. It is for this reason (together with payload limitations and the desire for simplicity of design) that American space capsules are employing pure oxygen. On the other hand, there are other factors (such as fire hazards, unnatural environment for conduction of body heat exchange, and lack of information concerning the necessity, if any, for respiratory nitrogen) that have led the Soviets to employ a more natural atmospheric environment.

Absolute Pressure Effects

The state of material can be influenced by the absolute magnitude of the ambient pressure. Greater pressures would tend to drive a material into the state which requires the least volume. For this reason, ice skates lower the melting temperature of ice to furnish a lubricating layer of water which persists long enough for the skater to pass. The influence of pressure upon the boiling temperature of material (particularly of water) is of greater biological significance.

As there is a large volume change when a material changes from a liquid to the vapor or gaseous stage, pressures can markedly influence the boiling temperatures of fluids. A liquid can release vapor in proportion to its vapor pressure, but boiling will not occur until a liquid's vapor pressure is equal to the magnitude of the ambient pressure. As previously discussed and as illustrated in Figure 6-6, boiling or at least rapid desiccation would be expected at body temperatures with pressures of 87 mm Hg or lower. As protoplasm occupies a given volume at a given viscosity, similar considerations of pressure and volume would predict that high pressures should drive protoplasm to states of lowered viscosity. This is, indeed, found to be the case for the protoplasm of a number of different organisms when exposed to hydrostatic pressures in excess of 70 atmospheres.

Life is certainly possible in pressures of several hundred atmospheres. In fact, organisms are known to inhabit this planet's seas to depths (3½ mi) where pressure exceeds 600 atmospheres. Pressures to be found at the surface of planets possessing very dense atmospheres would probably not forbid the existence of some form of life. Cells and organisms can tolerate exposure to gradually applied pressures as great as 1000 atmospheres.

Although activity is decreased, the effects can be reversed if pressure is removed at the onset of inactivity. These reversible effects are attributable to a change in the viscosity of materials and to the solubility of reactive gases.

Pressures required to inactivate proteins and cause other molecular changes are of the order of from 1,000 to 15,000 atmospheres. Although such intense pressures can undoubtedly be found sufficiently deep inside any heavenly body, the ability to tolerate them would not be a requirement for survival at the surface.

Transplanetary migration of life within meteors might require tolerance to such pressures. Objects which reach our atmosphere from space are drawn into it with such speed that frictional heat destroys these bodies before they can reach the ground (see pages 36, 76-77). Only life which could be packed deep within large meteors might receive adequate thermal insulation. Meteors were once thought to have originated from an exploding planet (see page 265, footnote 5). The explosion would have generated intense pressures within the core of a meteor which might possibly carry surviving organisms.

Pressures in excess of 1,000 atmospheres can alter the energy changes associated with a chemical reaction. At any constant pressure P, a change $\triangle V$ in volume in going from one configuration to another (say from reacting chemicals to the products of the reaction) will cause a potential energy change $P\triangle V$. In reactions at low pressures which involve only solids and liquids but not gases, the change is insignificant as compared to the other energy changes associated with a reaction. At high pressures, this energy change can become appreciable and may alter the direction of a biologically significant reaction.

Johnson et al. (1954) reviewed the influence of this volume difference upon the energy μ^* necessary to create activated complexes. Pressure influences magnitude and temperature dependence of reaction rates for such processes as protein inactivation.[8] Thus high pressures (i.e., those in excess of 1000 atmospheres) can change not only the rate of biologically significant reactions but the temperature dependence as well (see Chapter 5, footnote 3). Intense pressures are known to enhance the inactivation of some proteins.

Bibliography and References

ADLER, H. F. (1964): "Dysbarism." *Aeromedical Reviews*, Review 1-64, USAF School of Aerospace Medicine, Brooks AFB, Texas.

BURTON, A. C. (1960): Hemodynamics and the physics of the circulation. *In* "Medical Physiology and Biophysics" (T. C. Ruch and J. F. Fulton, eds.), 18th ed., pp 643-666. W. B. Saunders Co., Philadelphia.

---

[8] The activation energy changes with pressure, so that

$$\mu^* = \mu_o^* + P\Delta V^*$$

where μ_o^* is the energy for activation at zero pressure and $\triangle V^*$ is the difference between the volume of a reacting molecule and the activated molecule.

HEILBRUNN, L. V. (1952): "An Outline of General Physiology," 3rd ed., pp. 503-509. W. B. Saunders Co., Philadelphia.

JOHNSON, F. H., EYRING, H., AND POLISSAR, M. J. (1954): "The Kinetic Basis of Molecular Biology," pp. 286-368. John Wiley and Sons, Inc., New York.

LANPHIER, E. H. (1964): Man in high pressures. *In* "Handbook of Physiology, Sec. 4: Adaptation to the Environment" (D. B. Dill, E. F. Adolph, and C. G. Wilber, eds.), pp. 893-909. American Physiological Society, Washington, D. C.

SIMONS, D. G. (1964): Animals in high altitudes: in space capsules. *In* "Handbook of Physiology, Sec. 4: Adaptation to the Environment" (D. B. Dill, E. F. Adolph, and C. G. Wilber, eds.), pp. 877-892. American Physiological Society, Washington, D. C.

STANTLER, D. (1965): Vacuum technology. Paper No. 1. *In* "Proc. of Conf. on Role of Simulation in Space Technology," *Engineering Extension Series Circulator No. 4, Part A*, Va. Poly. Inst., Blacksburg.

7 | Metabolism and the Chemical Environment

The success of the various chemical reactions necessary for metabolism[1] and growth (Fig. 7-1) obviously depends upon the precise nature of the chemical environment. The state of knowledge pertaining to human nutrition is such that, given adequate storage space, all of man's metabolic needs can be satisfied for an indefinite period of time. The mineral and vitamin requirements would be too small to seriously crowd the precious cargo space of a rocket vehicle. The metabolically important supplies which would occupy valuable cargo space are oxygen, water, proteins, carbohydrates, and fats.

Energy Requirements for Metabolism

In order to maintain life, the average resting individual must metabolize sufficient food (approximately 0.8 lb., dry weight) to produce approximately 1800 kcal of energy per day. Considerably more energy would be necessary for individuals who are performing work or displaying other types of activ-

---

[1] *Metabolism* is concerned with the building up (*anabolism*) and tearing down (*catabolism*) of living material as well as the release of energy necessary for these and other processes within an organism. When anabolism proceeds at a faster rate than catabolism, the net result is growth (Fig. 7-1) or storage of food materials. In any conceivable type of life, anabolism would involve the synthesis of complex chemical compounds from less complex ones, while catabolism would involve the reverse phenomenon. In animals, all the energy which is necessary for these processes is obtained from the potential energy which has been stored in chemical form in various compounds. As is the case for all energy utilized on this planet, save the energy arising from some nuclear processes, the ultimate source for the energy used in metabolism is the Sun. The radiant energy of visible sunlight is converted by the process of photosynthesis in the green plants into potential chemical energy. This process stores the Sun's energy in a form which can be utilized in the conversion of the gas, carbon dioxide, and water into carbohydrates and gaseous oxygen. The carbohydrates can at some later time react with oxygen to release energy for the synthesis of other food materials and protoplasm or to bring about other metabolic processes. Photosynthesis is the first step whereby most of the Sun's energy can be utilized by life on this planet. Like green plants, some bacteria can utilize sunlight while other bacteria can utilize heat (which itself is the result of the Sun's radiant energy) to produce food materials and usable energy sources.

106

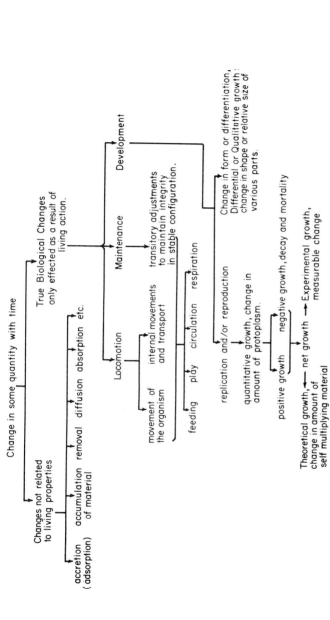

Figure 7-1. Categories of growth and change (Wunder and Lutherer, 1964). As loosely employed in the text of this chapter the term "growth" refers to a measurable increase in some dimension of an organism's size. This is a rather loose criterion because it would include increases associated with storage of such non-living matter as water and stored fat. Although more difficult to achieve operationally, but more satisfactory theoretically, one might consider growth to be a measure of the increase in living material (which is itself capable of producing more such material).

For the sake of completeness in this figure, arbitrary distinctions between some processes were necessary. Some replication of living material is necessary not only for growth but also for maintenance in the replacement of destroyed or catabolized protein.

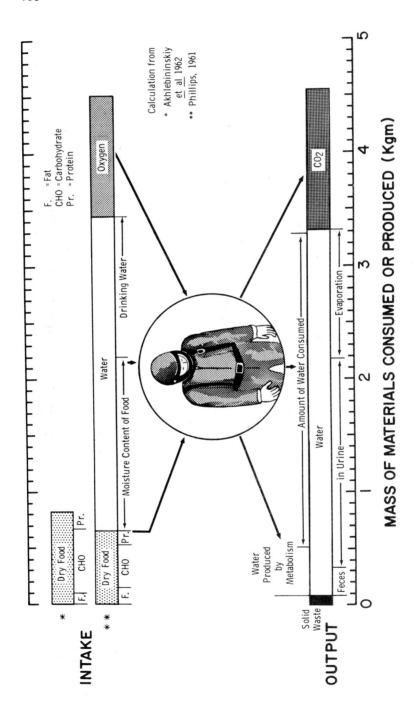

Figure 7-2. Typical turnover of material in a man producing 3600 kilocalories per day. (Based in part on data in the articles by Keller, 1960; Welch, 1963; and Akhlebininskiy, et al. 1962.)

ity. It seems likely that an astronaut remaining sufficiently active to maintain normal health throughout an extended voyage into space would consume something in the neighborhood of twice the basal requirement (3600 kcal per day or 1.6 lbs.) of food. Typical breakdowns of the total masses of material intake and output associated with this rate of metabolism are shown in Figures 7-2 and 10-5. If the metabolizing individual exhibits neither net growth (see Fig. 7-1) nor other changes in mass, the mass of the waste output (gases, liquids, and solids) by the individual will be equal to the mass of materials consumed. A breakdown of the manner in which ingested food or its energy equivalent might be utilized is shown in Figure 7-3.

Interesting speculation has arisen relative to changes which might be expected in this metabolic balance when the gravitational environment is altered. Even in the absence of gravity, a certain amount of energy must be expended in overcoming the resistance which opposes the movement of air, blood, fluids other than blood, and tissue during such processes as respiratory ventilation and circulation. However, a large amount of energy is consumed by the body in opposing gravity to move these materials as well as to move the body itself. In the absence of knowledge concerning this specific caloric requirement, several possibilities can be considered. A concomitant decrease in caloric intake may take place with the same amount of food materials being allocated to gravity-free processes and to storage. If there is no change in the total caloric intake or in the gravity-free activity, the only alternative would be a greater storage of food materials in the form of growth or of laying down of additional fat. As a major decrease in the total activity of the individual could result in a detrimental deterioration of all muscle (smooth, skeletal, and cardiac), it would be most desirable to maintain the original degree of food intake and total activity by subjecting the individual to a regimen of physical conditioning which would increase the amount of gravity-free work in proportion to the decrement in the work which would normally oppose gravity. There is also the possibility that astronauts will consume more energy in pursuing certain tasks associated with rendezvous or assembly of space stations. This is due to the fact that (in the absence of gravitationally imposed friction) men will be required to exert an "anchoring" force to counterbalance the reaction to their useful forces.

At the present time, there is only indirect evidence to verify the prediction that prolonged exposure to weightlessness would result in a decreased metabolic requirement and a resulting gain in body mass. No one denies that the individual who is resting in bed (and therefore doing much less work to oppose gravity than an active, standing individual) will require less food and less oxygen for his metabolism. It is also common knowledge that obesity increases with caloric intake and decreases with physical exertion. In experiments where individuals are subjected to some simulation of weightlessness (such as bed rest, immobilization, or water immersion), there is evidence of a decreased intake of food and oxygen accompanied by some deterioration of the skeletal and vascular musculature (see pp. 158-169). Con-

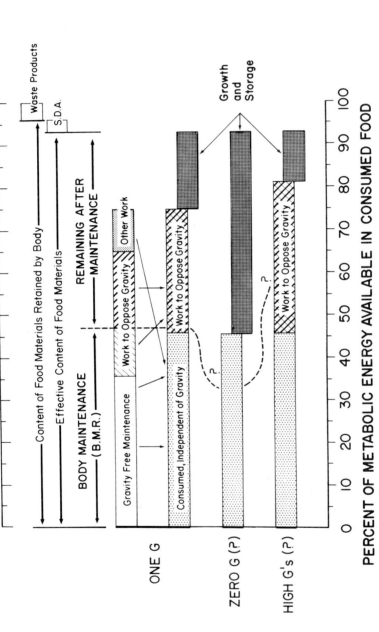

PERCENT OF METABOLIC ENERGY AVAILABLE IN CONSUMED FOOD

Figure 7-3. Utilization of the energy obtained from food materials. Of the total energy consumed not all of it will be utilized for metabolic energy. A portion of the energy content of food (approximately 6 percent) is used in converting the chemical nature of food materials or in other processes whereby these materials may be utilized by the cells of the body. This property of food is referred to as "specific dynamic action" (SDA). The lower two bars are suggestions as to the alteration in the availability of food for growth under gravitational conditions which would not normally be encountered on this planet but might become of significance either during extended space voyages or upon another planet.

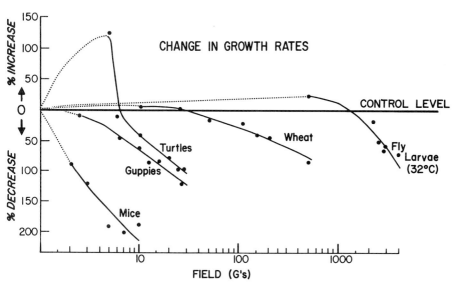

Figure 7-4. Immediate (first 24-hour) change in growth rate upon exposure to centrifugation. (Wunder and Lutherer, 1964.) The wheat data are for the coleoptile of wheat observed by Gray. Fly data are for fruit fly larvae centrifuged at 31.5° C. Mouse data are for males of the NLW strain at the age of 5 weeks. Guppies were 1 week of age at the onset of exposure. Turtle data are for hatchling red-eared turtles which were hatched in the winter or spring. After several days of exposure, certain animals (such as mice, Fig. 4-9) demonstrate better growth at the same fields.

versely, animals subjected to sufficiently high gravitational fields do display a decreased growth and fat storage (Wunder and Lutherer, 1964). The smaller size of such organisms is illustrated in Figures 4-9, 4-10, 7-4, and 8-17. Extrapolation of certain experimental findings, together with the assumption of constant caloric intake, would predict that individuals exposed for extended periods to the type of weightless environment expected in the voyages to other planets would result in abnormal growth, producing individuals which by Terrestrial standards would be considered obese weaklings.

The metabolic implications of weightlessness are actually somewhat more complex. Under certain conditions the food intake of animals exposed to moderate increases in gravity decreases (Wunder, 1961). Under other conditions (presumably when the added exercise imposed by gravity becomes more important than immobilization and nausea), food consumption increases (Dodge and Wunder, 1962; Smith, 1963). Although a certain amount of food is undoubtedly diverted from growth and storage to overcome gravity, some gravity is probably necessary in order to orient this growth. Figure 7-4 shows that a moderate increase in gravity can accelerate the growth of some organisms while intense gravitational exposures will result in a decelerated growth.

No machine, including the living organism, is 100 percent efficient. When man does work, only about one fourth of the energy content contained within the food consumed for this work is released as useful work. Isolated cells are somewhat more efficient (30 to 50 percent). Evidence exists that the metabolic efficiency of living material can be influenced by the intensity of the gravitational environment (Wunder and Lutherer, 1964). After developing at high gravity, some plants and animals require less oxygen than those which develop at normal gravity, even though they might be growing at a faster than normal rate. After return to normal gravity, mice which had been previously centrifuged developed diaphragms (the major respiratory muscle in mammals) which were smaller—on the basis of percent by mass of dry material—than was the case for normal mice. On the same basis, when our astronauts are transferred from the Earth's gravity to the lower gravitational intensity of a space ship, some muscular degeneration might occur, which will decrease the astronaut's tolerance to fields of gravity and acceleration that he would have to meet upon returning to this or some other planet.

Dissipation of Metabolic Heat

All energy produced by the body must be dissipated as heat from the body's skin and respiratory surface unless it can first serve as useful work upon the surrounding environment. All of the energy resulting from metabolism is eventually converted into heat energy. This heat must be dissipated from a space capsule or pressure suit to avoid intolerable temperatures. With increasing heat dissipation by the occupants of a vessel or pressure suit, the assembly will require a greater surface for radiant heat emission (see page 76, footnote 2). When this limit is exceeded, other means of heat dissipation (such as water evaporation) could require consumption of life support supplies (see Fig. 10-6).

Several factors influencing metabolic rate were discussed in Chapter 5. One of these factors is the temperature of the tissue. With all plants and also with the vast majority of the animal kingdom, body temperature and therefore metabolism is not constant but varies with the temperature of the external environment. Since mammals and birds tend to maintain a constant body temperature, the rate of heat loss and rate of metabolism are regulated primarily by the amount of heat which an organism must exchange with the environment in order to maintain a constant equilibrium temperature of the body tissues. From reference to Figures 5-10 and 5-11, it is obvious that the major mechanisms for heat loss (conduction, convection, radiation, and evaporation) occur across surfaces (either the skin or the linings of the lungs and respiratory tract). With the smaller surface-to-mass ratio, the larger warm-blooded animals demand less oxygen and food per gram of tissue than do smaller ones. Thus, satellites carrying small mammals will require a payload designed to transport a *relatively* larger proportion of food, oxygen, and heat-dissipating machinery than will a satellite carrying larger mammals.

The Oxygen Environment

Molecular oxygen is undoubtedly a strategic chemical compound in both the external gaseous environment and in the internal liquid environment of man. Aerobic metabolism requires that oxygen be consumed as the oxidizing agent through which energy is released from food materials. Anaerobic metabolism, which does not require oxygen for the release of energy, occurs with some bacteria and a few parasitic animals. In the absence of light, most animals and even green plants require molecular oxygen for prolonged metabolism. Human tissue can achieve some degree of anaerobic metabolism for a short period of time (oxygen debt); but in order that oxidizing agents within the cells be regenerated, additional oxygen must be supplied to the tissues in proportion to the amount of anaerobic metabolism which occurred.

As oxygen proceeds from the air to the site of metabolism, there is a gradient of concentration from the concentration of oxygen found in the air. It is diluted by carbon dioxide and water vapor in the gases of the lungs (see Figs. 6-6 and 7-5). From the smallest compartments of the lungs, the alveoli, the oxygen diffuses to the alveolar lining, and across through the walls of the lung capillaries, and into the serum of the blood. The capacity of the blood to hold oxygen or some other gas would, as predicted by Henry's Law, be in proportion to the partial pressure of the gas and its solubility in the liquid. Its ability to diffuse from the alveoli to the blood is proportional to the partial pressure gradient between these two regions (air of alveoli and plasma of blood in lungs), the total surface of the lungs, and the solubility of the gas in water.

Actually the solubility of oxygen in blood serum is a relatively minor factor in determining the actual capacity of blood to carry this gas. At any given partial pressure of oxygen in contact with arterial blood, by far the largest proportion of the oxygen is carried within the red blood cells bound to the protein molecules of the respiratory pigment, hemoglobin (see Fig. 7-6). The solubility of oxygen merely indicates the rate at which the gas is available to be picked up by the hemoglobin for transportation to the tissues. The hemoglobin is almost saturated with oxygen at the alveolar partial pressure of oxygen found at sea level. The barometric pressure must almost be halved before there is an appreciable decrease in the carrying capacity of the blood. By the time the blood reaches the tissues, however, there has been an appreciable drop in the partial pressure of oxygen, so that there is a lowered affinity of hemoglobin for oxygen, and it is thus released for diffusion into the tissues. The ability of hemoglobin to bind oxygen is also influenced, although to a lesser extent, by the partial pressure of carbon dioxide. The higher partial pressures of carbon dioxide found in

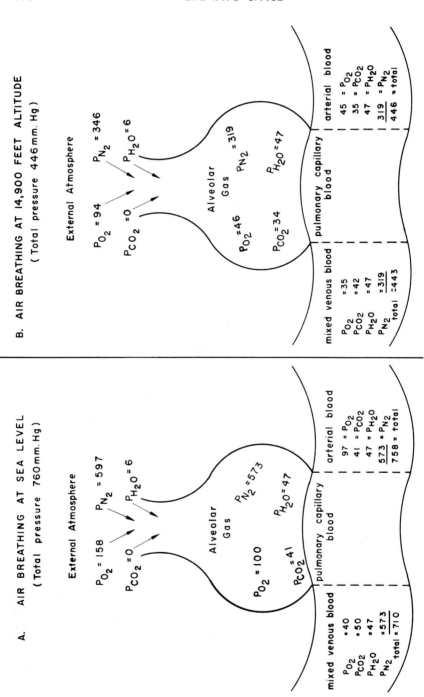

Figure 7-5. Partial pressures of various gases throughout the respiratory and circulatory system at two different conditions of altitude. (C. J. Lambertsen, 1963.)

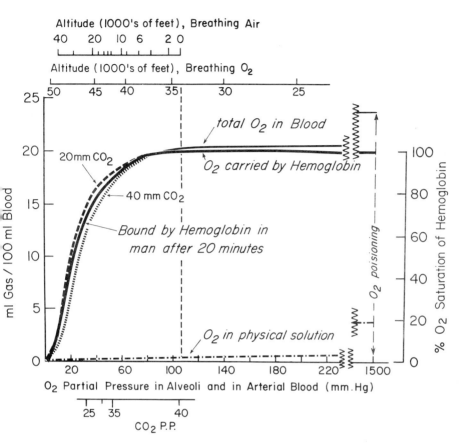

Figure 7-6.   The oxygen-hemoglobin dissociation curve. The heavy solid line indicates the amount of oxygen which is bound by the hemoglobin in the blood for individuals who have been taken from a sea-level environment and placed in pressure chambers which simulate various altitudes. Amount of saturation was determined after men had been exposed for a 20-minute period of time. Although the physiological dissociation curve resembles that for a partial pressure of 40 mm of carbon dioxide at sea level, the curve shifts over at high altitudes to resemble one for which the partial pressure of carbon dioxide is approximately 20 mm of mercury. Note that only a very small portion of this gas, oxygen, is actually carried in physical solution. The uppermost scale indicates the altitude that would be effected by these partial pressures to correspond to the individual who is breathing oxygen through a mask. (Data is for arterial blood leaving the alveoli. After mixing with some venous blood shunted past the alveoli, systemic arterial blood would contain slightly less oxygen.) The information displayed in this figure is compiled from a number of sources, including Figure 3-1 and the "Handbook of Respiration" (1958).

the tissues will slightly decrease the ability of the hemoglobin to bind oxygen, thus permitting even more to pass into the tissues.

For the best human performance it will be necessary to maintain the partial pressure of oxygen at nearly the same pressure found at the Earth's surface (160 mm of mercury). At lower pressures, oxygen would not be present in the quantities appropriate for optimum metabolism. Upon explosive decompression (even if the effects of dysbarism could be avoided [see pp. 95-97]), only a few seconds exist during which adequate oxygen would be available and in which an astronaut could seek emergency supplies of oxygen (Fig. 7-7). Higher pressures of oxygen are likely to injure either

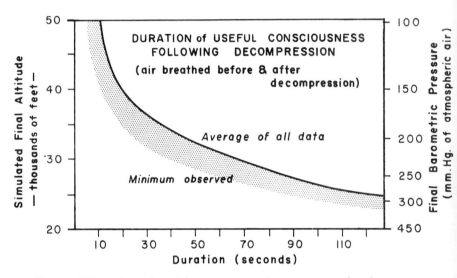

Figure 7-7. Time of useful consciousness in men exposed to low oxygen tension. (Modified from Committee Report, 1964.)

the surface of the lungs or certain metabolically significant chemicals within the tissues, so that a greater partial pressure of oxygen may actually result in an effective decrease in the concentration of oxygen which is available to the tissues. The concentrations of the other components of air are not so critical. Their concentration could be more drastically changed from that which is found in our atmosphere without profound metabolic effects.

The Gaseous Environment

Although oxygen is undoubtedly the most important component of our gaseous environment, the other constituents cannot be overlooked. American space capsules are employing pure oxygen at a partial pressure comparable to that or slightly greater than that found in our atmosphere. Some relatively inert material is probably necessary as a "filler" in maintaining the optimum total ambient pressure for inflation of the lungs. In the prolonged absence of a total ambient pressure which approximates that of our atmosphere, there is some fear that atelectasis (collapse) of the lungs is likely to occur, particularly during periods of intense acceleration. It is believed that the Russian space vehicles now employ some nitrogen in the artificial environment of the chamber. The disadvantage of employing nitrogen or some other gas in addition to the oxygen of the mixture is twofold. In the first place, the explosive decompression following puncture of the pressurized space cabin is more likely to result in bends when the pressure drops from a full atmosphere than when it drops from only a fraction of an atmosphere. The second disadvantage is that in the event of appreciable leakage or other inability to reuse the nitrogen there is a considerable addition to the payload necessary for a rocket vehicle. For these reasons, some consideration has been given to helium as the "filler" gas.

Most of the studies with abnormal atmospheric conditions have been accompanied by decrease in oxygen pressure as the predominant physiological factor. Very few biomedical studies have been pursued with a normal partial pressure of oxygen under conditions wherein the other constituents of air were at subnormal pressures over extended periods of time. Some amount of nitrogen (see pp. 234, 238) and carbon dioxide might well be necessary to man's normal functioning.

We know that carbon dioxide (as detected by receptors in the brain and by receptors in the circulatory system) plays a major role in stimulating adequate respiratory movements. There is almost none of this gas in the normal atmosphere. Adequate quantities of this material are produced by the body's metabolism, so that there would be no requirement, so far as we know, for additional quantities of this gas to be carried aloft in a space vehicle.

The major difficulty with the gaseous environment of a space vehicle will be that it is a completely closed system. Under the usual atmospheric conditions, most of the potentially hazardous gases and vapors are dissipated throughout the Earth's effectively infinite atmosphere. In industrial situations, men have been forced to work in close proximity to various toxic gases and vapors, and, as a result, some measure of the maximum allowable concentration of such materials has been determined. This information, however, may not be appropriate to conditions in space flight. Industrial data are usually based upon exposures of from 40 to 48 hours per week at normal gravity and at normal ambient pressure. A constant buildup of toxic materials during months of recycling of air has not been encountered. Various materials which are not normally a hazard may be a serious problem. A few of the gases and vapors which may cause difficulties are listed in Table 7-1. The problems likely to be encountered during constant rebreathing of the same air may be elucidated from experiences in submarines (Ebersole, 1960). Submarines, however, are usually able to effect some exchange with the atmosphere or with the surrounding ocean.

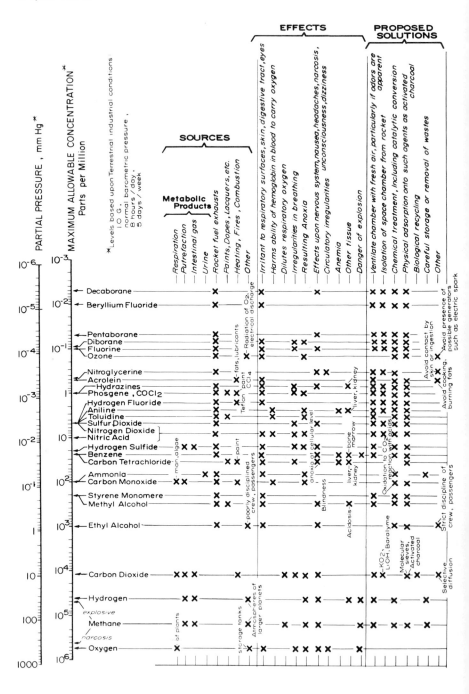

* Footnote on page 119.

As an example of the type of difficulty to be expected during maintained recycling of cabin air, we may consider an exaggerated "crowded-elevator effect," which could result from intestinal gases. As a by-product of their metabolism, some putrefying bacteria, including those commonly found in man's intestinal tract, release certain "exotic" respiratory gases. During interplanetary trips in a perfectly sealed space vehicle, accumulations of hydrogen sulfide and methane could be matters of concern (Keller, 1960). A calculated 14 months has been proposed as the time necessary for hydrogen sulfide concentrations to attain toxic levels. The primary danger with other intestinal gases is that they are highly explosive particularly when mixed with pure oxygen. An estimated 4 to 6 months would be required for accumulation of these gases in sufficient concentration to pose such a hazard.

Water

As water is the solvent in which practically all chemical reactions essential for Terrestrial life occur, a consideration of its availability is of the utmost importance. An adequate water intake, moreover, will probably be necessary to prevent two potentially adverse effects of prolonged weightlessness: the formation of kidney stones and contraction of the plasma volume of the blood. When adequate supplies of appropriate foods and fresh water are available, the various physiological control mechanisms of the human body are able to maintain the appropriate environment for man's cells and tissues. For long space voyages, adequate supplies of fresh water must be available. The freshness and potability of available water will depend upon the reliability and efficiency of the mechanisms for recycling. Constant recycling may result in the progressive accumulation of unexpected toxic materials. Without appropriate treatment, there is also the danger of biological contamination. As is shown in Figure 7-2, man releases more water into his environment than he consumes. The difficulty, then, is not the quantity of the water but its quality.

The duration of each flight thus far accomplished was short enough to permit transportation of the required water supplies. In the Gemini program, water will be produced as a by-product from fuel cells used to generate power. There can be no question that more extended voyages will demand adequate recycling procedures (see Chapter 10).

Bibliography and References

AKHLEBININSKIY, S. S., BYCHKOV, V. P., IL'INA, I. A., KONDRAT'YEV, YU. I., AND USHAKOV, A. S. (1962): On the problem of supplying the crews of spaceships with animal foodstuffs. *In* "Problemy Kosmicheskoy Biologii" [Problems of Space Biology] (N. M.

---

* Maximum allowable concentration in parts per million refers to the concentration in moles of material relative to the total number of moles of air. These values are for a total atmospheric pressure of 760 mm of mercury and for the Earth's normal gravity of 1 G. In most cases, the period of exposure corresponds to 48 hours per week. Tolerable values for space travel are not necessarily the same as those indicated here. This material was compiled from several sources including Slager, 1962; Kraul and Duguid, 1961; Montgomery and Reeves, 1960; and Stewart and Stolman, 1960. Additional values are available in Morrow, 1964.

Sisakyan, ed.). *Vol. 1,* pp. 161-168. As translated from Russian in NASA TT F-174, National Aeronautics and Space Administration, Washington, D. C.

COMMITTEE REPORT (1964): Medical aspects of business aviation. *Aerospace Med. 35,* 783-793.

DODGE, C. H., AND WUNDER, C. C. (1962): Growth of turtles during continual centrifugation. *Iowa Academy of Science 69,* 594-599.

EBERSOLE, J. H. (1960): The new dimensions of submarine medicine. *The New England J. of Med. 262,* 599-610.

"Handbook of Respiration" (1958). (Dittmer, D. S., and Grebe, R. M., eds.). Aero-Medical Laboratory, Wright-Patterson AFB, Ohio.

HURTADO, A. (1964): Animals in high altitudes: resident man. *In* "Handbook of Physiology, Section 4: Adaptation to the Environment" (D. B. Dill, E. F. Adolph, and C. G. Wilber, eds.), pp. 843-860. American Physiological Society, Washington, D. C.

KELLER, D. M. (1960): Cabin atmospheres: their physical and chemical control. *In* "Lectures in Aerospace Medicine," (Paper No. 13). School of Aviation Medicine, Brooks AFB, Texas.

KRAUL, C. W., AND DUGUID, R. H. (1961): Toxicity problems with solid missile propellents. *Archives of Environmental Health 3,* 680-683.

LAMBERTSEN, C. J. (1963): The philosophy of extremes for the gaseous environment of manned, closed ecological systems. *Aerospace Med. 34,* 291-299.

MONTGOMERY, V., JR., AND REEVES, J. L. (1960): Toxicity of chemicals. *In* "Lectures in Aerospace Medicine" (Paper No. 16) School of Aviation Medicine, Brooks AFB, Texas.

MORROW, P. E. (1964): Animals in toxic environments: mammals in polluted air. *In* "Handbook of Physiology, Section 4: Adaptation to the Environment" (D. B. Dill, E. F. Adolph, and C. G. Wilber, eds.), pp 795-808. American Physiological Society, Washington, D. C.

SLAGER, U. T. (1962): Toxicology. *In* "Space Medicine," pp. 307-337. Prentice Hall, Inc., Englewood Cliffs, N. J.

SMITH, A. H. (1963.): Chronic acceleration studies—physiological responses to artificial alterations in weight. *In* "Annual Progress Report," No. 8, Office of Naval Research Project, NRx: 102-448,, National Aeronautics and Space Administration Contract: R-53 with the University of California, Davis.

STEWART, C. P., AND STOLMAN, A. (eds.) (1960) (1961): "Toxicology: Mechanisms and Analytical Methods." *Vol. I, Vol. II.* Academic Press, New York.

WEBER, T. B., DICKEY, J. R., JACKSON, N. N., REGISTER, J. W., AND CONKLE, J. P. (1964): Monitoring of trace constituents in simulated manned spacecraft. *Aerospace Med. 35,* 148-152.

WELCH, B. E. (1963): Ecological systems. *In* "Physiology of Man in Space" (J. H. U. Brown, ed.), pp. 309-334. Academic Press, New York.

WUNDER, C. C. (1961): Food consumption of mice during continual centrifugation. *Iowa Academy of Science 68,* 616-624.

WUNDER, C. C. (1964): "A Survey of Chronic Weightlessness Simulation in Biological Research." HQARSC-TDR-64-1, Andrews AFB, Washington, D. C.

WUNDER, C. C., CRAWFORD, C. R., AND HERRIN, W. F. (1960): Decreased oxygen requirement for growth of fruit fly larvae after continual centrifugation. *Proc. Soc. Exper. Biol. and Med. 104,* 749-751.

WUNDER, C. C., AND LUTHERER, L. O. (1964): Influence of chronic exposure to increased gravity upon growth and form of animals. *In* "International Rev. Gen. Exp. Zoo.," *Vol. 1,* pp. 333-416. Academic Press, New York.

8

Influence of Inertial Fields and Motion: Acceleration, Gravity, Weightlessness, Rotation, and Vibration*

Nature of Gravitational and Inertial Fields

Gravity is one of the few attributes of our environment which is essentially constant both spatially and temporally over the surface of this planet. An appreciable change in its magnitude can be obtained only as we leave the surface of the planet and travel into space. Although it is possible to simulate certain conditions of an altered gravity by means of introducing another inertial field, such as would be the case with the physical acceleration of a system, man has very little actual firsthand experience of the effects of a true change in the gravitational environment.

The reader will remember that in any force field the force acting upon a body is proportional to the intensity of the force field and some specific property of the body under the influence of the field. With inertial fields, we call this force *weight*. This force of weight is proportional to the gravitational field intensity g and the mass of the body m:[1]

$$\text{Force of weight} = g \times m \tag{8-1}$$

---

* This chapter is in part a condensation of an article, "Influence of Chronic Exposure to Increased Gravity upon Growth and Form of Animals," by Charles C. Wunder and Lorenz O. Lutherer, which appeared in Vol. I of *International Review of General and Experimental Zoology,* 1964. Those portions printed here have been reproduced with the kind permission of Academic Press. Other portions are condensed from a technical report titled, "A Survey of Chronic Weightlessness and Simulation in Biological Research," prepared by the author in June, 1964, for the U. S. Air Force. The reader is referred to those works for complete citations to the original literature.

[1] The symbols used to designate inertial field intensity and units of this intensity have not been altogether standardized. Some writers use g to designate units of gravitational field intensity. Other writers employ the same symbol (g) to designate the actual field intensity. For the purposes of this text, g will designate the actual field intensity, and G will be understood to refer to a unit amount of field intensity: multiples of the Earth's normal gravity of 980 cm per $\sec^2$. Multiples of this unit will be expressed in terms of G's. The designation for the direction of an inertial field with respect to the orientation of the human body is shown in Figure 8-14.

TABLE 8-1. Quantities Related to Gravity and Acceleration*

Quantity (Appropriate Formulae and Typical Units)	Description	Significance
Speed (v) (cm/sec)	A *scalar* quantity which describes the rate at which some object traverses a path	Although a body moving in a straight line can have the same magnitude for both speed and velocity, such would not be the case when the path is not a straight line. For instance, a body moving in a circular path at constant speed does not experience a constant velocity: This is because the *direction* of motion is constantly changing
Velocity (v) (cm/sec)	A *vector* quantity which describes both the rate and direction of moving relative to some point and some direction of reference	
Acceleration ($\dot{v}$, a) $a = F/m$ (cm/sec², dynes/gm)	A *vector* quantity which describes the rate of change in velocity	The force experienced by a body in an accelerated system relative to that system is actually opposite in direction to the system's acceleration
Mass (m) (gm, pounds of mass)	A fundamental measure of the absolute quantity of material in a body	As the gravitational force or *weight* of a body is proportional to *mass*, these two quantities (mass and weight) are frequently confused. This confusion is compounded by the unfortunate circumstance that the very same words are frequently employed to refer to separate units for either quantity (mass or weight). Biologists often refer to the body *weight* of an animal when they are actually concerned with the animal's body *mass*. Only at 1 G will the magnitude of both quantities be equal when expressed in terms of grams
Momentum or motion (mv) (gm-cm/sec)	Product of both the mass and velocity of a body	Motion is a better indication of an object's movement than the velocity alone. For systems in the same g field (such as the Earth's field of 1 G) one would expect motion to be a fairly good index of activity. However, as the effort or work required for the same amount of motion against gravity is proportional to the g field intensity, the concept of motion is unsatisfactory for comparing the activity of individuals exposed to fields of different intensities

Force (F) $F = ma$ This equation holds for conditions of classical mechanics (i.e., when the velocities under consideration are much less than that of light) (gm-cm/sec^2 = dyne, gram of force, pound of force)	As defined by Newton this would be the action required to accelerate the mass: it would be expressed in terms of the rate at which a given force is capable of changing a body's motion	Although defined in terms of change in motion, it is frequently thought of and measured in terms of the ability to cause distortion When a distorted body obeys Hooke's Law (see Stress, Strain), the amount of distortion will be proportional to the distorting force which is equal in magnitude but opposite in direction to the restoring force Thus, spring balances can measure forces and weights but not true masses. The displacement of a spring balance by a mass is proportional to the force (weight) which is equal to the product of the mass and the intensity of the existing g field
Force field (field of force) (dyne/[unit quantity])* * Examples of appropriate unit quantities would be a gram or an esu (electrostatic unit of charge).	An influence in a region where force is exerted upon a body in proportion to the amount of some specific property (such as mass or charge) of the body	This influence expresses itself in terms of a force whose magnitude depends upon the properties of both the field and the body upon which it acts. Although the intensity of these fields is expressed in units of force divided by some other unit (such as grams of mass) there is an erroneous tendency among many people to think of a field as actually being a force
g Field or field of inertial force (g) (cm/sec^2 = dynes/gm, G's)	Any field of force which acts upon mass in the same way that a gravitational field will act This would include gravity itself as well as centrifugal and other types of acceleration The effective g field is the vector sum of all the individual fields Thus g fields can be combined in such a way as to increase or decrease the effective gravity	Various types of acceleration are of such a nature that not all parts of a system are receiving uniform acceleration. Thus, unlike the essentially uniform gravitational field encountered upon a planet's surface, the field in the accelerated system might vary from time to time or place to place within the system and vary with the motion of an organism

TABLE 8-1. Continued

Quantity (Appropriate Formulae and Typical Units)	Description	Significance
Gravity (g or g_0) ($cm/sec^2 =$ dynes/gm) The Earth's gravity $= 1.0$ G $= 980$ cm/sec² $= 980$ dynes/gm No. of G's $=$ no. of multiples of 980 cm/sec²	A force field originating from one mass (such as the Earth) and acting upon a given body in proportion to the given body's mass (the constant of proportionality depends upon the mass from which the field originates and also upon the distance between the two masses)	Although a *field of force*, this influence is frequently erroneously spoken of as a *force* The gravitational intensity is almost of constant magnitude over the Earth's surface (978 cm/sec² at the equator and 983 cm/sec² at the poles). Its intensity has also been constant with respect to time (over at least the past several million [10^6] years). This constancy has caused gravity to be more or less taken for granted. Thus, confusion has arisen with respect to weight and mass, pressure and pressure head, together with motion and activity. For most instances this confusion is not important as long as the environmental g field remains constant With the advent of such situations as space travel, the confusion can reach significant proportions. When one leaves this planet's surface, it would be expected that, in accordance with the inverse-square law, gravitational intensity would decrease by an order of 4 with every twofold increase in separation from the center of the Earth or some other planet. Also gravity is different upon the surface of different planets (the field to be experienced upon a planet's surface increases directly with planetary mass and inversely with the square of the planet's radius)
Centrifugal acceleration ($-a$) or (g) or (g_c) magnitude of centrifugal field intensity $= \dfrac{\pi^2 (\text{RPM})^2 (\text{radius in cm})}{900 \cdot 980}$	The apparent acceleration which a body experiences with respect to a system which is caused to move in a circular path. *Centripetal acceleration* is that shown by a rotating body forced from translational motion toward the cen-	The *centrifugal* field as generated in a centrifuge represents essentially the only manner in which a chronic, high g field can be generated in an Earth-bound laboratory. The speed component of the velocity remains constant but the directional component can be altered constantly, thus accelerating

ter of rotation, while *centrifugal acceleration* results from the force on the same body which is directed outward from the center of rotation

The *centripetal acceleration* constitutes the actual acceleration acting upon a rotating system with respect to a stationary frame of reference

a system without requiring extreme speeds and paths of astronomical proportions. It should be noted that in a centrifuge system there is a gradient in field intensity along the centrifuge arms, with the intensity increasing with distance along the arms from the center of rotation (see formula). With experiments designed to study the effect of field intensity alone and not that of a gradient, the gradient must be minimized by employing centrifuge arm lengths (radii) which are large with respect to both the speed of rotation and the size of the organism under study. The *centrifugal acceleration* is equal in magnitude to the *centripetal acceleration* but opposite in direction. The *centrifugal acceleration*, although not real with respect to a stationary system, can describe in the rotating system a g field which predicts the g forces which are actually attributable to the inertial reaction in opposition to acceleration

Moving organisms within a centrifuge will be subjected to a g field which would not be computed from the centrifugal field and which would be different in nature from a purely gravitational field. Upon a planet's surface, organisms would not experience any significant influence upon the effective g field as a result of this motion. However, within a centrifuge possessing a radius of rotation which is small in comparison to the speed of rotation or in comparison to the speed of an animal's motion, the effective field can vary markedly with movements. A stationary animal whose ventral surface is directed outward from the center of rotation would have the same orientation with respect to centrifugal field as would normally be assumed with respect to the Earth's gravity. However, consider a moving animal whose head is oriented into the direction of rotation; forward movements by the

(a) is customarily employed when speaking of the centripetal acceleration necessary to overcome a body's inertial opposition to circular motion

(g_c) is customarily employed when speaking of the effective gravity which appears to exist within the rotating frame of reference

Coriolis acceleration
The Coriolis contribution to the total g field in G's

$$= \frac{2\pi(\text{RPM})(v)}{30 \cdot 980}$$

(cm/sec²)

(G or G's)

where v is in cm/sec, and RPM refers to the rate of centrifuge rotation.

This is a second-order effect of rotation which will contribute to the impurity of the artificial gravity generated by a centrifuge. It is a type of g field which acts upon moving objects within such rotating systems as the Earth or a centrifuge. This action appears because trajectories which are consistent with respect to a stationary system must be distorted with respect to a centrifuged cage's or container's frame of reference In the equation to the left, v represents the magnitude of the pertinent component of the velocity vector v for an animal moving in a centrifuge. The velocity v is relative to a system represented by the centrifuged cage. The speed equals $|v| \cos \alpha$, where α is the

TABLE 8-1. Continued

Quantity (Appropriate Formulae and Typical Units)	Description	Significance
	angle between the direction of relative motion and the direction of a right-hand screw parallel to the axis of centrifuge rotation	animal would increase the g field; backward movements would decrease it. Vertical movements would deflect the direction of the g force vector toward the caudal direction. Imagine the bizarre and conflicting sensations which would occur when an animal turns its head. Thus, in order to rule out the secondary effects of unnatural psychophysical disturbances, centrifuge studies designed to simulate the influence of uniform gravity must employ centrifuges of sufficient arm length in comparison to an organism's movements and in comparison to the magnitude of the centrifugal field. As should be obvious from the equation to the left, this gravitational distortion becomes less significant for slow centrifuge speeds or for slow animal movements
Weight (W) weight $= $ (mass $\times$ g field intensity) $= mg$ $= $ volume $\times$ density $\times g$ (gm of force $= 980$ dynes $= $ weight of 1 gm, pounds of force)	Force exerted by a g field upon mass	(See section on Mass relative to the unfortunate confusion between mass and weight) A mass of 1 gm possesses a weight of 1 gm of force only when it is placed in a g field comparable to the Earth's gravity (980 cm/sec^2)
Weightlessness (or free-fall) Total g fields $=$ zero	Condition in which a mass experiences no weight	The mass which has definite weight in a g field experiences no weight in the absence of gravity and other g fields A simulated weightlessness can be generated by causing a body to fall (free-fall) toward a gravity source at a rate of acceleration which is equal in

magnitude but opposite in direction to the gravity. Thus, the vector sum of the opposing inertial forces or fields is zero

Organisms orbiting about the Earth in artificial satellites are actually within the realm of the planet's gravity. The satellite with its orbit about the planet amounts to a centrifuge system in which the centrifuge field exactly counterbalances the gravity. This can also be thought of as a system which is constantly falling toward the Earth at an acceleration equal to gravity under conditions such that its translational motion causes it to continually fall at a constant distance beyond the horizon

Amount of force being exerted normal to a surface divided by the area of the surface

Pressure (P)

$$P = \text{force} \div \text{area}$$
$$= mg \div \text{area}$$
$$= (\text{volume}) \times (\text{density})\, g \div \text{area}$$
$$= \frac{\text{volume}}{\text{area}} \times (\text{density})\, g$$
$$= (\text{height of fluid column}) \times (\text{fluid density})\, g$$

(dynes/cm²)

Occasionally, misinformed individuals think of gravity as being a type of pressure. While gravity can cause the weights of fluids to exert a downward force, gravity is not in itself a pressure

g fields can cause hydrostatic pressures to be generated in proportion to the field intensity. Such gravitationally induced pressures can have pronounced effects upon fluid systems (such as the circulatory system) within an organism

In accordance with the formula shown to the left, one can see that the ability of an organism to tolerate gravitational effects mediated due to pressures should be inversely proportional to an organism's height (see Pressure Head)

Ambient pressures generated by centrifugal fields can cause effects upon organisms centrifuged in a fluid medium. Such effects should be attributable to the pressure environment and not to the gravitational environment. Pressures of the order of 500 atmospheres can have effects at the molecular level

However, such gravitationally generated ambient pressures can be used to counterbalance the internal pressures which are generated by action upon body fluids and which would tend to distend an organ-

TABLE 8-1. Continued

Quantity (Appropriate Formulae and Typical Units)	Description	Significance
		ism's body walls and vessel walls. This would be most effective when the fluid heights and densities are comparable inside the organism and in the ambient fluid. Internal pressures can also be counteracted by application of special corsets called g suits which exert force about the abdomen and legs
Pressure head $$\text{head} = \frac{\text{pressure}}{(\text{fluid density}) \times g}$$ (mm of mercury, mm of water, mm of blood)	Height to which a column of a given fluid can be raised by a given pressure	When a fluid of constant density is specified, the units for the length of these heights have been employed in such a manner as to imply that these length units are interchangeable with more classical pressure units. This thinking is satisfactory when all references are relevant to a constant g field. However, drastic errors could result if heads in different g fields were thought proportional to pressure alone
		In a normal, healthy human, sufficient arterial blood pressure exists to raise a head of pressure to three times the height to the eyes. However, at 3 G's there would, without physiological adjustments, be hardly enough hydrostatic pressure to raise a head to eye level. Without adjustment, greater fields would cause loss of vision or "black out"
Buoyancy buoyant force $=$ (displacement volume of fluid) $\times$ (density) g net force acting upon a completely submerged body $=$ volume $\times$ (density of body $-$ density of suspending medium) $\times g$ $= m(1 - V_{\delta_0})g$	An upward (in a direction opposite to g fields) force which in accordance with Archimedes' Principle is exerted upward by an amount equal to the weight of a suspending fluid which is displaced by a wholly or partially submerged body	Buoyancy helps to support massive animals against gravity. Animals the size of whales would probably be mechanically unstable in 1 G without buoyant support and therefore collapse under their own weight. The larger dinosaurs probably spent a considerable portion of their time in water or swamps. The first of our distant ancestors required to undergo a major struggle against gravity were probably the fish-like animals which attempted an existence on land.

where V represents volume of a unit mass of submerged body and δ_0, the density of the suspending medium (*dynes*)	The rate (at which a sedimenting body is drawn downward by g forces through a fluid in opposition to buoyancy and friction) divided by the intensity of the g field acting upon the fluid system	Most structures within an organism possess densities closer to that of body fluids than to that of the surrounding air. Buoyancy should exert less force to displace one organ with respect to another. Therefore, the major effect of gravity upon terrestrial organisms (under conditions of adequate cardiovascular adjustment) would normally not be upon the internal arrangement of an organism but upon the walls of the integument, the skeleton, and the muscles of support
Sedimentation constant (S) rate of sedimentation $= v = Sg$ total net force acting upon sedimenting body $= F = O$ $=$ (downward forces) $-$ (upward forces) $=$ weight due to gravity $-$ (weight due to linear acceleration) $-$ (buoyancy) $-$ (frictional forces opposing downward motion) $= Vg - [V\delta a + V\delta_0(g - a) + fv]$ $= Vg - [V\delta a + V\delta_0(g - a) + fsg]$ where V is the volume of a sedimenting body and δ is its density. The g field acting upon the fluid which contains the body is g Acceleration of the body with respect to fluid system equals a; δ and δ_0, the densities of the body and the fluid. A body's frictional coefficient is represented by f and its velocity of sedimentation by v In a viscous medium, the rate of sedimentation will be accelerated at first but will eventually drop to zero as ter-		This is a constant independent of field which can predict the rate at which sedimentation will occur in a given field The end result of sufficiently long and intense sedimentation with an organism would be stratification of its contents according to density. Thus, intense fields (of the order of 10^4-10^6 G's) are useful in determining the physical characteristics of macromolecules and cellular constituents. As indicated in the equations to the left, buoyancy and friction can delay settling. Various types of mixing phenomena tend to reverse sedimentation toward a more uniform distribution of otherwise sedimentable particles. Examples of such phenomena would be turbulence, cyclosis, and diffusion. As field increases, sedimentation tends to overcome these phenomena. Thus, material which is evenly distributed at one field might sediment at another. An intermediate state between sedimentation and mixing by diffusion is described by the last two equations in this section of the table. As mixing increases with temperature, it has been suggested that increased temperature might enhance the ability of organisms to tolerate high gravity. On the other hand, several animals seem better able to tolerate centrifugation at lower temperatures. Larger organisms are often influenced by lower gravities than would be necessary to sediment macromolecules.

TABLE 8-1. Continued

Quantity (Appropriate Formulae and Typical Units)	Description	Significance
minal velocity approaches zero. Under that condition, the above equation can be rearranged to give $$S = \frac{v}{g} = (1 - V\delta_0)\frac{m}{f}$$ For most protein molecules, S is in the order of from 10^{-13} to 10^{-10} sec. Since f increases with fluid viscosity and with departure from spherical shape, the inverse would be true for S. For a sphere, $f = 6\pi\eta r$ where η is viscosity and r is radius of sphere. For sedimentation equilibrium, concentration at given height in a fluid medium $$= C_0 e^{-m(1-V\delta_0)gh/RT}$$ When $m >> V\delta_0$ this reduces to $$C_0 e^{Mgh/RT}$$ where C_0 is the concentration at a lower reference height, h is the difference in height, k is the Maxwell-Boltzman constant, M the molecular weight of a sedimenting particle. R is the ideal gas constant, T is the absolute temperature, and e is the natural number (2.7182) Units: (cm/sec) $\div$ G (cm/sec) $\div$ (cm/sec^2) = sec		Sedimentation of growth-enhancing agents has been suggested as a method whereby gravity can encourage plant growth. Centrifugation of cells or organisms in fluids containing a suspension of significant particles (such as food material) could result in an experimental artifact due to effective concentration changes

Strain	A description of the relative distortion which a body experiences when exposed to an applied force	One type of force possessing a straining potential is gravitational force or weight. Since weight = mass $\times$ g, the applied straining force in this instance would be (assuming constant density and shape as a function of size) proportional to (length)^3 and field g

$$\text{strain} = \frac{\text{change in size}}{\text{original size}}$$

(As this is a pure number without units, it can be expressed in terms of a unitless fraction or in terms of a percentage)

| **Stress** | The force (attributable to the elastic properties of a strained body) which acts to restore an elastic, strained body to its unstrained configuration. This restoring force is equal to but opposite to the applied straining force. | The ability of a given material which obeys Hooke's law to exert the stressing (or resting) force would be proportional to area. Assuming constant shape and constant modulus of elasticity as a function of size, the magnitude of the restoring force would therefore increase only with area or (length)^2 |

As can be seen from the discussion of strain, the straining or distorting weight would increase faster with size than would the stressing or restoring ability. Thus one would expect from the simplest mechanical considerations that the relative distortion (stress) would increase with length or height and with field g. Thus one would expect small organisms to be more mechanically stable in a given field and the maximum stable size for a given living structure (or any other structure) to decrease with field g

Forces of true mechanical stress as discussed here are *passive* ones. Unfortunately some biologists have referred to a so-called biological "stress" to describe the various *active* reactions undertaken by an organism to restore its physiological integrity after exposure to some agent which caused distortion to the physiological integrity. Sometimes biologists even refer to the distorting influence or the distortion itself as "stress"

"Gravitational stress" could mean either of two quite distinct things: (1) the true passive physical forces opposing distortions brought about by a body's weight, or (2) the various active, internal, unconscious reactions within an organism subjected to adverse gravitational conditions

stress = (restoring force)/area when the area measured is normal to the direction of stretching

$$\text{stress} = y \text{ (strain)}$$

under conditions in which Hooke's law is obeyed; y is a proportionality constant known as Young's Modulus

$$y = \frac{\text{stress}}{\text{strain}}$$

$$= \frac{(\text{restoring force})/\text{area}}{(\text{increase in length})/(\text{original length})}$$

(dynes/cm^2)

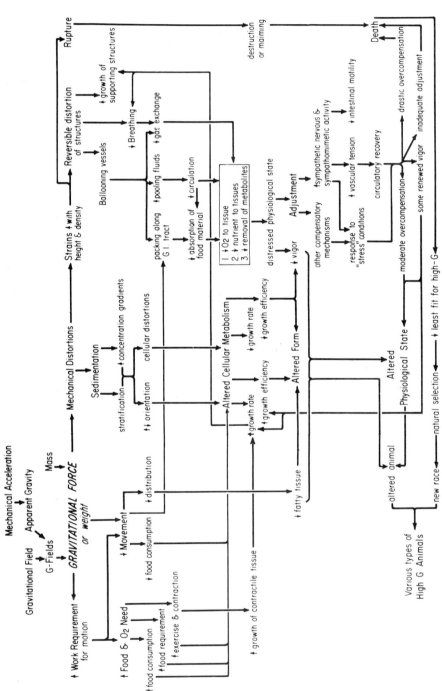

Figure 8-1. Pathways for some of the responses which one might expect as a result of exposure to increased gravity. This diagram should serve as a guide to some of the many effects of high gravity which are possible rather than the specific effects obtained with any given animal. (Wunder and Lutherer, 1964.)

The constancy of the Earth's gravitational field has caused many quantities which are proportional to each other only under conditions of constant field intensity to be thought of in equivalent or synonymous terms, for example, the frequent misuse of the term weight in reference to mass. A number of the attributes related to gravity and acceleration which are likely to be imprecisely understood by the biologist are listed in Table 8-1.

One can predict from simple considerations the action of forces upon inanimate objects with a fair degree of certainty. Living organisms, however, possess certain compensatory homeokinetic potentialities which limit the validity of predictions made on the basis of a study of inanimate objects. Provided that this is borne in mind, basic physical considerations may serve as groundwork for the study of living material. Some of the many diverse changes to be expected from a change in gravitational field are outlined in Figure 8-1. A number of as yet unproven responses may eventually result from gravitationally induced forces and distortions.

The weight of a body is the result of the gravitational force acting upon it and is directly proportional to the mass of that body. The gravitational field thus restricts the maximum stable size of an object, necessitates an expenditure of energy in opposition to the field, causes fluids to exert a pressure, and promotes the settling of denser constituents toward the bottom of a system. The more massive an object is, the greater is its weight. The ability to support weight, however, does not necessarily increase with size. Probably the first serious discussion of animal size and gravity as specifically related to space biology dates back to the work of the early Russian space scientist, Tsiolkovsky (in a 1960 reprinting of material cited by Gazenko and Gurjian, 1964).

It is instructive to recall Galileo's observation (Thompson, 1942, p. 27) that gravity causes the mechanical stability of a body to decrease with size. If one object is twice the size of another while density and character of shape remain unchanged, the weight will be eightfold greater, while the ability to resist force will be only fourfold greater (Fig. 8-2). Thus, a 60-foot giant could walk in a low gravitational field, as might be encountered on the Moon, whereas on Earth his bones would collapse under his own weight. Larger structures require relatively thicker supporting members. A short, stout individual with thick bones and bulging muscles should be best suited to endure the force of greater gravitational fields. A tall individual with flat bones and slight musculature would be better fitted for slight fields.

That the shape of an elephant's leg is relatively thicker than that of a less ponderous animal is obvious to the casual observer. In accordance with the dependence of strength upon cross-sectional area, it has been found that champion weight-lifters possess weight-lifting ability in proportion to their (body mass)$^{2/3}$. If appropriate anatomical adjustments occur, the requirement for greater weight support should lead to relatively larger supporting structures of rounder cross-sections. As the tension acting upon

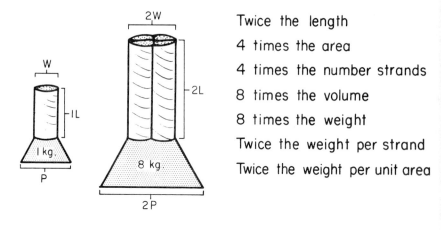

Twice the length

4 times the area

4 times the number strands

8 times the volume

8 times the weight

Twice the weight per strand

Twice the weight per unit area

% distortion $\propto$ height x gravity

Force to Support   =   Force to Distort

y x %distortion x c.s. area = mg

$$\% \text{ distortion } = \frac{mg}{y \text{ c.s.area}} < \frac{h^3 g}{y \, h^2} < hg$$

Figure 8-2. Influence of size upon mechanical stability (Wunder and Lutherer, 1964). Two weights of different sizes are compared so as to illustrate that gravitational field intensity g has a more marked effect upon the mechanical stability of larger objects. Young's modulus of the rope supporting the weight is equal to y. It is assumed that mass is proportional to the height h raised to the power of 3:

$$\text{Mass} = m = (\text{volume}) \times (\text{density}) \propto h^3$$

a bone increases, there is a tendency toward deceleration of longitudinal growth and acceleration of cross-sectional growth.

An altered gravitational field will influence the manner of movement. Most walking patterns differ in altered gravitational fields. In the discussion later in this chapter dealing with vibrational motion, it is noted that the greater the gravitational field, the faster will be the optimum rate at which a pendulous extremity, such as the leg, would swing in executing motion. At the same time, the rate of frequency of swings or steps permitted would decrease with the size of a limb (see pp. 174-176).

Other forces become more important as weight decreases. Most mammals are of such a size that weight, at least on the gross level, is the most important single force. Many insects are small enough so that gravitational factors are in part negated by other forces, as is exemplified by the fly walking on the ceiling and the water skipper which, supported by surface tension, walks on water. On a cellular level, factors such as thermal motion, electrical attraction, molecular interaction, and chemical bonds are paramount. Most theoretical considerations suggest the requirement of extremely intense field strength before gravity would become an important force within the animal cell. The extremely intense field, however, may not be necessary to produce cellular changes in the plant cell. Botanists at the Argonne National Laboratory have found indications of effects upon cellular growth in plants with a field as low as 10^{-5} G's (see also Pollard, 1965).

The amount of energy expended by an individual involves two considerations: (1) the energy necessary in supporting and moving gravitationally imposed weight, and (2) the energy expended on processes independent of the gravitational state. When the acceleration due to gravity remains constant, the force involved in opposing gravity is proportional to the mass. Therefore, the individual with the least mass will expend the least amount of energy for upward movements and for maintenance of posture. Work (by definition proportional to distance) will be greater as it is exercised through a greater field. Thus, if two individuals have the same mass, the taller of the two will, in exerting normal motion through a greater field, do a greater amount of work, and expend more energy. Short individuals and individuals with little mass require less energy to oppose gravity than do their larger counterparts. On this basis, the former may be better able to withstand an increase in the force of gravity. Existence in decreased gravitational fields will require less expenditure of energy in opposition to the force of gravity, thereby making more energy available for growth and other body functions.

There are several sensory receptors whereby man becomes aware of the attributes in the inertial field in which he is present (Table 8-2) The sensory receptors which have as their primary function the detection of inertial properties of the environment are located in the labyrinths of the inner ear (Fig. 8-3). The static magnitude and direction of an inertial field is detected as a result of the weight exerted upon hair cells by tiny calcareous bodies in the macula (Fig. 8-4). Changes in the field intensity are detected by means of action (i.e., distortion of flaps of tissue brought about by flow of endolymph fluid which is caused to move when inertial forces change) upon other hair cells within the ampullae of the semicircular canals. As these canals are arranged in three mutually perpendicular planes on each side of the head, changing field intensities in any of the three dimensions can be detected. As a change in rate of rotation involves changing inertial fields, the semicircular canals are frequently thought of as an organ for the detection of rotation. We are also aware of gravity due to the gravitationally imposed forces detected by other receptors throughout the body (Table 8-2).

Assuming freedom from the influence of the gravitational fields of other celestial bodies, one can theoretically reduce the force of gravity acting on a body by increasing the distance of that body from the Earth. At a distance of 4000 miles from the Earth's surface, the distance from this planet's center would be doubled, so that, in accordance with the inverse-square law,

Table 8-2. Some of the Sensory Receptors Capable of Detecting Properties of an Inertial Field*

	Those Responding Directly to Inertial Fields	
Factors influencing temporal and spatial pattern of discharge from sensory nerves	Static magnitudes and direction of field	Changes in field intensity or in direction are likely to be encountered at the beginning or end of linear acceleration and/or during angular acceleration
Sensory end-organ	*Macula* of the *utricle* of the *inner ear* due to weight of calcareous otolith bodies acting upon *hair cells* (See Figs. 8-3 and 8-4)	*Semicircular canals* of the inner ear due to the changing force resulting from the flow of fluid within these canals. This force causes a distortion which is detected by *hair cells* in the *ampullae* of these canals.

* This information is based primarily upon summaries by King *et al.*, 1961; Ruch, 1960 and Barnett *et al.*, 1961.

Those Likely to Be Stimulated as a Result of Actions Effected by Inertial Fields

In Response to Force- or Force-Induced Distortion						*From Conscious Interpretation of Visual Cues*
1. Static magnitude of muscular stretching 2. Changing magnitude of muscular stretching 3. Muscular contraction	Static magnitude of tendon stretching	Touch (changing magnitude of pressure)	Deep pressure (static magnitude of pressure)	Static magnitude of joint flexion	Changes in magnitude of joint flexion	Static magnitude (primarily in cones) and changing magnitude (primarily in rods) of light pattern
Muscle spindles within skeletal muscle	*Golgi tendon organ* at the insertion of tendons in muscle	*Meissner's corpuscles* and *free nerve endings* (at hair follicles) in the skin	*Pacinian corpuscles* beneath the skin and in muscle	Spray-like ("Ruffini type") nerve endings in the fibrous capsule of joints, firing in response to deformation End-organs in the joint ligament which resemble Golgi tendon organs	Laminated capsules (which are apparently modified Pacinian corpuscles) in the fibrous capsule of joints	*Rods* and *cones* of the eye's *retina* after focusing by the eye's lens system and prior to information processing by other neural elements in the retina itself and in the visual cortex of the brain

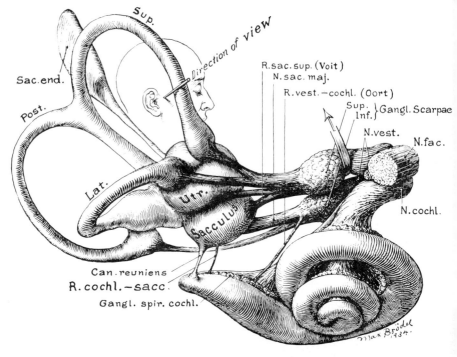

Figure 8-3.   The inner ear.   (Hardy, 1934.)

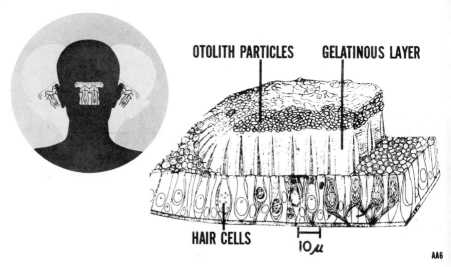

Figure 8-4.   Otolith organ.   (Courtesy of Dr. Raphael Levine, of Lockheed Aircraft Corp., as modified from Kolmer, 1927.)

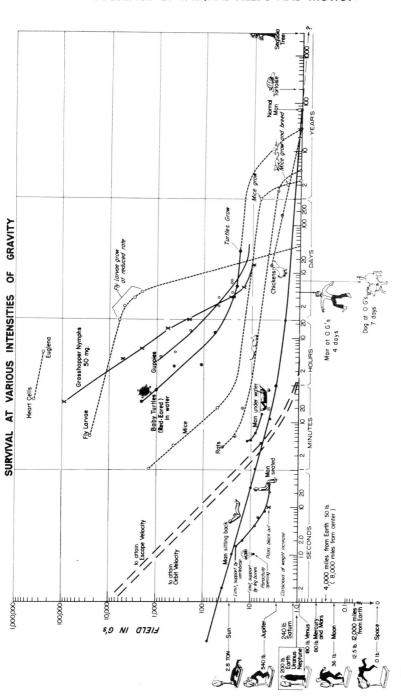

Figure 8-5. Survival at various intensities of gravity. This figure indicates the intensities of either a simulated or natural gravitational field at which living material is known to have survived. Times for 1 G would correspond to the life expectancy in the Earth's normal gravity. (Modified from figures described elsewhere [Wunder, 1963; Wunder et al., 1963].)

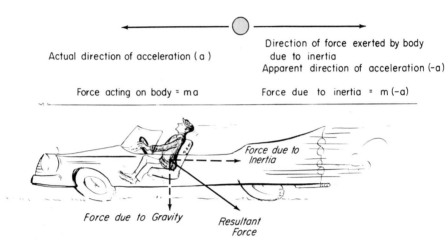

Figure 8-6. Direction of actual acceleration and forces acting upon a body and apparent direction of inertial forces relative to accelerated system. (Wunder and Lutherer, 1964.)

the field strength would be one fourth of that experienced on the surface, or 0.25 G's (Fig. 8-5). If the distance were sufficient, a space traveler would approach a zero gravity state.

When one considers that the dimensions of gravitational intensity are distance divided by time squared (cm/sec^2 in cgs units), a method of simulating varied gravitational field intensities is immediately suggested. These are the same dimensions as those expressing acceleration, which exhibits essentially the same action upon mass as does gravity.[2]

The exact magnitude of a centrifugal field can be computed from the equation:

$$\text{Field in G's} = \frac{\pi^2 \ (\text{RPM})^2 \ r}{900 \times 980} \tag{8-2}$$

[2] A force applied to a body to produce a change in velocity is designated as acceleration. This change in velocity can be either in magnitude or direction or both. The rate of change is directly proportional to the force acting on the mass and inversely proportional to that mass. Thus, mass opposes acceleration exactly as it opposes the force of gravity. To an unaccelerated observer, the direction of acceleration appears to be opposite to that of the actual acceleration (see Figs. 8-6 and 8-7).

Any unidirectional acceleration would result in tremendous speeds in a relatively short period of time. It is obvious that prolonged artificial gravitational states cannot be produced in this manner within the dimensions of a planet. Thus, it is necessary to vary the other parameter of acceleration, the directional vector. The most common laboratory procedure for simulating maintained increased gravitational fields is centrifugation (see Figs. 8-8 and 8-9). Field intensity depends upon speed of rotation and radius of rotation. The nomogram in Figure 8-12 can be employed for computations of centrifugal fields.

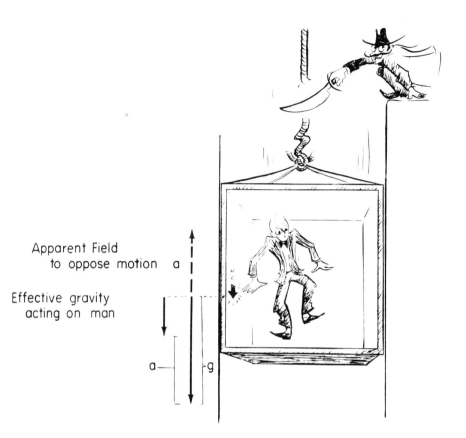

Figure 8-7. Simulation of a lessened gravitational field by means of downward (negative) acceleration. (Wunder and Lutherer, 1964.) Similar results are obtained when an airplane executes an outside loop (see Fig. 8-11).

The radius or distance from the axis of rotation to the body under consideration is designated by r and in this equation is expressed in centimeters. The magnitude of the field in units of cm/sec² rather than in G's can be obtained upon omission of the value 980 from the above equation. The factor 900 derives from conversion of the translational speed S into rotational rate and from conversion of seconds into minutes.[3]

---

[3] When expressed in cgs units, the centrifugal field g, as a function of the translational speed v about a circular path, would be:

$$g = \frac{v^2}{r} = \frac{(2\pi[\text{RPS}])^2}{r} = 4\pi^2 r[\text{RPS}]^2 \times \left[\frac{\text{RPM}}{60\ \text{RPS}}\right]^2$$

where RPM refers to rev/min and RPS to rev/sec.

A space vehicle in orbit around the Earth comprises part of a large-scale centrifuge system which has the Earth as the center of rotation. In this system, the gravitational field acts as the centripetal force which opposes the centrifugal force. Maintained orbit is achieved when the force from the gravitational field is just balanced by the centrifugal force of the vehicle.[4] While laboratory centrifugation simulates increased-intensity fields (above 1 G), the condition in an artificial satellite results in decreased intensity which approaches the weightless state (zero G). By combining changes in the scalar dimensions of speed and direction, it is also possible for a subject in an airplane to achieve briefly an acceleration which balances the gravitational field (Figs. 8-7, 8-11). Until the historic journeys of Russian and American astronauts, acceleration techniques had achieved weightless states lasting for little more than one minute.

As the animals which presently exist on Earth have evolved in a gravitational field of almost constant intensity, it seems reasonable that nature would have selected organisms which are extremely well adapted to this particular field intensity. The extent to which an animal can adjust to a different field intensity would probably depend upon the extent to which this type of adjustment has been useful in surviving other types of changes that affect the organism in the same manner as gravitational change.[5]

Scientists at the Davis campus of the University of California (Smith and Kelly, 1963; Burton and Smith, 1965) have reported development of a strain

---

[4] The perfect balance of centrifugal and gravitational fields is strictly true only in a circular orbit, during which a constant magnitude of velocity and rate of rotation are maintained. During elliptical orbit, the speed becomes less at greater distances from the Earth, so that there is a net balancing not only of gravitational and centrifugal forces but also of forces arising from translational acceleration or deceleration of an orbiting body. Unrestrained objects in space fall with accelerations that negate biological effects of weight.

The planets, as they orbit about the Sun, and the satellites, as they orbit about their planets, are held in their orbital path due to counterbalancing of the centrifugal field generated by their own physical acceleration and the gravitational force arising either from the Sun or the appropriate planet. So long as these two forces are at all times balanced, they do not necessarily require a constant value. As demonstrated by Kepler several centuries ago, the planetary paths are elliptical with one of the foci of the ellipse (i.e., one of the two points from which the sum of the distances from these two points to a third point on the ellipse is always of constant magnitude) at the location of the Sun or at the center of a planet for satellite orbit. (This focus would actually lie at the center of mass for the entire system but with large discrepancies of mass such a mass center would be closely approximated by the center of mass for the larger body; i.e., the Sun for a planetary orbit and planet for a satellite orbit.) The point in a satellite orbit of greatest distance from the Earth would be referred to as the *apogee*. The nearest point would be referred to as the *perigee*.

[5] Some physical agents, such as ionizing radiation, are capable of directly causing random mutations. The energy concentration attainable in gravitational fields which known life can tolerate is much too low to have the direct effects at the molecular level required to induce a mutation. A change in the gravitational intensity, therefore, could not induce true genetic change. The only way in which gravity could act to alter the genetic makeup of organisms would be by indirect influence through the process of natural selection.

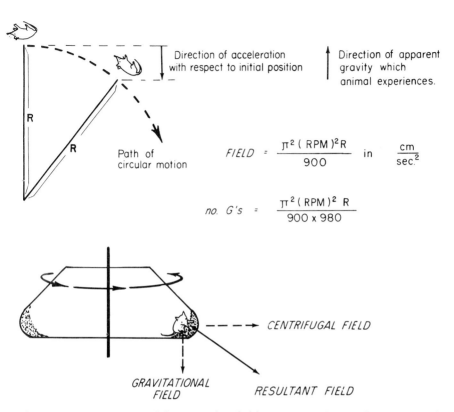

Direction of acceleration with respect to initial position

Direction of apparent gravity which animal experiences.

R

R

Path of circular motion

$$FIELD = \frac{\pi^2 (RPM)^2 R}{900} \quad in \quad \frac{cm}{sec.^2}$$

$$no. \ G's = \frac{\pi^2 (RPM)^2 R}{900 \times 980}$$

CENTRIFUGAL FIELD

GRAVITATIONAL FIELD

RESULTANT FIELD

Figure 8-8. Direction of forces and g fields in a centrifuge. The centripetal force constantly pushes the animal toward the center of rotation, away from a transverse path, and into a circular path. Note that the total g field acting on a centrifuged animal is the vector sum of the centrifugal and gravitational fields. The magnitude of this resultant field is essentially the same as that for the centrifugal field at high rates of rotation. At lower rates of rotation the contribution of the gravitational vector assumes relatively greater proportions. (Wunder and Lutherer, 1964.)

of chickens which, after 5 generations, now has increased tolerance to the rigors imposed by a centrifugal field. In each of the generations, only those animals which could survive centrifugation could live to breed. It is not surprising, therefore, that a strain of high gravitational tolerance has evolved as a result of "experimental, natural selection." If all the factors influencing the tolerance of an organism to high gravitational intensities were known and observable, comparable strains of high-tolerance animals—even man—could be obtained by means of arbitrary selection.

Inertial Fields of High Intensity

Although the physical acceleration of rockets and airplanes imposes exposure to short bouts of intense, artificial gravity upon man, the likelihood that man will, within the foreseeable future, experience natural gravity of greater than 1 G is remote. Materials are not available which would afford man protection from the Sun's (28 G's) intense heat. On Jupiter (2.65 G's), Saturn (1.17 G's), Uranus (1.05 G's), and Neptune (1.23 G's), the surface temperatures are believed to be too low and the barometric pressures too high to encourage a visit by man. The energy requirements for a rocket which would permit one to return from these planets, moreover, would be prohibitive due to the large mass of these heavenly bodies (Figs. 3-2, 10-2) serving as a "gravitational sink."

Should man decide at some time in the far distant future to attempt a long voyage (one which might require several generations to complete) to planets which lie beyond our solar system, exposure to prolonged bouts of acceleration may become necessary. Even at the speed of light, a voyage to the closest star would require a period of 4 years. A much longer period of time would be required in accelerating the rocket ship at the rate of 1 G or 980 cm per sec^2 toward a final velocity approaching the speed of light (see page 228).

Upon returning to the Earth's gravity from some other body of our solar system or from outer space itself (zero G unless artificial gravity is employed), man is likely to encounter a physiological condition similar to that of continual exposure to high gravity. After an extended voyage in a weightless state or in the lower gravity of the moon (0.16 G), Mars (0.39 G), Venus (.86 G), Mercury (.38 G), or the natural satellites of one of the planets, organisms might change in such a manner that they would best be adapted or adjusted to a sub-Terrestrial gravity. Until reconditioning could be achieved, there is a high probability that the Earth's normal gravity would be most oppressive. Some clue as to how man might react under such conditions can be obtained from experimental studies with animals which are forced to live for long periods of time in the artificial gravities generated by slow-speed centrifuges.

The type of inertial field which is of most immediate concern involves short bouts of high-G exposure during acceleration to orbital and escape velocities or during the deceleration necessary in returning to the Earth's atmosphere. The amount of inertial field to be experienced in addition to that of the planet's normal gravity would be equal to the velocity to be attained divided by the time for attaining this velocity. Products of 19 and 13 G-minutes are involved in attaining the Earth's escape and orbital velocities of 11 and 8 km per sec respectively. The total inertial field g to be experienced by an organism in achieving a given velocity can be described by the equation:

$$g = \frac{v}{time} + \text{planet's field} \qquad (8\text{-}3)$$

The total field involved for various times of acceleration is shown in Figure 8-5,

Figure 8-9. Proposed human centrifuge for chronic exposure. (Courtesy of Drs. G. N. Hoover and R. T. Donaldson, North American Aviation, Inc., Downey, Calif.) Although fields as great as 2 G's can be generated for as long as 120 man-days of exposure, most studies with this machine will be at less than 1.5 G's and intended primarily to study rotation *per se* rather than high gravity. Maximum rate of rotation will be 12 RPM. When completed by Rucker Co., Oakland, Calif., for North American in June, 1965, the radius will extend to 75 feet. Eventual plans call for a diameter of 300 feet. This centrifuge will be employed to establish design requirements for rotating space stations by determining levels of human tolerance to rotation. Smaller human centrifuges have been employed primarily for study of intense acute acceleration as great as 50 G's.

indicating that man could tolerate a constant acceleration which would require *more* than 2½ minutes to place him in orbit and more than 4 minutes for escape. The rockets which are presently in use or proposed for use involve several stages of acceleration similar to the patterns shown in Figure 8-13.

Tiny centrifuges have been developed in which it is possible to generate fields as intense as 500,000,000 G's. As long ago as 1926, centrifuges were available which would permit the observation of protein sedimentation during exposure to tens of thousands of G's. Single cells have survived exposure to 500,000 G's for as long as 30 minutes. Since 1935, several centrifuges have been developed for experiments with man as the subject (Fig. 8-9). Fields up to 30 G's can be produced for extended periods in "human" centrifuges. Among such centrifuges presently in operation are the ones at the Mayo Clinic in Rochester, Minnesota, Wright-Patterson Air Force Base at

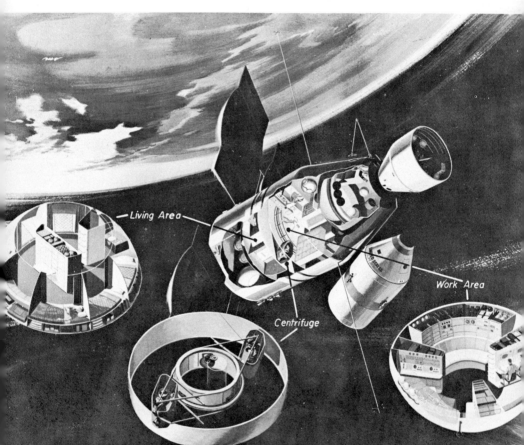

Figure 8-10. Space-based human centrifuge proposed by Douglas Aircraft Co. (White, 1964.)

Dayton, Ohio, the Naval Air Development Center in Johnsville, Pennsylvania, the School of Aerospace Medicine at Brooks Field near San Antonio, Texas, and the University of California at Los Angeles. Greater fields of shorter duration can be produced by rapid acceleration of the rocket-driven sleds. Man has survived fields as intense as 80 G's for a fraction of a second and 2 G's for 24 hours.

As a rule, survival time is greatest at lower field intensities (Fig. 8-5). Some mice at the University of Iowa have survived at 2 G's for as long as 2 years, during which time they have conceived, delivered, and reared litters. Scientists at Cambridge University in England have maintained breeding rats in the centrifuge at 3 G's for three generations. Mice have grown and survived for as long as one year at fields as intense as 7 G's.

The ability of animals to make environmental adjustments is important. The threshold for mechanical damage to bone and other structures imposes the endurance limit for intense, acute exposures lasting less than one second. Distribution of blood determines tolerance to lower fields lasting for a number of seconds. At still lower fields, which can be endured for several minutes,

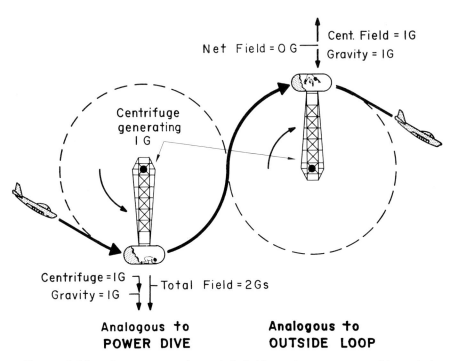

Figure 8-11. Comparison of inertial fields acting upon a subject during inside and outside loops of aerodynàmic flight and in a centrifuge. (Modified from figure in *Physiology of Flight.* Air Force Manual 160. July, 1953.)

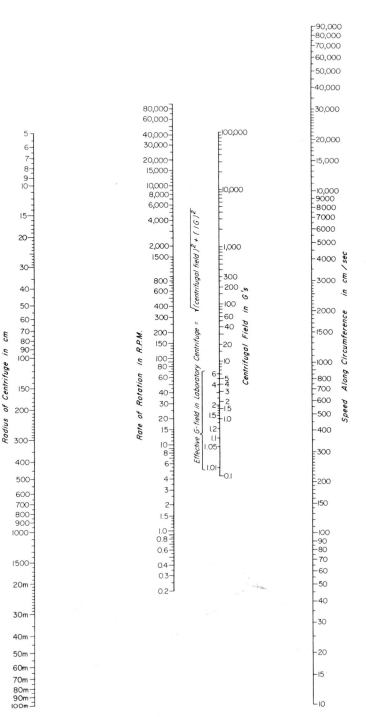

Figure 8-12. Nomogram for computation of centrifugal and total effective g fields as a function of centrifuge radius and as a function of either rate of rotation or of transverse speed. (As modified from Wunder and Lutherer, 1964.)

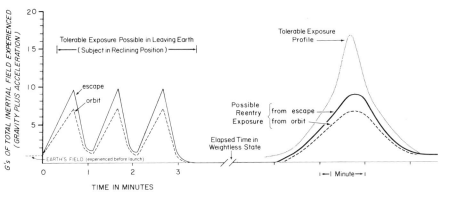

Figure 8-13. Possible three-stage acceleration pattern and reentry patterns for orbit and escape of manned rockets. (Based in part on data of Stapp, 1961.)

the ability to breathe becomes the primary consideration. At the fields which are low enough to permit prolonged exposure, limitations are imposed by the ability of the animals to maintain adequate nourishment.

Responses of the circulatory and respiratory systems to acute acceleration have been tested to some extent in man and other mammals. Some of the responses of centrifuged men are listed in Table 8-3. Greater gravity gives effectively greater weight to columns of blood or other fluids and results in greater hydrostatic pressures (see pp. 93-96). The heart, blood vessels, and the veins in the regions beneath the heart balloon with pooling of blood. Various degrees of circulatory shock can appear unless these vessels are able to increase tone. There is an impediment to venous return, and, as a result, cardiac output is momentarily decreased. At a time when a greater pressure is required to supply the brain with blood, the blood pressure at head level of standing or sitting individuals is severely reduced (Figs. 6-4, 8-15, and 8-16). Temporary visual defects and loss of consciousness are expected and often occur. As the field intensity increases, there is a corresponding increase in the heart rate and in the systemic vascular resistance which promotes the recovery or eventual elevation of the blood pressure. Acceleration also imposes difficulties on the mechanical function of respirations.

Procedures which reduce the ability of *g* fields to cause large pressure heads and pooling of blood below heart level would offer protection from intense fields. The principle of opposing gravitational force by the buoyancy factor has not only been utilized to simulate lowered intensity fields but has also been experimentally demonstrated to be capable of protecting the body against high-intensity fields. This actually amounts to simulating a lower field than is being generated by the acceleration. As water is of nearly the same density as the body, the increased force would cause comparable pressure changes inside and outside the body with little change in the net

TABLE 8-3.   Effects of Acute Acceleration upon Man as Tabulated from Review by Lindberg and Wood (1963)

	Direction of Acceleration (as indicated from Fig. 8-14)		Transverse		
	Positive	Negative	Eyeballs In	Eyeballs Out	Lateral
1. *Cardiovascular*	Limiting factor for exposures of several seconds		Little effect due to lower columns of blood		
a. Arterial pressure	*At head level:* Fall with increasing field. Some compensation (apparently due to reflexes arising from pressure receptors at the carotid sinus acting through the autonomic nerves to increase blood pressure) after 7 sec of exposure *At heart level:* No immediate change (5 G's) with increase during compensation for low pressure at head. Can be maintained for as long as 10 min at 4 G's	*At head level:* Increases. This activates reflex to increase influence of vagus nerve upon heart with possible resulting decreased circulation to head			
b. Heart rate	Increase rate	Sometimes decreases due to reflex action			
c. Cardiac output	(Volume rate of pumping): Decrease				
d. Venous return of blood	Decrease due to pooling of blood as vessels balloon out in the abdomen and legs				
2. *Vision*	*Decreased peripheral vision* after 3 sec at 3.5 G's (due to decreased oxygen delivery by	Some reddening of visual field (possibly due to engorgement of retinal blood vessels)	Normal vision up to 20 G's		

	blood to the retina as a result of the inability of the lowered arterial pressure to overcome intraocular pressure of eye) *Complete loss of vision* ("black-out") after 7 sec at 4 G's with some recovery during exposure (due to pressure compensation) but with no recovery during exposure to higher fields		
3. *Consciousness*	*Unconsciousness* after 5 sec at 4.5 to 5 G due to decreased circulation with greater tolerance than for vision. Circulation tends to be maintained due to the siphon-like arrangement for circulation within the rigid skull	*Unconsciousness* in some subsides due to overcompensation to decreased heart rate after 7 sec at 6 G's. Discomfort in head	
4. *Respiration*	*Decreased saturation* of blood with oxygen presumably due to gravitationally induced shunting of blood or due to uneven expansion of alveolae Increased total and tidal lung volume with greater effort required for large expirations	*Decreased lung volume* and impaired breathing due to weight of abdominal viscera. Effective breathing impossible above 12 G's	Limiting factor in tolerance Decreased lung volume Increased rate
5. *Other*	Low tolerance in comparison to positive acceleration	High tolerance in comparison to positive acceleration	Not extensively investigated

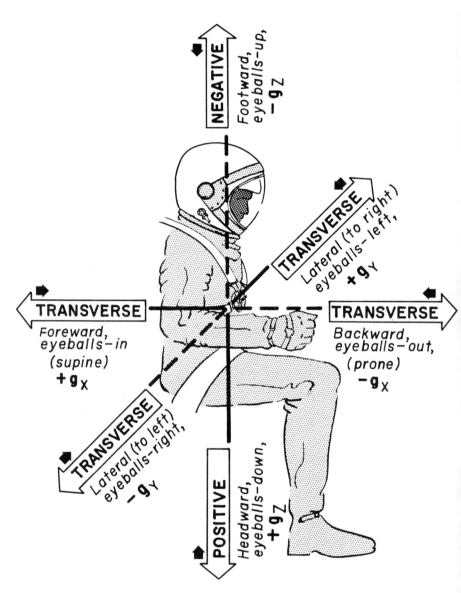

Figure 8-14. Direction of forces and effective acceleration (solid line) and actual direction of acceleration or of centripetal force (broken line) for various notations of acceleration.

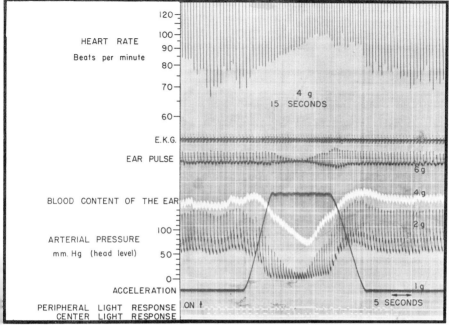

Figure 8-15. Sequence of physiological events during exposure of human subjects to 4 G headward acceleration in a centrifuge. Note that there is a drop initially in the arterial pressure at head level with some recovery occurring within a few seconds resulting in part from an increasing heart rate. (Figure courtesy of Dr. Earl H. Wood [Fed. Proc. 5, 327-344, 1946].)

pressure difference. Essentially, the body is supported against a greater field by a greater buoyancy. This phenomenon is exemplified by the whale, which is crushed by its own weight when removed from the water. In the cases reported for this type of protection, human beings were able to endure given fields for approximately twice the usual period of time (before visual impairment [Fig. 8-5]).

Since men are able to survive the acceleration pattern of our existing rockets, an immersion technique is not being employed for space vehicles. In order to reduce some of the distortions, however, astronauts are placed in specially constructed couches which conform to the shape of the body. The anti-g suit (mentioned in Chapter 6) serves as a corset resisting internal pressure changes induced by the high *g* fields. It prevents displacement by actively compressing the body by means of inflated air bladders about the abdomen and legs. The positioning of the subject in a supine position so that the force acts in a direction which will least interfere with circulatory and respiratory functions is an obvious method of protection. In Figure 8-5,

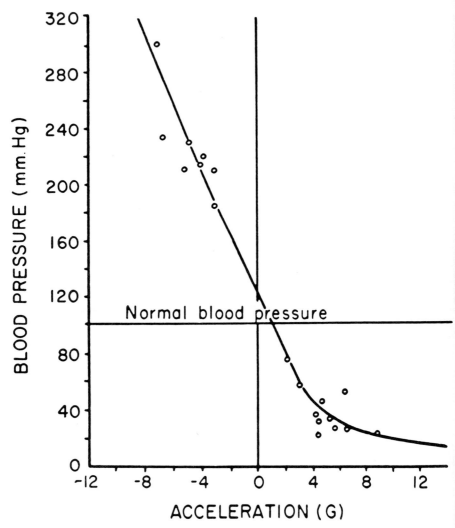

Figure 8-16. Effect of angular acceleration upon arterial blood pressure at neck level. Note that the pressure heads indicated here would not actually be the height to which a column of mercury would be raised during acceleration but the height to which mercury would be raised if it were matched at 1 G against the pressures developed during centrifugation. (Arthur C. Guyton, 1961, after Armstrong, 1943.)

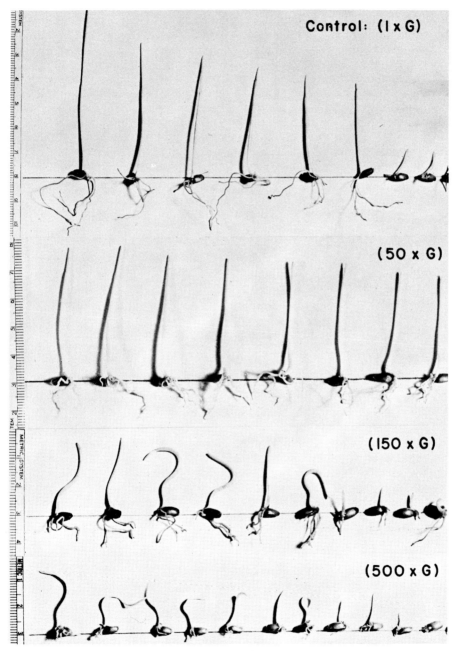

Figure 8-17. Wheat seedlings after 4 days of growth in a centrifuge. (This figure was supplied through the courtesy of Stephen W. Gray. It has been described by him elsewhere in more detail [Gray and Edwards, 1955].)

it will be noted that the man who is sitting back and is therefore closer to the prone position exhibits a greater tolerance than the man sitting in a more erect manner.

Different organisms, including wheat, chickens, mice, rats, hamsters, fish, insects, and turtles, are known to be capable of growth during exposure to chronic centrifugation. Alterations in development do result. The most pronounced observable changes are with respect to quantitative or general growth in the animal's size. Although gravity can influence the form of an organism, intrinsic factors are of such importance in controlling the animal's differentiation that experimental changes in form are more difficult to detect. Sufficiently intense fields tend to decelerate growth (Figs. 4-10 and 8-17).

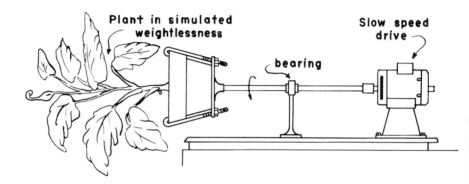

Figure 8-18.   Clinostat for simulation of zero G by tumbling plants in horizontal position.

Moderate intensities of centrifugation can, in some cases, however, cause an accelerated growth rate. The nature of response is a function of field intensity, the age, the size, and the biological and physical characteristics of the organism as well as other environmental factors. Terrestrial animals could live and perhaps multiply at gravitational intensities differing from that found on the Earth.

Weightlessness and Inertial Fields of Low Intensity

Although physical principles of weightlessness[6] are well understood, no adequate simulation of it exists. It is necessary to approach this problem by various indirect methods.

Two conditions to be met during space travel can cause man to exist in an effectively weightless environment. One condition occurs when the space craft is such a distance from any heavenly body that there is present

---

[6] *Weightlessness and zero G* are employed here as synonymous terms. Some authorities (Gerathewohl, 1965) employ the latter to designate the true absence of gravity and weightlessness as conditions (such as water immersion) which simulate zero G.

little or no true gravitational field. The other condition occurs when the centrifugal field generated by an artificial satellite counterbalances the gravitational field originating from the Earth or some other heavenly body. The first exposure to a natural gravitational field which, although still significant is substantially less than that to which man is accustomed, will take place when manned colonies or stations are established on the Moon.

For 80 years, man has been aware that gravity influences the normal growth of organisms. The first attempts to simulate a weightless environment were performed in work with plant material. The work by Sachs in 1872 (as cited by Lyon, 1962) and later work of other botanists involved rotating or tumbling plants in a device known as a clinostat (Fig. 8-18). The clinostat tumbles plants with their axes of growth at right angles to the gravitational vector with a speed of rotation such that the direction of any settling within the plant cells would be constantly changing, thereby eliminating any net gravitational effect at the cellular level.

Before the turn of the present century, embryologists demonstrated that gravity is necessary for certain processes in animals. One of the earliest observations that normal gravity can influence biological processes was that of Pflüger (1884, as discussed by Morgan, 1897), in which the direction of cleavage in the frog's egg was observed to be dependent upon its orientation with respect to the Earth's gravity. A decade later, Schultze (1894, as discussed by Generales, 1963) noted that when the fertilized eggs of the frog, *Rana fusca,* were inverted abnormal development ensued. Megusãr (1906, as discussed by Generales, 1963) made comparable observations with the water beetle, *Hydrophilus arterrimus.*

Strughold in 1928 (as discussed by Hawkins, 1963), simulating short bouts of weightlessness by opposing acceleration in aircraft in the Earth's gravity, first made observations with man. His studies were concerned with the overshoot in positioning or aiming as a result of the absence of gravitational cues. During the following two decades, as the performance of aircraft improved, problems of aviation became more concerned with the influence of high or low gravitational environments. The first nonexperimental situation in which men were required to perform tasks during weightlessness occurred during World War II (Bourne, 1963). German fighter pilots executed a maneuver in which they first dived from above to beneath Allied bombers. Then they executed an outside loop, counteracting the Earth's gravity by a centrifugal field as they swung up to attack the belly of Allied airplanes.

With advances in rocketry, German scientists began to consider the implications of prolonged weightlessness which might accompany space flight. Mindful of the changes in the sensory threshold for other agents in our environment, Gauer and Haber (1950) warned that in the absence of the Earth's gravitational field the slightest of movements could generate inertial fields which, although of low intensity, would be capable of quickly disorientating human subjects. They explained this prediction in terms of the Weber-Fechner Law. (This law predicts that the detectable change in intensity of some stimuli varies in direct proportion to the initial intensity of that stimuli or agent.)

TABLE 8-4. Effects of Weightlessness Predicted from Various Types of Simulation (Wunder, 1964*†)

		Metabolic Rate	Obesity	Growth	Bone	Ca Excretion	Joint Stiffness or Pain	Muscle Size	Muscle Force	N Excretion	Urine Volume	Thirst	Hematocrit	Noradrenolin (urinary level)	Heart Rate	Heart Size	Orthostatic Hypotension	Diaphragm Edema & loss of dry mass	Disorientation	Tendency to Semi-Fetal Position	Stretch Reflex (knee jerk)
FLIGHT	Orbital	↓28		↓mass dessication 4		±4	↑4		±4	↓4	↑ dessication 4	↑4	↑4	+↓ 4,33 unstable 24,20			↑4,30		↑ only 1=1.30sec. 33,24,17	31,16	↓4
	Suborbital & Parbolic	↓5	↑5																		26 13,38
BED REST				↓body mass 3		↑3 ←2	↑3	↘2 ↘19	→3	←28 ↓2	←2 ↑3		↑28 ↓2	↑28	←28 stroke volume	↓28	↑31 3,2,28		31,16		
IMMOBIL-IZATION	Cast, Splint etc.		↑15	↓rabbit bone 7	±←	±5	↑5	↘5	↓5	↓5	↑5		±5	±5	+↓5	5	5			
	Tenotomy (animals)			↓bone 7 muscle 35				↘25	↓25												
	Denervation (animals)			→bone 1				↘6,18	↘6,18												
IMMERSION				↑plants 12		←10			↗10,11	←10	←10	←10	←21	→23	±10	↗10,23		→29 ↑21,14	←8	humans 13	↗36,37
TUMBLING								↘34													
CHRONIC CENTRI-FUGATION (animals)	Moderate	↓32		↓34									←32 acute 34 humans	↑32 acute 34 humans							
	High	↓32 34		↓34				34					27	→9							
	After removal	↓34		↓34													←34			

NOTE: Footnotes on page 159.

* Arrows indicate direction of changes; slanted arrows indicate only slight changes.

† References are given to an article discussing or reviewing an experimental finding but not necessarily to the original publication which described the work. The references are as follows: (1) Howell (1917); (2) Birkhead et al., 1963; (3) Brannon et al., 1963; (4) Catterson et al., 1963; (5) Deitrick et al., 1948; (6) Eccles, 1941; (7) Geiser and Trueta, 1958; (8) Dr. Jack Goldman, personal communication, 1964; (9) Goodall, 1962; (10) Graveline et al., 1961; Graveline and McCally, 1963; (11) Graybiel and Clark, 1961; (12) Handbook, 1963 (in discussion of Finn's work); (13) Hawkins, 1963; (14) Heilbrunn, 1943; (15) Helander, 1960; (16) Henry et al., 1952; Henry et al., 1962; (17) Hines and Thomson, 1956; (18) Hislop, 1963; (19) Kas'yan, 1963; (20) Levine, 1963; (21) McCally, 1964; (22) McCally and Graveline, 1963; (23) Parin, 1962; (24) Schottelius et al., 1954; (25) Capt. J. C. Simons, personal communication, 1964; (26) Smith and Kelly, 1963; (27) Taylor et al., 1949; (28) Thomson, 1955; (29) Volynkyn and Yajdovsky, 1962 (as cited by McCally, 1964); (30) von Beckh, 1954; (31) Vrăbiesco et al., 1964; (32) White and Berry, 1964; (33) Wunder and Lutherer, 1964; (34) Zelená, 1963; (35) Lilly and Shurley, 1961; (36) Margaria, 1958; (37) Capt. R. S. Kellogg, personal communication, 1964; (38) Gazenko and Gurjian.

TABLE 8-5. Conditions Which Achieve Some of the Effects of Weightlessness (Wunder, 1964)

Condition	Degree of Weightlessness	Disadvantages	Remarks
1. Remoteness from all heavenly bodies	Complete, save for natural or artificial gravity generated by the space vehicle containing living material	Theoretically, the time is still several years in the future when this will be possible with living material. Spinning or any change of a space ship's motion would still effect gravity-like forces	
2. Opposing acceleration or changing a body's motion just sufficiently to counterbalance the gravitational acceleration	Complete to the extent that the applied acceleration is uniform with respect to distance, time, and direction	Difficult to place sizable quantities of living material in this situation while maintaining spatial and temporal purity of the apparent gravitational field	
2a. Orbital flight in an artificial satellite for which the satellite's centrifugal field just	Almost complete, particularly at the center of the satellite. However, spinning could gen-	Same as above. High fields must accompany going into and leaving orbit. Extreme care is	A well-controlled experiment would in all likelihood require that control material be ex-

TABLE 8-5. Continued

Condition	Degree of Weightlessness	Disadvantages	Remarks
counterbalances the Earth's gravitational field	erate centrifugal fields, and the opposing centrifugal and gravitational fields could disagree at the rim of a space station by 1.5×10^{-4} G per mile of the station's radius	necessary to assure that control animals are exposed to all the non-weightless aspects of orbital space flight, such as radiation, vibration, short bouts of acceleration, and heating due to reentry.	posed to the same space voyage as the experimental organisms. A 1-G environment would be maintained by centrifuging the control organisms within the space vehicle
2b. Suborbital trajectory flight in the nose cone of ballistic rockets	Duration of only a few minutes (poor uniformity of field)	Same as 2 and 2a above. Furthermore, the period of post- and pre-weightless acceleration is sizable in comparison to the actual period of weightlessness	
2c. Parabolic or Keplerian flight in high-performance aircraft	Duration of approximately 1 minute (poor uniformity of field)	Same as 2, 2a, and 2b, save for the fact that experimental material can be somewhat more easily placed in this condition and be more readily available to the observer	
2d. Falling in drop towers or slides	Duration of seconds or less (poor uniformity of field)	Too short a period to detect many biological responses to weightlessness	
3. Reducing the influence of gravity without actually decreasing its magnitude	The extent to which gravitational effect is reduced can only be qualitatively estimated; it cannot be accurately quantified	Various methods of reducing gravitational effect do not act equally on all parts or systems of an organism. Moreover, these methods frequently impose various types of restric-	Many studies, particularly the earlier ones, employing this approach were designed primarily to investigate factors other than the absence of gravity. For this reason, the type

		tion upon an organism which would cause experimental artifacts	of control is not of the optimum type with respect to weightlessness
3a. Reduction of activity or work load	Perhaps a fair qualitative comparison from the aspect of weight support and work. However, weightlessness would not restrict that aspect of activity which is primarily motion (mass $\times$ velocity) rather than work (force $\times$ distance)	A certain amount of activity would be necessary even in the absence of gravity. Absence of gravity would reduce the amount of force required to support force or weight (isometric muscle work or static work). However, one would not expect such a drastic effect upon actual motion (isotonic, muscle contraction or kinetic activity)	
3a(1). Bed rest			Assumption of the horizontal position would not merely reduce the work to support gravitational force. It would also reduce the effective height of columns of fluid (such as blood), thus reducing the hydrostatic pressure which could be imposed by gravity
3a(2). Suspension or support by frictionless devices			Would primarily be useful only in considerations of performance in evaluating responses to the absence of *external* gravitationally-imposed frictional forces
3a(3). Immobilization by means of casts, splints, and tenotomy	Only for a portion of a body		This might impose a greater reduction in movement and in sensations of strength or tension from the muscles or tendons than would be the case for true weightlessness. Imposes unnatural environment for immobilized subjects. Also in certain respects weightlessness

TABLE 8-5. Continued

Condition	Degree of Weightlessness	Disadvantages	Remarks
		would afford a certain freedom of movement which would have the opposite effect of immobilization	
3a(4). Denervation	Only for the denervated portion of a body	As in 3a(2) above, this would exaggerate the absence of sensory information and absence of muscle stimulation and movement beyond that of the weightless conditions. Also, it would have effect only with respect to the specific denervated areas rather than the entire system, as would be the case for denervated muscles	
3a(4.1). Complete denervation		Would permit less nervous control than occurs in the weightless state	Achieved in experimental animal by complete sectioning of a nerve
3a(4.2). Sensory denervation			Achieved in experimental vertebrates by sectioning the dorsal route of spinal nerves as they enter the spinal cord
3a(4.3). Motor denervation			Achieved in experimental vertebrates by sectioning the ventral route of spinal nerves as they leave the spinal cord
3b. Buoyant support by means of water immersion to oppose gravitational forces	Fairly good simulation of reduced force requirements for slow body movements, body support, and opposition of gravitationally induced pressures	A greater force would be necessary for fast body movements due to the greater viscosity for water than for air. Would not negate the gravitational effect upon structures (such as the	

otolith bodies of the gravity-detecting end-organs or of air-filled spaces, such as the lungs) the specific gravity of which is different from that of the surrounding medium or structure. Moreover, unless air is applied at a positive pressure, more work would be required for ventilation of the lungs, and experimental artifacts would arise as a result of negative-pressure breathing. There are also the difficulties associated with an unnatural heat exchange and unnatural ambient environment for the skin. Additional psychological difficulties associated with isolation, sensory deprivation, and boredom can result

This method has been employed with plant material for approximately 100 years (Sachs, 1872). When combined with water immersion, it has been proposed for use with animal material. Rotation with a seated subject tumbling from head to foot has been attempted and abandoned at the NASA-Langley Installation. Rotation of a prone subject in a sideways direction has met with greater success and is still under development at Lockheed in Marietta, Georgia (Levine, 1963)

Nearly complete at center of rotation

Centrifugal fields would occur with increasing distances from the axis of rotation or with increasing rates of rotation. Moreover, high rates of rotation can cause a certain amount of disorientation due to a bizarre stimulation of such sensory organs as the semicircular canals of the middle ear

3c. Tumbling of a subject about an axis which is at right angles to gravitational vector with a speed of rotation such that no net sedimentation or settling of structures or materials occurs

TABLE 8-5. Continued

Condition	Degree of Weightlessness	Disadvantages	Remarks
4. Studies of chronic exposure to high gravitational loads		Imposes many potential effects of rotation, such as uneven g fields	It is necessary in such studies that the arm length of the centrifuge be large in comparison to animal size, animal motion, and rate of rotation
4a. Chronic centrifugation and extrapolation of results with the assumption that subgravity would evoke the opposite response	Depends upon the extent to which a response to gravity would increase in a linear manner with field intensity	Not all of the responses observed in these studies are of the type which increase linearly with gravity. Biological growth is frequently enhanced by slight intensities of centrifugation but is discouraged by more intense fields (Fig. 7-4)	Most of these studies have been performed with growing animals, so that many of the results reflect the influence of gravity upon development but would not necessarily indicate the influence of weightlessness upon adult men. In many instances, these investigations were directed rather toward the problems of growth than those of weightlessness
4b. Removal from chronic centrifugation to a less intense field (normal gravity or one G)	Qualitative indication of effect of subgravity upon factors resulting from adjustment to gravity	Would not indicate any effects which result directly from less gravitational force. It should indicate only the response due to properties which can be influenced in one way or another by the gravitational environment itself	Involves developing or breeding organisms into a special organism possessing exaggerated characteristics. These organisms should respond to normal gravity in the same manner as normal animals should respond to subgravity.
4c. High-gravity strain of organisms evoked by maintenance of surviving animals over generations of centrifugation	Qualitative indication of effect of subgravity upon factors displaying best survival during gravitational adversities	Same as 4b above	

It was known even at that time that some disorientation could occur during the first few seconds of weightlessness. Fortunately, it has since been found that, after a few seconds, man can adjust to weightlessness. The complications to be expected if the range of applicability of the Weber-Fechner Law extended to the very low gravitational intensities are not now apparent.

At the time of this writing (July 1965), there has been no well-controlled experiment which involves exposure of biological material to a completely weightless condition. On the basis of known theory and experiments, however, such as those outlined in Tables 8-4 and 8-5, some predictions of the possible effects can be made (Fig. 8-19).

With less energy required to oppose gravity, a surplus of available energy might cause certain mechanisms which normally would conserve energy to fall into disuse. A decreased efficiency might arise and later persist when the organism requires more energy.

With less force required to stretch or strain muscular and tendon tissues, there would be a decreased stimulation of sensory receptors within these structures. Altered thresholds of response by these receptors and altered postural reflexes for equilibrium could result. The decrease in the force to stretch muscles and tendons would come not only from the direct decrease in gravitational force but also from the reduced need for muscular contraction. Decreased muscular and gravitational forces would decrease the normal skeletal strain. Moderate strain (or the resulting mechanical stress) is believed to be one of the factors responsible for stimulating and directing the growth of bone (Thompson, 1942, pp. 958-1025; Sissons, 1956). Should the rate of bone anabolism be slower than the rate of bone catabolism, there would be an excretion of extra calcium and phosphorus. If high urine levels of these minerals persisted, kidney-stone formation could occur. (With man this probably would not be encountered until after at least 3 weeks.)

The decrease in muscular work to oppose gravitational force would not necessarily result in decreases in muscular movement. In the case of immobilization, the muscles doing less work decrease in size and in ability for maximum exertion of force. With the greater ease of body motion under low gravity fields, greater isotonic contraction of the muscles could occur, so that an individual exposed to weightlessness might possess muscle which, although smaller than normal, would still possess a greater ability for light muscular work than would muscle which had been completely immobilized (Elliott and Thomson, 1963). A program of conditioning including static exercise ("dynamic tension" or isometric contraction) and also other exercises involving body movement might be necessary for extended space voyages.

With the lowered gravitationally induced internal pressure differences across both the integument of the body and the walls of such structures as blood vessels, decreased distention of all these structures would occur. With the lower pressure gradients to oppose the return of venous blood to the heart, blood would return more readily and distend the auricles. It is believed that this would stimulate certain sensory receptors of heart volume

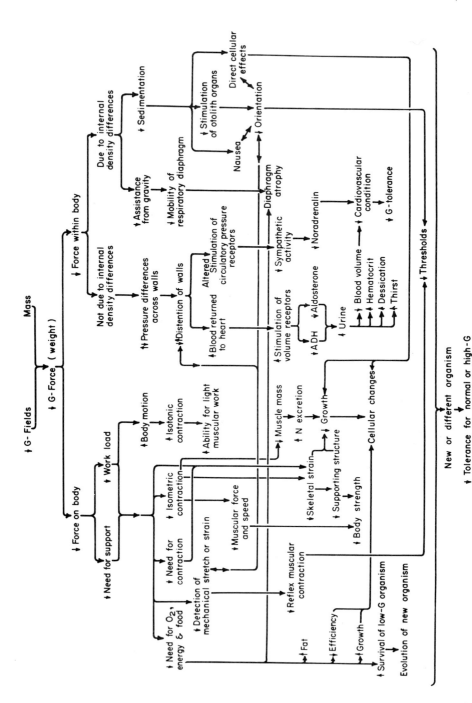

Figure 8-19. Some possible effects of weightlessness (Wunder, 1964).

(Gauer and Henry, 1963), reflexively causing a decrease in the amount of antidiuretic hormone (ADH). This would result in a faster rate of urine formation from the kidney, a decreased blood volume, a greater concentration of red blood cells, and a greater thirst. If the thirst could not be satisfied, desiccation of the body could also occur. Whether or not reflexes arising from auricular volume receptors might also influence the electrolyte secretion by the kidney is an unsettled question. With decreased work by the animal and with the lesser forces required to oppose gravity, the heart would be called upon to exert less pressure. A decreased stimulation of sensory receptors for pressure in the circulatory system, together with a decrease in the other efforts necessary for maintaining satisfactory circulation, could result in a decreased sympathetic activity of the autonomic nervous system and adrenal medulla. Less norepinephrine would be released. The blood vessels would more readily distend should high pressures result from a sudden return to a gravitational environment.[7]

Since air has a density drastically different from that for water, certain changes might be expected in the ventilatory respiration as well as the distribution of blood in the lungs. Erect individuals normally receive gravitational assistance in pulling the viscera down as the diaphragm contracts. The absence of gravity would therefore tend to immobilize the diaphragm. If the major ventilatory effort is eventually met by intercostal breathing, some diaphragm atrophy could result. This might be enhanced by a lower total expenditure of energy and therefore less demand for oxygen.

With the decreased settling of the calcareous otolith particles in the utricle of the inner ear, some disorientation would occur. This disorientation could be compounded by lack of sensation arising from the sensory-end-organs for stretch, strain, and pressure from other parts of the body. This, together with the possible unnatural distribution of gases and liquids within the various parts of the digestive tract, could cause nausea.

The possibility for decreased sedimentation and stratification of subcellular components has been considered as a possibility for causing effects at the cellular level (Pollard, 1965). The smaller a structure, the more mechanically stable it is and therefore the less likely to be influenced by the existence of or change in gravitational intensity. Random forces, such as those associated with diffusion, are believed normally to cause redistribution of material faster than it would be sorted by gravitational fields. Nevertheless, a different

---

[7] This type of cardiovascular deconditioning has been most frequently tested by means of a tilt table, which involves suddenly tilting a person from a recumbent to an erect or nearly erect position in the Earth's gravity. The deconditioned individual should resemble persons with *orthostatic hypotension*. With both the decreased blood volume and lessened tension in the walls of the blood vessels (particularly of the veins, beneath heart level), pooling of blood would occur with less blood returning to the heart, causing the arterial blood pressure to drop and the pulse rate to increase in an attempt to correct this condition. If cardiovascular adaptation is not adequate, the blood could supply less oxygen to the brain and fainting would occur.

distribution of structures (e.g., the mitochondria) could occur in some of the larger plant cells.

It is reasonable that in the absence of the effects of gravity certain adjustments will be made. Perhaps it might be more accurately stated that the body will fail to maintain the adjustments normally necessary in the presence of gravity. This deconditioning could eventually result in an organism which would be less able to sustain gravitational forces. Even though an astronaut may be able to tolerate the Earth's normal gravity, this deconditioning might place him at a serious disadvantage during the period of intense deceleration which accompanies the return into the Earth's atmosphere.

Developmental changes would be expected. Structures which experience a reduced functional need might also experience a reduced growth or a net loss in size. With less food required for energy to oppose gravity, more food materials might be available for growth or storage, particularly with respect to body fat. If appropriate procedures are not taken to prevent this deconditioning, the result may be an obese weakling.

As is indicated in Table 8-4, information suggestive of the possible effects of weightlessness can be obtained when this condition is simulated by means of accelerations which oppose gravitational field using various procedures which, although they do not eliminate the gravitational field, do reduce or negate its taxing effects. Some of the details as well as the advantages and disadvantages of these various approaches are listed in Table 8-5.

Mention has been made of the occurrence of a weightless state in an orbiting satellite. Limited data obtained from man and other animals under these conditions indicate that the heart rate and the blood pressure tend to drop slightly below normal, at least as an initial effect. Exposure to this type of simulated weightlessness is known to be a pleasant sensation by American astronauts (but reported as unpleasant by Yegorov, as cited by Volynkin and Vasil'yev, 1965) and is not believed to be dangerous for periods of exposure as long as 4 days. Although some nausea (for the Russian cosmonaut, Titov [see next section of this chapter]) and changes in the relative frequency of certain types of white blood cells have been observed during or after orbital flight, it is not yet possible to attribute specifically the effects to the absence of gravity (Berry, 1963; Catterson et al., 1963). Unfortunately, any attempt to correlate bed rest or immobilization effects of space travel and the effects of weightlessness could be misleading. Scientists at the School of Aerospace Medicine at Brooks Field, Texas, feel that some of the results of space travel are attributable to the immobilization imposed by the small size of existing space capsules rather than to weightlessness (Lamb, 1964; Lamb et al., 1964a,b).

Partial and total immersion of human subjects in water has also been used to simulate fields approaching zero G, since the force of 1 G is counteracted by the buoyant support of the water. This technique can be further refined by rotating the tank and its contents just fast enough to eliminate any sedimentation due to density differences. Heart rates, spatial orientation, lung capacities, oxygen consumption, and muscular strength have been measured on human subjects during and after varying periods of immersion. Results are fragmentary and evaluation is limited because of restrictions imposed on the length of time for which the experiments can be performed and the number of subjects used. Indications are that subjects consume less oxygen, develop a weaker skeleton and musculature, and experience difficulty in readjusting to a Terrestrial existence. The weaker musculature would be predicted on the basis of the decreased force needed to oppose gravity, and the oxygen intake decrement would follow from the ensuing reduction in energy requirements. The skeletal weakness is assumed to result from the bone demineralization indicated by high urinary calcium reported to occur both during submersion and bed rest.

As has been emphasized earlier, there are definite inadequacies in any experiment performed thus far in attempts to determine the effects of weightlessness. Even the satellite experiments which have been performed to date cannot be considered of a definitive nature.[8]

Manned orbiting laboratories are planned in which exposure to essentially weightless conditions of various types of animate and inanimate material can be studied. The Air Force anticipates that a non-rotating laboratory will be functional in 1968 (Fig. 2-6). Eventually rotating orbiting laboratories (Fig. 4-5) will be employed to compare the effects of exposure to inertial fields of essentially Terrestrial magnitude with exposure to little or no field. Rotation itself introduces a new environmental factor which will require examination.

Rotation

In the discussion of weightlessness, the use of a rotating station or orbiting centrifuge as a space platform was suggested as a necessity in maintaining control subjects for the study of weightlessness. If prolonged exposure to weightlessness proves intolerable, some sort of artificial gravity will be necessary during extended voyages (Fig. 4-6). Centrifugation will be the only practical method of simulating this necessary gravity. A chart (Fig. 8-20) presents some of the possible rotational speeds and sizes which have been computed for such fields by Hill and Schnitzer (1962), whose figures indicate

---

[8] Although the cause has not been definitely established, it seems reasonable to assume that the orthostatic hypotension exhibited by American and Russian astronauts can be attributed to exposure to weightlessness. On the other hand, the suggestion by American and Russian scientists that certain effects observed at the cellular level in satellite experiments are attributable to weightlessness seems only remotely plausible. All of the experiments were based upon comparison with ground-based control subjects, but adequate compensation was not made for the pattern of acceleration, the thermal pattern of heating as the satellite passed through the atmosphere, various types of radiation, vibration, effects of change in the magnetic field, and possible unknown factors. The possibility that there are unknown factors in space which might be of biological consequence should not be overlooked; the existence of cosmic rays has been known for only 60 years and that of the radiation belts for less than 10 years. In order to correct for these various factors, it is essential that the control material in weightlessness studies be placed in the satellite and centrifuged at 1 G.

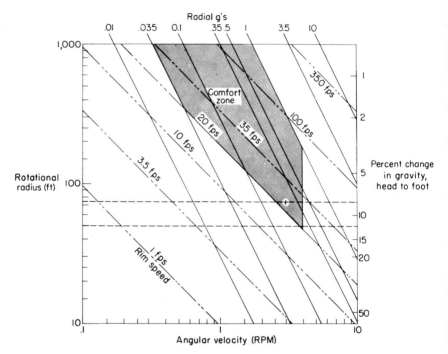

Figure 8-20. Rotational parameters for supplying artificial gravity to men in space stations. Shaded area indicates those combinations of rotation and radius which some authorities suggest might be comfortable to man. (Hill and Schnitzer, 1962.)

that a rotating system which would be comfortable to man in creating a field of 1 G would have a rotational radius of almost 200 feet, a rotational rate of 4 feet per minute, and a change in gravitational field from head to foot of approximately 3½ percent.

The principal disadvantage in using the centrifuge as a means of simulating gravitational fields lies in what might be termed the "impurity" or lack of uniformity of the field. As the radius within a centrifuge system is increased, the force on the rotating subject will increase. Thus, although a subject under experimental conditions might be considered to be at a fixed radius, certain parts of that subject will be farther from the center of rotation than other parts and thereby will experience greater force. Another factor is the existence of various Coriolis forces which do not present problems when an organism is stationary during rotation, but rather when the organism moves within a rotating frame of reference (Table 8-1). These variations in the field become increasingly important when the size or motion of the subject is large relative to the radius of rotation and when experimental artifacts may arise to confuse any conclusions drawn with respect to the effects of true gravitational fields. Although the effects of rotation depend upon the size of a centrifuge or spinning platform, studies by Navy scientists (Graybiel *et al.*, 1961) indicate that, except for a certain degree of psychophysical disorientation, men can adjust to speeds of rotation as high as 10 per minute. The primary psychophysical difficulty involved with rotation seems to be attributable to the uneven stimulation of the semicircular canals relative to that expected under conditions of comparable orientation or motion in a non-rotating system.

At the end of prolonged rotation the individual who has adjusted to the rotation might feel nausea in readjusting to the stationary state. This could cause difficulties for some future astronaut when he leaves a rotating space station for return to Earth. These difficulties could be further compounded if, while dependent upon a pressurized suit, the astronaut's nausea should be so drastic as to cause vomiting.

It has been suggested that the nausea experienced by the Russian cosmonaut Titov resulted from the spinning of his space ship. As the rotation of the Vostok was slow and the axis of rotation was at right angles to the vessel's long axis, some Soviet scientists feel emphatically that the effect was due solely to weightlessness and not to any side effects of rotation (conversation between Dr. O. G. Gazenko, U.S.S.R. Acad. Sci., and Mr. C. H. Dodge, Library of Congress, at the author's request). Ballet dancers by appropriate motions and exercise can learn to adapt themselves to high speeds of rotation without the accompanying disorientation. It is believed that since Titov's experience the Soviets have included in their training program for cosmonauts a series of conditioning exercises similar to ballet movements.

Vibrational Motion

Since mechanical vibrations cannot travel through a vacuum, they would not be considered a natural attribute of outer space.[9] On the other hand, there are many motions associated with the operation of a rocket vehicle which would give rise to vibrations: adjustments by the control mechanism, exhaust of gases from the rocket jets, burnout of the rockets, tumbling and rotation of the vehicle, and turbulent interaction with the atmosphere upon reentry. The nature of some of these vibrations is indicated in Figures 8-21 through 8-25.

When either a portion of the environment or the space vehicle itself undergoes or transmits certain vibrations, the extent to which it will influence

---

[9] The to and fro motion of vibration involves a cyclical transition between kinetic energy of a body or part of a body and the potential energy stored in a body as it is drawn away from an equilibrium position and which tends to return the vibrating body back to its equilibrium position. Examples of vibration of a single body would be those of a swing or a displaced spring with a weight on the end. Mechanical vibrations are transmitted through material in various wave patterns, such as surface waves (as exemplified with ripples in water) and compression waves (as exemplified by sound in air).

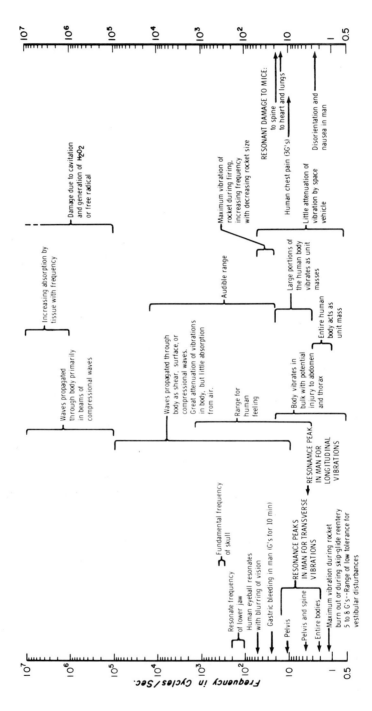

Figure 8-21. Frequency in cycles per second of various sounds and vibrations of significance to living material or to rocket flight. (Values listed here are compiled primarily from three sources: Stapp, 1961; Slager, 1962; von Gierke, 1959.)

part or all of an organism as well as any other object depends largely upon the ability of the object to resonate at a given frequency,[10, 11] Some of the

---

[10] This is exactly the same phenomenon as occasions the maximum motion of a swing-mounted bell or other pendular object if the timing of pushing or pulling is coordinated with the displacement of the swing. As a general rule, the resonant frequency f tends to be greater for the smaller object.

The stiffer an object is (i.e., the greater the force which it exerts in returning to an equilibrium position and in opposing displacement), the faster will be its fundamental frequency:

$$f \propto \sqrt{stiffness} \propto \sqrt{spring\ constant}$$

For a rod-like pendulum swinging at one end like a human leg, the fundamental frequency would be indicated by the equation:

$$f = \frac{\sqrt{3g/2l}}{2\pi}$$

[11] In an elementary description of sound or other vibration, it is generally assumed that the vibratory displacement is essentially the same as the vertical displacement of a point executing circular motion on the surface of a wall. The displacement in such simple harmonic motion is described by equation (a):

$$displacement = X \sin (2\pi ft), \tag{a}$$

where X is the amplitude or maximum displacement above and below the equilibrium position and t refers to time. When considerable friction is offered to oppose vibration, the amplitude of vibration would decrease in an exponential manner such that the displacement could be described by equation (b):

$$displacement = X_o e^{-kt} \sin (2\pi ft) \tag{b}$$

where X_o would be the initial maximum displacement and k would refer to the coefficient for decay of amplitude. Readers familiar with the methods of differential calculus will remember that the rate at which the displacement itself is occurring can be described by equation (c):

$$velocity\ of\ displacement = 2\pi fX \cos (\pi ft) \tag{c}$$

This velocity of displacement should not be confused with the velocity at which a sound or vibration is propagated through a medium. Rate of propagation is equal to the square root, as predicted by equation (d):

velocity or propagation in a liquid or solid

$$= \sqrt{\frac{modulus\ of\ bulk\ elasticity}{density}} \tag{d}$$

The modulus of bulk elasticity refers to the restoring force per unit of fractional compression or displacement and would be expressed in such units as dynes per cm^2. This equation can be modified for use with propagation through a gas:

$$velocity\ in\ a\ diatomic\ gas = \sqrt{\frac{1.40 \times RT}{Molecular\ Weight}} \tag{e}$$

from the assumption that volume elasticity would be:

$$1.40 \times Pressure,$$

from the assumption that density per mole of gas would be:

$$Molecular\ Weight \div Volume,$$

and from the assumption that the Ideal Gas Law would accurately predict the pressure-volume product per mole to be: RT.

For monoatomic gases, such as helium, a factor of 1.66 would replace 1.40. For any given gas, the propagation velocity is independent of the pressure but does decrease with density or molecular weight of the gas.

resonant frequencies of biological significance for space travel are indicated in Figure 8-21. It will be noted (Fig. 8-21) that the resonant frequency for the entire body is lower than for portions of the body and that those for man are at lower frequencies than for smaller animals.

With pendulums, the restoring force of which is determined by weight, the frequency is a function of the gravitational field. With an individual

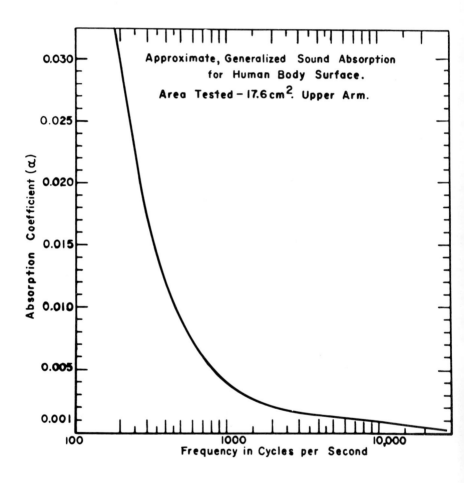

Figure 8-22. Approximate fraction of airborne sound energy which will be absorbed by the human body. (von Gierke, 1959.)

possessing a leg 100 cm. long and moving on the Earth where field g is equal to 1 G (980 cm per sec^2), it can be shown that frequency f is equal to 0.60 cycles per second. The frequency would be slower for a longer leg. It would increase if the leg were shorter, and it would also increase if the gravity were greater. On the moon, where the lower gravity is equal to 0.16 G's or 155 cm/sec^2, the leg could move most readily at a frequency

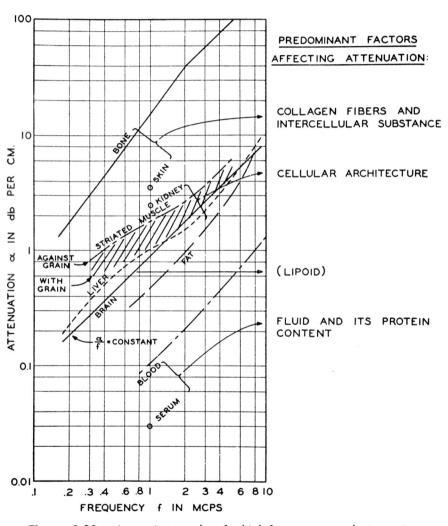

Figure 8-23. Approximate values for high-frequency sound attenuation in various tissues. (von Gierke, 1959.)

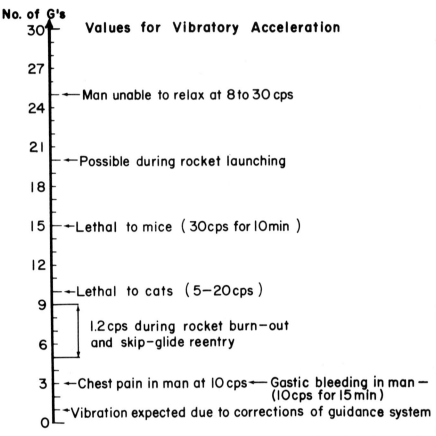

No. of G's

Values for Vibratory Acceleration

30

27

← Man unable to relax at 8 to 30 cps

24

21

← Possible during rocket launching

18

15 ← Lethal to mice (30 cps for 10 min)

12

← Lethal to cats (5–20 cps)

9

1.2 cps during rocket burn–out
and skip–glide reentry

6

3 ← Chest pain in man at 10 cps ← Gastic bleeding in man —
(10 cps for 15 min)

← Vibration expected due to corrections of guidance system

0

Figure 8-24.   Some values for vibratory acceleration. (This is based primarily
upon values cited by Stapp, 1961 and Slager, 1962.)

of 0.15 cycles per second. Although each stride may be longer the rate at
which each stride would occur may well be slower.[12]

Vibrations of relatively low frequency (i.e., those of less than 100 cycles
per second) are the ones of greatest significance (Fig. 8-21). Due to the
fact that a tissue can be less readily compressed than air, airborne sounds

---

[12] To consider human locomotion entirely from the assumption of legs as simple
pendulums is an oversimplification. Complete agreement does not exist for walking
patterns anticipated at a lower gravity. In a theoretical discussion of possible locomotion, Margaria and Cavagna (1964) suggest that traction in the Moon's gravity would
be almost too weak for walking. They propose as possible a gait which would resemble
the running pattern seen in motion pictures viewed at reduced speed. Energy requirements for this would be lower than for comparable velocities on Earth. The maximum
velocity for this "running" they contend could not exceed 8 miles per hour. It is
suggested, however, that by means of jumping movements, speeds of locomotion would
be as fast or even faster than in the Earth's gravity.

cannot exert sufficient pressure to permit absorption of much sound energy. Most of the sound, except with specialized structures like the human eardrum, is reflected like an echo. Very little audible sound energy is absorbed and therefore such sound is incapable of causing damage to the human body except with extreme intensities (Fig. 8-22).

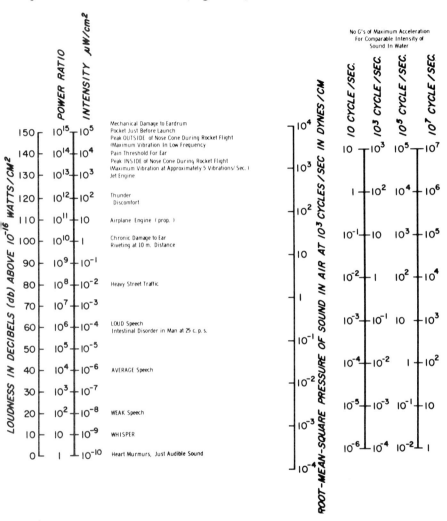

Figure 8-25. Loudness of various sounds. The loudness, power ratio, intensity, and root-mean-square pressure all refer to the sound transmitted in air. The values for acceleration in G's refer to sounds of the same energy intensity if transmitted in water. If sounds are transmitted from air into body tissue due to the high amount of reflection, very much lower accelerations would be possible. (Values are based primarily upon those listed in Stuhlman, 1943; Ackerman, 1962; and Slager, 1962.)

The two primary considerations pertinent to audible sound are more concerned with communication than with biology. (1) Because sound must be transmitted through a medium, no sound could be transmitted through the vacuum of space or above the airless surface of the Moon. Two individuals not within the same pressurized chamber would be compelled to depend upon visual or radio contact. (2) The frequency or pitch of sound through a gas varies with the velocity v of propagation (f = v ÷ wave length) and velocity would decrease with molecular weight (see footnote 11, Eq. [e]). Thus, if helium (presently under consideration as a replacement for nitrogen) is employed as a "filler" gas in an artificial medium, an astronaut's voice would become shrill and unnatural. As oxygen and nitrogen possess nearly similar molecular weights and as velocity is not affected by pressure, no communication difficulty would be expected with pure oxygen at $\frac{1}{5}$ to $\frac{1}{3}$ atmospheric pressure.

For vibrations in excess of 100,000 cycles per second, there is increasing absorption of transmitted vibrational energy by the human body (Fig. 8-23). When sufficiently intense, ultrasound can cause the disintegration of material and the rupture of cell walls. These effects are attributed to cavitation, which involves the expansion and collapse of bubbles of dissolved gases within tissues or liquid. Even more intense ultrasonation can produce free radicals of the type produced during ionizing or ultraviolet radiation. With biological material, however, the intensity necessary for the production of free radicals is so great that most life would have been destroyed by the rupture of cellular membranes before lethal quantities of free radicals were produced.

The magnitudes of vibrational energy and sound are variously described in terms of intensity, acceleration, pressure, or logarithmic indices of relative intensities (decibels). The magnitude of such acceleration is proportional to the square of vibrational frequency f and to the displacement amplitude X.

$$\text{vibratory acceleration} = -4\pi^2 f^2 X \sin 2\pi f t \qquad (8\text{-}4)$$

This equation gives an acceleration in terms of units[13] which are identical with those for gravitational or centrifugal acceleration and are frequently expressed in terms of the maximum acceleration, as indicated by the equation:

$$\text{maximum acceleration} = \pm 4\pi^2 f^2 X \qquad (8\text{-}5)$$

The energy content of sound or propagated vibrations are usually expressed in terms of intensity (energy per unit of area).[14] When the velocity v of sound propagation and density δ of the medium are known, values of acceleration are proportional to the square root of intensity I.

---

[13] For expression of vibratory acceleration in terms of G's, it would be necessary to multiply the terms in Eqs. (8-4) and (8-5) by 1.0 G/(980 cm/sec²).

[14] The intensity I would be equal to:
$$I = 2\pi^2 v f X^2 \delta$$

$$\text{number of G's} = \frac{4\pi f}{980 \text{ cm/sec}^2/G} \sqrt{\frac{10 \quad \text{I in microwatts/cm}^2}{2v/\delta}}$$

where the values if not otherwise indicated are expressed in cgs units.

For sounds with frequencies in the audible or ultrasonic range, it is usual to refer to pressure rather than to acceleration. The effective pressure is expressed in terms of the square root of the average square of the pressure difference from the equilibrium value. Like acceleration, it is proportional to the square root of intensity:

$$\text{root mean pressure} = \sqrt{2\delta vI}$$

The change in intensity of most stimulatory energy is detected by man or other organisms not in proportion to the actual magnitude of the change but more nearly in proportion to the fractional magnitude of the change (i.e., the ratio of the change in intensity to the initial intensity with logarithmic quantities for this ratio being expressed in *bels* or *decibels*). This relationship (Weber-Fechner Law) has been applied to many agents in the environment which can stimulate sense organs.

Bibliography and References

ACKERMAN, E. (1962): Sound and the ear. *In* "Biophysical Science," Chap. 1, pp. 3-25. Prentice-Hall, Englewood Cliffs, N. J.

ARMSTRONG, H. G. (1943): "Aviation Medicine." Williams and Wilkins Co., Baltimore.

BARNETT, C. H., DAVIES, D. V., AND MACCONAILL, M. A. (1961): "Synovial Joints," pp. 108-111. Charles C Thomas, Springfield, Ill.

BEAMS, H. W. (1951): The effects of ultracentrifugal force on the cell with special reference to division. *Ann. N. Y. Acad. Sci. 51,* 1349.

BERRY, C. A. (1963): Aeromedical preparations. *In* "Mercury Project Summary Including Results of the Fourth Manned Orbital Flight," pp. 199-209. NASA Sp-45, National Aeronautics and Space Administration, Washington, D. C.

BIRKHEAD, N. C., BLIZZARD, J. J., DALY, J. W., HAUPT, G. J., ISSEKUTZ, B., JR., MYERS, R. N., AND RODAHL, K. (1963): "Cardiodynamic and Metabolic Effects of Prolonged Bed Rest." AMRL-TDR-63-37, Wright Air Development Division, Wright-Patterson Air Force Base, Ohio.

BOURNE, G. H. (1963): Neuromuscular aspects of space travel, "Physiology of Man in Space" (J. H. U. Brown, ed.), pp. 1-59. Academic Press, New York.

BRANNON, E. W., ROCKWOOD, C. A., JR., AND POTTS, P. (1963): The influence of specific exercises in the prevention of debilitating musculoskeletal disorders: implication in physiological conditioning for prolonged weightlessness. *Aerospace Med. 34,* 900-906.

BURTON, R. R., AND SMITH, A. H. (1965): Chronic acceleration sickness. *Aerospace Med. 36,* 39-44.

CAIN, C. C. (1963): Predictions on the biological effects of weightlessness, "Physical and Biological Phenomena in a Weightless State." Proceedings of the Second AAS Symposium on Physical and Biological Phenomena under Zero Gravity Conditions, Los Angeles, January 18, 1963 (E. T. Benedikt and R. W. Halliburton, eds.) *Vol. 14,* pp. 318-349. *In* "Advances in the Astronautical Sciences." Amer. Astronautical Soc., Baltimore.

CATTERSON, A. D., McCUTCHEON, E. P., MINNERS, H. A., AND POLLARD, R. A. (1963): Aeromedical observations. *In* "Mercury Project Summary Including Results of the Fourth Manned Orbital Flight," pp. 299-327. NASA SP-45, National Aeronautics and Space Administration, Washington, D. C.

CHAMBERS, R. M., AND FRIED, R. (1963): Psychological aspects of space flight. *In* "Physiology of Man in Space" (J. H. U. Brown, ed.), pp. 173-256. Academic Press, New York.

DEITRICK, J. E., WHEDON, G. D., AND SHORR, E. (1948): Effects of immobilization upon various metabolic and physiologic functions of normal men. *Amer. J. Med. 4,* 3-36.

ECCLES, J. C. (1941): Disuse atrophy of skeletal muscle. *Med. J. Australia 2,* 160-164.

ELLIOTT, D. R., AND THOMSON, J. D. (1963): Dynamic properties of denervated rat muscle treated with electrotherapy. *Amer. J. Physiol. 205,* 173-176.

GAMOW, G. (1962): "Gravity." Doubleday (Anchor), Garden City, N. Y.

GAUER, O., AND HABER, H. (1950): Man under gravity-free conditions. *In* "German Aviation Medicine, World War II," *Vol. I,* pp. 641-644. Dept. of the Air Force, Washington, D. C.

GAUER, O. H., AND HENRY, J. P. (1963): Circulatory basis of fluid volume control. *Physiol. Rev. 43,* 423-481.

GAUER, O. H., AND ZUIDEMA, G. D. (eds.) (1961): "Gravitational Stress in Aerospace Medicine." Little, Brown and Co., Boston.

GAZENKO, O. G., AND GURJIAN, A. A. (1964): "On the Biological Role of Gravity" (a Soviet translation into English of paper presented at COSPAR Symposium, Florence, May 1964) Zak. 2144, USSR Acad. Sci., Moscow.

GAZENKO, O. G., AND GURJIAN, A. A. (1965): Physiological effects of gravitation (as presented at 8th COSPAR Plenary Meeting, Buenos Aires, May 1965, and as translated into English by C. H. Dodge) *A.T.D. Press 3* (243), 9-16. Library of Congress, Washington, D. C.

GEISER, M., AND TRUETA, J. (1958): Muscle action, bone rarefaction and bone formation; an experimental study. *J. Bone and Joint Surg. 40-B,* 282.

GENERALES, C. D. J., JR. (1963): Weightlessness: its physical, biological, and medical aspects. *In* "Medical and Biological Problems of Space Flight" (G. H. Bourne, ed.), Chap. 6. Academic Press, New York.

GERATHEWOHL, S. (1965): Effect of low-gravity on physiological processes. Paper No. 23. *In* "Proc. of Conf. on Role of Simulation in Space Technology," *Engineering Extension Series Circular No. 4, Part D,* Va. Poly. Inst., Blacksburg.

GOODALL, Mc. C. (1962): Sympathoadrenal response to gravitational stress. *J. Clin. Invest. 41,* 197.

GRAVELINE, D. E., BALKE, B., McKENZIE, R. E., AND HARTMAN, B. (1961): Psychobiologic effects of water-immersion-induced hypodynamics. *Aerospace Med. 32,* 387-400.

GRAVELINE, D. E., AND McCALLY, M. (1963): Body fluid distribution: implications for zero gravity. *Aerospace Med. 33,* 1281-1290.

GRAY, S. W., AND EDWARDS, B. F. (1955): Effects of centrifugal forces on growth and form of coleoptile of wheat. *J. Cell. and Comp. Physiol. 46,* 97-123.

GRAYBIEL, A., AND CLARK, B. (1961): Symptoms resulting from prolonged immersion in water: the problem of zero G asthenia. *Aerospace Med. 32,* 181-196.

GRAYBIEL, A., GUEDRY, F. E., JOHNSON, W., AND KENNEDY, R. (1961): Adaptation to bizarre stimulation of the semicircular canals as indicated by the oculogyral illusion. *Aerospace Med. 32*, 321-327.

GUYTON, A. C. (1961): Aviation, high altitude, and space physiology. *In* "Textbook of Medical Physiology," 2nd ed., Chap. 44, pp. 587-601. W. B. Saunders Co., Philadelphia.

"Handbook of Instructions for Aerospace Systems Design: Reduced Gravity," *Vol. 3.* (1963). USAF AFSCM 80-9, Andrews Air Force Base, Washington, D. C.

HARDY, M. (1934): Observations on the innervation of the macula sacculi in man. *Anatomical Record 58-59,* 403-418.

HAWKINS, W. R. (1963): Space flight dynamics—weightlessness. *In* "Physiology of Man in Space" (J. H. U. Brown, ed.), pp. 287-307. Academic Press, New York.

HEILBRUNN, L. V. (1943): "An Outline of General Physiology," 2nd ed. rev. W. B. Saunders Co., Philadelphia.

HELANDER, E. (1960): Muscular atrophy and lipomorphosis induced by immobilizing plaster casts. *Acta Morph. Neerlando Scand. 3,* 92-98.

HENRY, J. P., AUGERSON, W. S., BELLEVILLE, R. E., DOUGLAS, W. K., GRUNZKE, M. K., JOHNSTON, R. S., LAUGHLIN, P. C., MOSELY, J. D., ROHLES, F. H., VOAS, R. B., AND WHITE, S. C. (1962): Effects of weightlessness in ballistic and orbital flight. *Aerospace Med. 33,* 1056-1068.

HENRY, J. P., BALLINGER, E. R., MAHER,, P. J., AND SIMONS, D. G. (1952): Animal studies of the subgravity state during rocket flight. *J. Aviat. Med. 23,* 421-432.

HILL, P. R., AND SCHNITZER, E. (1962): Rotating manned space stations. *Astronautics 7, No. 9,* 14-18.

HINES, H. M., AND THOMSON, J. D. (1956): Changes in muscle and nerve following motor neuron denervation. *Amer. J. Phys. Med. 35,* 35-37.

HISLOP, H. J. (1963): Quantitative Changes in Human Muscular Strength during Isometric Exercise. *J. Amer. Phys. Therapy Assoc. 43,* 21-38.

HOWELL, J. A. (1917): An experimental study of the effect of stress and strain on bone development. *Anatomical Record 13,* 233-252.

KAS'YAN, I. I. (1963): Cardiovascular and respiratory reactions of animals in sealed cabins during rocket flights up to an altitude of 212 kilometers. *Izvestiya Akademii Nauk SSR, Seriya Biologicheskaya 28,* No. 1, p. 24. As translated from Russian in *Fed Proc.: Trans. Suppl. 23,* T410-T416.

KING, B. G., PATCH, C. T., AND SHINKMAN, P. G. (1961): "Weightlessness—Training Requirements and Solutions," Technical Report NAVTRAD EVC EN 560-1, U. S. Naval Training Device Center, Port Washington, New York.

KNIGHT, T. A. (1806): On the direction of the radical and the germen during vegetation of seeds. *Phil. Trans. Roy. Soc. London 96,* 99.

KOLMER, W. (1927): Gehorogan. Von Mollendorf's *Handb. d. Microskop. Anat d. Menschen 3* (1), p. 250.

LAMB, L. E. (1964): An assessment of the circulatory problem of weightlessness in prolonged space flight. *Aerospace Med. 35,* 413-419.

LAMB, L. E., JOHNSON, R. L., AND STEVENS, P. M. (1964a): Cardiovascular deconditioning during chair rest. *Aerospace Med. 35,* 646-649.

LAMB, L. E., JOHNSON, R. L., STEVENS, P. M., AND WELCH, B. E. (1964b): Cardiovascular deconditioning from space cabin simulator confinement. *Aerospace Med. 35,* 420-428.

LEVINE, R. B. (1963): A device for simulating weightlessness. *In* "Medical and Biological Problems of Space Flight" (G. H. Bourne, ed.), pp. 85-113. Academic Press, New York.

LILLY, J. C., AND SHURLEY, J. T. (1961): Experiments in solitude, in maximum achievable physical isolation with water suspension, of intact healthy persons. *In* "Psychophysiological Aspects of Space Flight" (B. E. Flaherty, ed.), pp. 238-247. Columbia University Press, New York.

LINDBERG, E. F., AND WOOD, E. H. (1963): Acceleration. *In* "Physiology of Man in Space" (J. H. U. Brown, ed.), pp. 61-111. Academic Press, New York.

LYON, C. J. (1962): Gravity factor for auxin transport. *Science 137*, 432-433.

McCALLY, M. (1964): Plasma volume response to water immersion: implications for space flight. *Aerospace Med. 35*, 130-132.

McCALLY, M., AND GRAVELINE, D. E. (1963): Physiologic aspects of prolonged weightlessness: body-fluid distribution and the cardiovascular system. *New Eng. J. Med. 269*, 508-516.

MARGARIA, R. (1958): Wide range investigations of acceleration in man and animals. *J. Aviat. Med. 29*, 855-871.

MARGARIA, R., AND CAVAGNA, G. A. (1964): Human locomotion in subgravity. *Aerospace Med. 35*, 1140-1146.

MEGŬSAR, F. (1906): Einfluss abnormaler gravitation-swirkung auf die embryonalentwicklung bei hydrophilus aterrimus eschscholtz. *Arch. fur Enwicklungsmechanik der Organismen 22*, 141-148. As cited by Generales, 1963.

MORGAN, T. H. (1897): The effect of injuring one of the first two blastomeres. *In* "The Development of the Frog's Egg," pp. 106-122. Macmillan, New York.

PARIN, V. (1962): Capacities of the human organism: defense mechanisms and adaptations in conditions of maximum overload and the state of weightlessness. *Perspectives in Biol. and Med. 5*, 527-533.

PFLÜGER, E. (1884): Ueber die einwirkung der schwerkraft und angerer bedingungen auf die richtung der zelltheilung. *Pfluger's Arch. 34*, 607-616.

POLLARD, E. C. (1965): Theoretical studies on living systems in the absence of mechanical stress. *J. Theoret. Biol. 8*, 113-123.

ROGERS, T. A. (1962): The physiological effects of acceleration. *Sci. Amer. 206*, 61-70.

RUCH, T. C. (1960): Somatic sensation. *In* "Medical Physiology and Biophysics" (T. C. Ruch and J. F. Fulton, eds.), Chap. 13, pp. 300-322. W. B. Saunders Co., Philadelphia.

SCHOTTELIUS, B. A., THOMSON, J. D., AND HINES, H. M. (1954): Capacity of skeletal muscle to develop isometric tension after prolonged shortening. *Amer. J. Physiol. 179*, 491-494.

SISSONS, H. A. (1956): The growth of bone. *In* "The Biochemistry and Physiology of Bone" (G. H. Bourne, ed.), pp. 443-473. Academic Press, New York.

SLAGER, U. T. (1962): Noise and vibration. *In* "Space Medicine," Chap. 8, pp. 241-257. Prentice-Hall, Englewood Cliffs, N. J.

SMITH, A. H., AND KELLY, C. F. (1963): Influence of chronic acceleration upon growth and body composition. *Ann. N. Y. Acad. Sci. 110*, 410-424.

STAPP, J. P. (1961): The "G" spectrum in space flight dynamics. *In* "Lectures in Aerospace Medicine" (Paper No. 12). School of Aviation Medicine, USAF Aerospace Medical Center (ATC), Brooks AFB, Texas.

STUHLMAN, O., JR. (1943): Auditory biophysics. *In* "An Introduction to Biophysics," Chap. 7, pp. 253-310. John Wiley and Sons, New York; Chapman and Hall, London.

TAYLOR, H. L., HENSCHEL, A., BROZEK, J., AND KEYS, A. (1949): Effect of bed rest on cardiovascular function and work performance. *J. Appl. Physiol. 2,* 223-239.

THOMPSON, D'A. W. (1942): "Growth and Form." Cambridge University Press, New York.

THOMSON, J. D. (1955): Reaction of the diaphragm to denervation. *Amer. J. Physiol. 180,* 202-204.

TSIOLKOWSKY, K. E. (1960, as cited by Gazenko and Gurjian, 1964): "The Way to Stars," M., AN SSSR (in Russian).

VOLYNKIN, Y. M., AND VASIL'YEV (1965): Results of medical investigations conducted during the flight of "Voskhod-1" (paper presented at 2nd Int. Symposium, Basic Environmental Prob. of Man in Space, Paris, June 1965, as condensed and translated into English) *A.T.D. Press 3* (253), 1-4. Library of Congress, Washington, D. C.

VOLYNKYN, YV. M., AND YAJDOVSKY, V. T. (1962): "First Manned Space Flights," Academy of Science, USSR, Dept. of Biology. As cited by McCally, 1964.

VON BECKH, H. J. A. (1954): Experiments with animals and human subjects under sub- and zero-gravity conditions during the dive and parabolic flight. *J. Aviat. Med. 25,* 235-241.

VON GIERKE, H. E. (1959): Transmission of vibratory energy through human body tissue. *In* "Proc. of the First National Biophysics Conference," Columbus, Ohio, March 4-6, 1957. (H. Quastler and H. J. Morowitz, eds.), Chap. 186, pp. 647-668. Yale University Press, New Haven.

VRĂBIESCO, A., CIMPEANO, L., AND DOMILESCO, G. (1964): Vieillissement préce produit experimentalement par la surgravite de longue dure, *Rev. Française de Gérontologie,* Aout, 245-259.

WHITE, S. C., AND BERRY, C. A. (1964): Resume of present knowledge of man's ability to meet the space environment. *Aerospace Med. 35,* 43-48.

WHITE, WM. J. (1964): "A History of the Centrifuge in Aerospace Medicine." Missile & Space Systems Division, Douglas Aircraft Company, Inc., Santa Monica, California.

WUNDER, C. C. (1963): Inertial force (biological effect). *In* "McGraw-Hill Yearbook of Science and Technology," D. I. Eggenberger, ed., pp. 292-294. McGraw-Hill, New York.

WUNDER, C. C. (1964): "A Survey of Chronic Weightlessness Simulation in Biological Research." (Technical Report for U. S. Air Force) HQARSC-TDR-64-1.

WUNDER, C. C., AND LUTHERER, L. O. (1964): Influence of chronic exposure to increased gravity upon growth and form of animals. *In* "International Reviews of General and Experimental Zoology," W. J. L. Felts and R. J. Harrison, eds. Academic Press, New York. (In press.)

WUNDER, C. C., LUTHERER, L. O., AND DODGE, C. H. (1963): Survival and growth of organisms during life-long exposure to high gravity. *Aerospace Med. 34,* 5-11.

ZELENÁ, J. (1963): Development of muscle receptors after tenotomy. *Physiol. Bohemoslov 12,* 30-36. As abstracted in *Biol. Abst.,* No. 11385.

9 | Radiation and Electromagnetic Energy

Essentially all of the energy which has been utilized upon this planet comes from the Sun. Some of this energy has been stored for millions of years in the form of coal or oil after original production by the process of photosynthesis, which required light from the Sun. The Earth's atmosphere and magnetic fields have protected this planet's inhabitants from the more hazardous radiations found in space, but useful radiation has been transmitted to the Earth's surface. The early space voyages are concerned with providing the optimum conditions to prevent damage to man by hazardous radiations while carrying the minimum load of protective equipment. Extensive space voyages may later be concerned with the biological utilization of radiant energy in a manner that will permit the minimum payload of food materials.

The energies to be encountered in a magnetic or purely electrical form are probably of insufficient intensity to have a direct effect upon life. Nonetheless, a discussion of their effects is important because magnetic and electrical phenomena can have a profound effect upon the location and intensities of the various biologically significant radiations to be encountered. Furthermore, most of the radiations considered here possess properties which are related to magnetic or electrical phenomena.

In order for any energy to have an effect, it must first be absorbed. The absorption of energy depends primarily upon three factors: (1) the amount of incident or applied energy, (2) the amount of shielding or protection of the sensitive area from the applied energy, and (3) finally, the ability of a sensitive area to absorb the applied energy. The most damaging energies of space are the ionizing rays. For this reason, a large portion of the payload of our space vehicles will be devoted to protection from ionizing radiation.

Magnetic and Electrical Energy

In traveling to other parts of the Solar System, man will encounter magnetic fields, the intensities of which will range several orders of magnitude above and below those encountered on Earth. Magnetic field intensity drops roughly with the inverse third power of distance from a planet. Great intensities are necessary before the exposure of biological material can result in

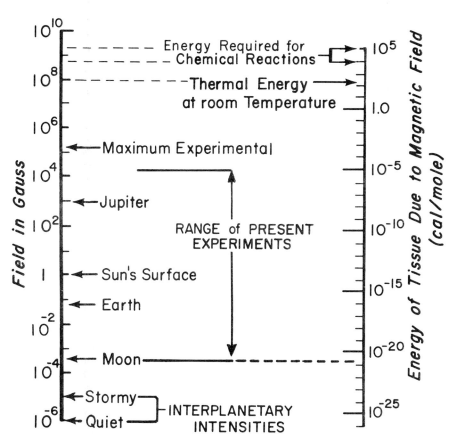

Figure 9-1.   Magnetic field intensities of significance to space biology.
(Modified after figures and data presented by Beischer, 1963.)

the induction of heat as a result of exposure to fields (Fig. 9-1). Although specific effects might result from electrical currents induced when an organism moves across magnetic lines of force, it has been argued that any effects at the molecular level induced by static fields as great as 10^4 Gauss would be obscured by effects of minute, natural, temperature fluctuations (Ragle, 1964).

Some scientists are skeptical of the possibility that specific biological effects result from magnetic fields. Nonetheless, a number of effects have been reported for fields (2,500 to 5,000 Gauss) which are more than 10,000 times the intensity of the Earth's magnetic field. A number of these effects have been reviewed by Barnothy (1960). In mice, such effects have included slower growth and development, greater mortality, lower body temperature, decreased food consumption, slower aging, altered mortality, changes in the concentration of certain blood cells, greater resistance to ionizing radiation, and arrested tumor growth. Inhomogeneous magnetic fields are reported to have a somewhat greater effect than homogeneous fields. The former would produce a separation of various chemicals in accordance with magnetic susceptibility. Barnothy suggests that other effects of magnetic fields could result from induced forces and electrical currents or potentials. Alternating, high-frequency magnetic fields are known to set up electromagnetic radiation in the microwave region, which can be employed therapeutically for the purpose of heating tissue.

It was thought at one time that the Earth's magnetic field could be detected in animals by some unknown receptor which could aid in guiding the migratory and homing behavior of these animals. However, the Earth's magnetic field is probably of too low an intensity to be of direct biological significance. No effects have been noticed when men have been placed in very low fields (1/2,000 of a Gauss, i.e., less than the normal Terrestrial gravity) for as long as 2 weeks (Beischer, 1963).

With magnetic fields, the effect which is of the greatest concern for space travel is the deflection of charged particles of ionizing radiation. When the intensity of a magnetic field is changed, electric current can be induced into a conductor. The movement of a conductor through a magnetic field can cause also the generation of electromotive force. This mechanism has been used to explain the capture of charged nuclear particles within the Van Allen belts of trapped radiation. As a result of electromagnetically induced forces, the charged nuclear particles are deflected back and forth within zones of radiation. Although the Earth's magnetic field has thus caused the existence of regions of highly hazardous radiation, it has also shielded this planet's equatorial zones from a large amount of cosmic radiation. Employment of relatively large artificial magnetic fields about space vehicles has been suggested as a method whereby the occupants could be protected from some types of radiation. Existing magnetic devices probably would not be feasible due to high mass and power requirements.

As with magnetic energy, the intensities of electrical fields to be encountered in space are probably not great enough to be a major hazard. Electrical forces are nonetheless of such paramount importance in determining the structure of matter and coordinating the functions of biological structures that electrical considerations cannot be overlooked in the interpretation of the response of organisms to various types of energy. Ionizing radiation acts on tissue primarily by overcoming the electrostatic forces which hold electrons in atoms. Furthermore, space ships like most other powerful equipment will carry with them a number of instruments which are dependent upon electricity for their functioning and which create strong electrical fields.

Types of Radiation

Radiation of the type which is considered to be moving particles or corpuscles has an energy content described in terms of the total kinetic energy attributable to the translational motion of all the radiant particles. The dependence of particle energy upon velocity is shown in Figure 9-2. The best examples of particulate radiation are the beams of submolecular particles (electrons, neutrons, protons, alpha particles, and atomic nuclei) which are

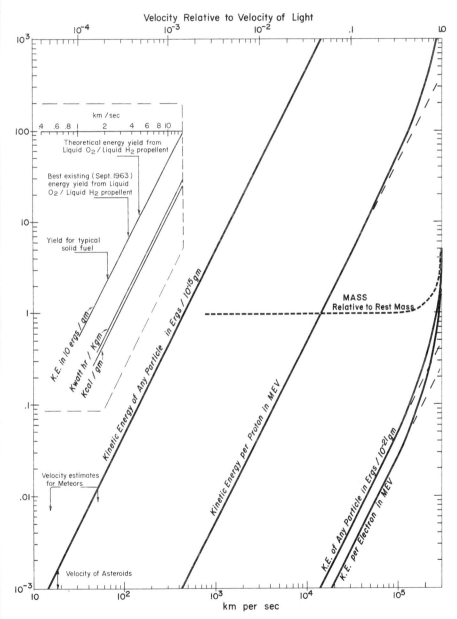

Figure 9-2.   Velocities and kinetic energies associated with high-speed particles.

TABLE 9-1. Some Biologically Significant Ionizing Radiations to Be Anticipated during Space Travel

	Location in Space	Approximate Unshielded Dose in Space at Earth Distance from Sun	Shielding Amount or Type of Necessary Shielding	Shielded Dose
A. Naturally occurring 1. Normal solar	Spreads out evenly from Sun	.1r/day	No more than a space suit	Almost nothing
2. Cosmic rays a. True cosmic or galactic rays	Throughout the galaxy	.02r/day	None for short exposures For longer exposures: Outer shield of hydrocarbons accompanied by an inner lead shield to absorb secondary X-rays	
b. Solar outbursts accompanying a solar flare	Spreads out unevenly from Sun			
1) Relativistic	Peak values	> 6000r/yr > 3000r/day and up to 10^4r/hr	$15gm/cm^2$ $2gm/cm^2$ (more than presently proposed but still not adequate)	Safe
2) Minor		50r/hr		

Significant Composition of Primary Radiation	Probable Source	Temporal Characteristics	Remarks
60-600 ev X-rays	Sun	Almost constant	Not considered a major hazard to space travel
Charged particles of 10^{-1} to 10^{10} Bev 1) *Protons* 85% 2) *α-particles* 14% 3) *Larger nuclei* 1%	Other stars in the galaxy with further acceleration as the particles pass through the various magnetic fields	Presumably of constant intensity in distant space but with some variation near Earth as influenced by solar activity and magnetic field	The large bare atomic nuclei are of considerable concern because their biological effect is not well known. Conflicting predictions have been advanced as to the potential hazards to be expected from these particles
	Sudden outbursts from areas on the Sun. These areas are usually characterized by brightness	Last about 2 days but means of predicting time of occurrence is not well developed as yet	
X-rays (.1 to 1.3 Kev) 10^{-8} watts/cm^2 *Protons* ($>$ 30 Mev) 5×10^9/cm^2-day		Average slightly less than one per year	During a relativistic flare, complete shielding of the entire crews' quarters would be too massive. Smaller shielded chests the size of a coffin have been proposed as "storm cellars"
Protons ($<$ 100 Mev)		Occur 5-15 times a year with the frequency of occurrence following an 11-year cycle. Peak in particle emission coincides with sunspot maximum	

TABLE 9-1.   Continued

Location in Space	Approximate Unshielded Dose in Space at Earth Distance from Sun	Shielding	
		Amount or Type of Necessary Shielding	Shielded Dose
c. Planetary belt of trapped radiation — Surrounding planets of sufficiently intense magnetic intensity: Earth and Jupiter but probably neither the Moon nor Venus			
1) Inner Van Allen belt (hard radiation zone) — From 600 to 10^4 km above Earth in an equatorial belt extending 40° to either side of the Equator	10gm/cm² 1gm/cm²		Safe 10-100r/day
2) Outer Van Allen belt (soft radiation zone) — From 15,000 to 70,000 km above Earth in an equatorial belt extending 40° to either side of the Equator	4×10^4r/sec	1gm/cm² hydrocarbons 1gm/cm² of hydrocarbons plus 4 gm/cm² of lead	50r/hr 1r/hr

Significant Composition of Primary Radiation	Probable Source	Temporal Characteristics	Remarks
Relatively few trapped charged particles which are moving within these zones. However, their constant movement across the belts at about 10 times per second is sufficient to effect a high intensity	Reflection of charged nuclear particles (primarily electrons and protons) as a result of the electrical current induced as they cut magnetic lines of force		Magnetic fields (which cause such belts to exist) tend to decrease the amount of cosmic radiation which will reach a planet's surface. For this reason, cosmic-ray intensity is higher near the Earth's magnetic poles than at the Equator
Protons: > 40 Mev, $2 \times 10^4/cm^2$ sec *Electrons:* > 600 Kev, $10^7/cm^2$ sec	Material ejected from Sun Decay products of neutrons produced by cosmic rays in Earth's upper atmosphere	Relatively stable except following solar activity, geomagnetic storms, and man-made atomic explosions. The former two can cause a 200% increase in activity	As a 12-ft sphere would require 5 tons of material for safe shielding, it might be necessary for a space ship to leave and depart from the Earth's polar region. Otherwise a very fast transit through this belt would be necessary. It has also been suggested that radiation might be "swept" out of this belt within one month to a year by means of an "area broom" of 1.0 km²
Electrons: > 500 Kev, $2 \times 10^7/cm^2$ sec *Protons:* > 10 Mev, $> 100/cm^2$ sec; > 140 Kev, $10^8/cm^2$ sec	Material ejected from Sun	Highly unstable 2000% increase in activity is possible	The protons are not considered of biologically significant composition in comparison to the electron intensity. The radiation in this, the outer belt, is less intense than in the inner belt. Therefore a lesser shielding problem is anticipated

TABLE 9-1.   Continued

	Location in Space	Approximate Unshielded Dose in Space at Earth Distance from Sun	Shielding Amount or Type of Necessary Shielding	Shielded Dose
d. Nuclear rocket (figures cited are at a distance of one meter from a ten billion watt reactor)		2 to 20 × 10^9 rem/min (higher figure assumes 10% efficiency)	Liquid hydrogen fuel followed by 20 cm (23 gm/cm²) of lead.*	

* In space, away from atmospheric scattering, the shield could be arranged as a truncated cone radiating outward from the reactor.

Significant Composition of Primary Radiation	Probable Source	Temporal Characteristics	Remarks
Protons: (gamma) .15-3.5 Mev 5×10^{19}/sec 3.5-6.5 Mev 10^{18}/sec *Neutrons:* >3 Mev 10^{19}/sec; 3-10 Mev 2×10^{17}/sec	Reactor placed as far from the living quarters as possible	Will probably need only about 5 min. of actual operating time	An interplanetary rocket will probably require the order of ten billion watts of power. Intensities can be computed for a given reactor power and for a given separation by assuming dose and intensity proportional to power and inversely proportional to the square of distance from reactor

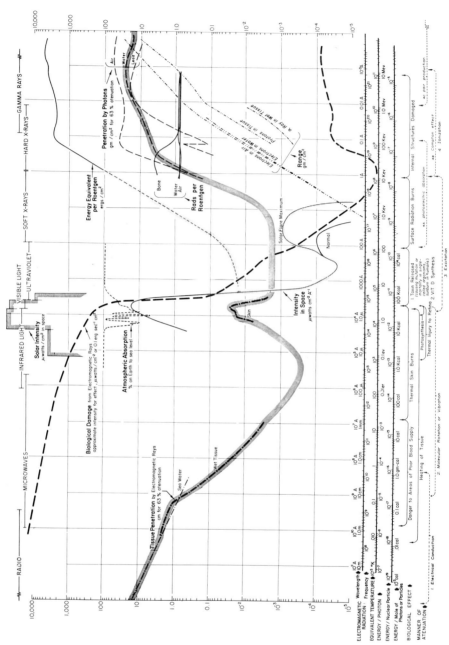

Figure 9-4. Caption at bottom of opposite page.

Electromagnetic Radiation

The reader will recall that light and other forms of electromagnetic radiation theoretically possess the highest attainable velocity. Although matter and other forms of energy propagation may approach this velocity, they can never exceed it. This finite velocity of electromagnetic rays in a vacuum is designated by the symbol c and is equal to 3×10^{10} cm/sec.[2]

The reader will also remember that the alternating flow of electrical current through appropriate conductors will result in the conversion of electrical energy into electromagnetic radiation possessing the same frequency as the electrical current. The frequency of these waves is generally designated by the symbol ν. For a vacuum with wavelength designated by λ

$$c = \nu\lambda \text{ or } \nu = \frac{c}{\lambda} \qquad (9\text{-}1)$$

The behavior of the longer wavelengths of electromagnetic radiation, such as radio waves, can be explained from the model describing the wave nature of light. At higher frequencies, light will react with matter in reactions which involve the absorption of discrete quantitized bundles of energy. Each one of these corpuscles or bundles is referred to as a *photon*. The energy per photon can be computed from Eq. (9-2):

$$E \text{ [per photon]} = h\nu \qquad (9\text{-}2)$$

where Planck's constant or h is equal to 6.63×10^{-27} erg-seconds. As the wavelength of radiation decreases, the nature of the absorption process is that which would be expected from moving particles of progressively greater kinetic energy, momentum, and impact.

Depending upon the wavelength or energy of radiation, several units are often employed to describe the relationships for the energy, intensity, and absorption of radiation. A number of such units are tabulated and described in Table 9-2.

---

[2] The velocity of electromagnetic radiation depends upon the electrical and magnetic properties of the matter through which it passes, as described by the equation:

$$\text{velocity} = \frac{c}{\sqrt{(\text{dielectric constant}) \times (\text{magnetic permeability})}}$$

Figure 9-4. Properties of some types of radiation as a function of wavelength or kinetic energy. Curve for threshold to biological damage from electromagnetic radiation must not be considered exact. Note that the atmosphere is transparent for wavelengths of from 1,000 to 10,000 Å *(Optical Window)*. Although not shown the atmosphere is also transparent to wavelengths of from 0.07 cm to 30 cm. *(Radio Window)* and for wavelengths shorter than 7×10^{-14} cm. *(Cosmic Ray Window)*. Intensities of X-ray emission lines from the Sun are also not shown.

TABLE 9-2. Units Employed in Describing the Properties of Radiant Energy

Property or Descriptive Term	Units	Conversions	When Employed	Remarks
Energy	Erg	Erg = dyne × cm 10^7 erg = joule		Ability to do the work of exerting a given force through a given distance Ability to do the work of exerting one dyne (980 gm of force) through one cm
	Calorie	cal = gm calorie = small calorie 10^3 cal = Calorie = large calorie = Kgm-calorie = 4.186 joules	Describing heat energy or chemical energy	
	Electron volt (ev)	ev = 1.60×10^{-10} ergs	Describing the energy of individual molecules, protons or particles of radiation	ev = the work necessary in moving the charge of one electron (4.8×10^{-10} electrostatic units) between two positions in an electric field for which the field intensity differs by one volt
Intensity of energy	Watts/cm²	watt/cm² = joule/(sec·cm²)	Intensity of electromagnetic radiation is usually described in terms of energy while that of radiant particles (which possess rest mass) is usually described in terms of number	The amount of some quantity (usually either energy or number of particles) which in a given unit of time passes through a given area at right angles to the surface of that area.
Flux of particles of radiation	Number/ (sec-cm²)			
Directional intensity of energy	Watts/ (cm² steradian)			If the radiation is not all oriented in the same direction the intensity for certain types of radiation in space is frequently expressed in terms of the amount passing through a unit solid angle (steradian or that portion of a sphere covered by an area equal to the square of the radius). Thus if the intensity

	Unit	Value / Formula	Reference / Purpose	Description
of particles	Number/(cm² steradian)			of a given radiation is the same in all directions, the total intensity passing through a point would be 4π or 12.57 multiplied by the average directional intensity
Brightness	Lux	lux = lumen/m² = .0929 ft-candles $\simeq 1.6 \times 10^{-7}$ watt/cm² (at 5560Å)		An index of the intensity of that light which can be detected by vision, photographic film, or a photoelectric cell. Classically one lumen would be the total rate of light production by an International Candle. The exact conversion from units for brightness to those for intensity would vary with the wavelength of the light
Effectiveness Quantum yield (also called quantum efficiency)	Molecules per photon		Primarily with reference to visible or other light which can cause a photochemical reaction (2000 to 30,000 Å)	The number of responses or the number of a given type of molecules affected for each photon which is absorbed. Although the bleaching of visual pigment has a quantum yield of unity, that for vision has been measured at from 0.1 to 0.5 units. For photosynthesis the quantum yield is approximately .25 units
Relative biological effectiveness (RBE)	rem/rad	(Values tabulated in Table 9-3)	For comparison of various types of ionizing radiations with respect to a specific type of biological damage with a specific organism	Ratio of the required absorbed dosage of X or gamma radiation to that for some other ionizing radiation necessary to evoke a specific biological effect (see page 201)
Dosage of ionizing radiation				Generally expressed in terms of the *total accumulated amount of energy* applied per unit amount of material in contrast to intensity which is expressed in terms of rate with respect to time

TABLE 9-2. Continued

Property or Descriptive Term	Units	Conversions	When Employed	Remarks
Energy applied to tissue	Roentgen (r)	Conversion to ergs/cm² by values on *Energy Equivalent Curve* of Figure 9-4	With X or gamma radiation a rather unsatisfactory index of exposure which unfortunately is the only easily performed measurement for this radiation	r = dosage of accumulated X or gamma radiation necessary to produce in each cc of air an absolute total charge (i.e., total magnitude of all positive charges plus total magnitude of all negative charges) of one electrostatic unit (2.08×10^9 ion pairs). The actual amount of applied energy incident in a Roentgen will vary with wavelength
	rep (Roentgen equivalent physical)	Represents 83 ergs absorbed per gm of air and 93 ergs per gm of water (also approximately 93 ergs per gm of wet tissue)	With ionizing radiations other than X or gamma (now an obsolete term)	rep = dosage of accumulated radiation which will result in the same amount of ionization of air as is the case with one roentgen of X-rays
Energy absorbed by tissue	rad (radiation absorbed dose)	100 absorbed ergs per gm of radiated material	To give the actual amount of ionizing energy absorbed by radiated material	rad = dosage of accumulated ionizing radiation necessary to cause the absorption of 100 ergs per gram of material
Effective energy absorbed by tissue	rem (Roentgen equivalent man)	Exposure in rem = (exposure in rads) × RBE	To indicate the amount of radiation in terms of the number of r necessary to produce the same effect as X-rays	rem = dosage of accumulated ionizing radiation necessary to cause some biological effect in man or some other given mammal as is caused by one Roentgen of radiation

	Units			
Relative effectiveness of absorbed energy. RBE (relative biological effectiveness)	rem/rad	Unity for X and gamma rays; some other values are listed in Table 9-3	For comparison of the relative effectiveness of different radiation in evoking a specific effect of radiation	RBE = ratio of dosage of X-rays necessary in evoking a given effect to that dosage required by some other radiation
Ionizing energy deposited per unit path Generally called "LET" (linear energy transfer) or *ionization density*	ev/μ	For a given tissue depth LET in ev/μ $$= (6.24 \times 10^9 \ \frac{ev}{rad\text{-}gm} \times \frac{cm}{\mu})$$ $\times$ (dose in rad at given depth) $\div$ [(density of irradiated material in gm/cm^3) $\times$ (flux of ionizing particles in $number/cm^2\text{-}sec$)]	In computing dose at given tissue depth In determining ionization pattern for computation of target size For theoretical predictions of RBE	LET of X-rays with a tube potential of 200 to 250 kv (possessing an effective energy of 80 Kev and a RBE of unity) is effectively about 3 Kev/μ. For particulate radiation LET increases with charge and decreases with energy For exponential destruction as described for simple target theory for dry virus or protein molecules, increasing values of LET beyond 3 kv/μ causes a decreasing RBE. This is attributed to the fact that ionizations are too closely packed to destroy separate units For complex animals including man, close packing of ionization assures destruction which requires more than one ionization per sensitive unit. With man, the RBE rises from unity at 3 Kev/μ to a maximum of 3 or 4 in the LET range of 100 to 200 Kev/μ (Langham et al., 1965, p. 28)

TABLE 9-2. Continued

Property or Descriptive Term	Units	Conversions	When Employed	Remarks
The relative effectiveness of ionizing radiation anticipated from LET: QF (quality factor)	rem/rad	As empirically described in Langham (1965, p. 29) $QF = 0.8$ rem/rad $+ 0.16$ (LET in Kev/μ) $\times \dfrac{\text{rem/rad}}{\text{Kev}/\mu}$	For prediction of effective radiation of known LET	
Dose equivalent exposure	rem	Dose equivalent exposure $= $ (exposure in rads) $\times$ QF		
Ability to pass through material Depth of penetration	cm	Depth of penetration in cm $= 1 \div$ (absorption coefficient) $= 1 \div$ ([density of absorber] $\times$ [mass absorption coefficient])	Can be used to describe any radiation which demonstrates exponential absorption with distance Assumes intensity $= I = I_0 e^{-\text{distance} \div \text{ by depth of penetration}}$ Although it is applicable throughout the entire electromagnetic spectrum it is most frequently employed with radio and microwave energy	Depth to which radiation will penetrate a material before its intensity will be attenuated by one natural logarithmic unit (1/e or 37% of original intensity). Depth in which 63% of the energy has been absorbed
	gm/cm²	Depth of penetration in gm/cm² $= 1 \div$ (mass absorption coefficient)		Mass of material per unit area which must be penetrated in order to attenuate the intensity of one natural logarithmic unit

Characteristic	Units		Description	Definition
Range	cm or gm/cm²		Used with particulate radiation (particularly alpha particles, protons or large charged nuclei) for which essentially all the radiation is absorbed within a measurable discreet distance, rather than being absorbed as an exponential function of distance. Also used with a lesser degree of satisfaction with some other radiation (such as electrons and neutrons)	Depth of absorbing material just necessary to absorb all of the primary radiation for a given type of ray
Half value layer (HVL)	cm			Depth of some shielding material (such as lead or copper) necessary to reduce the intensity of incident radiation by 50%
Ability to be absorbed by material Linear absorption coefficient	cm⁻¹	Absorption coefficient $= 1 \div$ (depth of penetration) $=$ density $\times$ (mass absorption coefficient)	Can be used to describe any radiation which demonstrates exponential absorption with distance $(I = I_o e^{-[\text{absorption coefficient}] \times [\text{distance}]})$ Although it is applicable to all electromagnetic radiation it is most commonly employed with infrared, visible, ultraviolet, X-, and gamma radiation. Although sometimes employed with electrons and neutrons, it does not describe their absorption with complete satisfaction	Instantaneous rate of fractional absorption per unit of path length Absorption coefficient $= \dfrac{dI/d(\text{distance})}{I}$

TABLE 9-2. Continued

Property or Descriptive Term	Units	Conversions	When Employed	Remarks
Mass absorption coefficient	cm²/gm			
Effective quantity of radioactive material	Curie = quantity of isotope undergoing 3.7 × 10¹¹ atomic disintegrations per minute	(in rads) Dose of radiation to tissue = #Curies/gm of tissue × average energy of emitted particle (ev) × 1.59 × 10¹² ergs/ev × rad ÷ (100 ergs/gm)	In dose computations one must assume that the active isotope is evenly distributed throughout the tissue and that the size of the tissue is large in comparison to the range or penetration of the emitted radiates	Classically defined as the activity of a gram of radium
	Rutherford = quantity undergoing 10⁶ disintegrations/ sec = 2.7 × 10⁻⁵ curies		Now an obsolete term	

There is no discrete depth within an absorbing material at which one can say that all electromagnetic radiation is absorbed. As the radiation penetrates into tissue or other material, it will be absorbed at a rate which is proportional to its intensity. Thus, the intensity at a given depth would be described by Eq. (9-3):

$$I = I_0 e^{-k \times depth}, \text{ or } \log_{10}I = -\frac{k \times (depth)}{2.3} \times (\log_{10}I_0) \qquad (9\text{-}3)$$

where I represents intensity, I_0 the initial intensity, and k the absorption coefficient. In the radio and microwave region of the spectrum, the term *depth of penetration* (for 63% absorption) is frequently employed to describe the absorption of a specific wavelength of radiation in a specific material. It can be shown that this depth is equal to the reciprocal of k (1.0/k). The influence of wavelength upon a given radiation's photon energy, penetrability, and effectiveness is shown in Figure 9-4. From the widest curve, we can see that the longer wavelengths, being the least energetic, are the least effective and, as a photon's energy increases, its effectiveness increases. There is no sharp demarcation over the range of electromagnetic radiation except that a region of electromagnetic spectrum which can be perceived by human vision is, by definition, visible light.

High intensities of energy are necessary with Hertzian waves (radio spectrum) because most effects upon living tissue are not evident until sufficient heat has been induced to produce the observed effect. Most of this heat is generated as a result of alternating currents of electricity which are induced into wet tissue by the radiation. The most susceptible regions of a body are those where the blood supply is poor and where the induced heat cannot be dissipated. Examples of such regions are implanted metal, the eyeballs, and the testicles. Microwaves may be able to cause some non-thermal effects upon tissue. Many authorities, however, consider existing reports of non-thermal effects to be far from convincing. When all induced heat is dissipated from experimental material, normal growth and survival are possible for living material exposed to radiation 30 to 100 times the safe dose (i.e., the intensity considered safe without cooling; Searle *et al.,* 1961; Moressi, 1964). Although detectable quantities of microwave radiation are found in space and are emitted from the Sun, these intensities are much too low to be hazardous. The primary hazard to be expected is that which could result from high-intensity radar, radio communication, or other electronic uses.

The shorter wavelengths of infrared light have very poor penetrating ability. They produce thermal burns on the surface of the skin (if not protected by a thin shield, such as the aluminized covering of a space suit) or corneal surface of the eye. Shorter lengths of infrared and visible light are of sufficient intensity in space to cause irreversible thermal damage to the retina of the human eye. This very rarely occurs within the Earth's atmosphere because the scattering of light by the Earth's atmosphere normally permits adequate illumination of areas shadowed from direct sunlight and thus eliminates the necessity of wide pupil openings during daylight hours.

(Without scattering, the vacuum of space will permit drastic contrast of illumination for sunlighted and shadowed areas; see Plate 3-1.)

Even though visible light is a relatively thin section of the total electromagnetic spectrum, it is the most important radiation from the point of view of man's life and economy. Although the photochemical process of vision is very important, the process of photosynthesis is even more so. Both of these processes include photochemical reactions in which photons of light can be absorbed by a sensitive pigment. The energy which is stored by the molecule of pigment can then be utilized in triggering energy necessary to stimulate a visual nerve fiber in the case of the retina or in converting molecules of carbon dioxide and water into oxygen and carbohydrates in the chloroplasts of plants. Only 2 to 10 photons need to be absorbed in order for an individual to detect a flash of light. An average of 4 photons is necessary for every molecule of carbon dioxide which is converted to oxygen and carbohydrate. The major output of electromagnetic radiation from Sun to Earth occurs in the region at or near the wavelength of visible light. If other forms of life are discovered, perhaps we can answer the question: "Did life evolve on Earth because its surface was exposed to the right kind of radiation or did the forms which exist on Earth evolve in the specific manner in which they did because this was the only path possible for their specific pattern of radiation?"

We should not overlook the role which the timing of visible light apparently plays in cueing the activity of various plants and animals, including man (Kleitman, 1939; Halberg, 1961; Strughold, 1963). Many forms of activity, as indicated by such indices as rate of cell division, rate of motion, body temperature, and oxygen consumption, are known to vary with time in a cyclical manner. Most of the reported cycles possess a predominant period of slightly more or slightly less than 24 hours and are referred to as *circadian rhythms*. In consideration of this planet's 24-hour cycle of alternate light and darkness and in consideration of studies in which the animals were exposed to varying periods of light and dark, the daily cycle of this planet's intensity of visible light is accepted by many scientists as a major factor in controlling biological rhythms.

The nature of the biological mechanism whereby a plant or organism maintains this rhythm is not resolved. Some biologists cite rhythms which persist and shift to new cues in the absence of natural cues. They argue for the existence of a biological "clock" or resonator with a fundamental frequency of nearly 24 hours. Others reporting a correlation between biological behavior and cosmic-ray intensity suggest that timing is imposed upon a sensitive locus in the organism by some external "clock" (Webb and Brown, 1959).

Once organisms are beyond the regimen of timing imposed by the rotation of this planet, they will (except when on Mars which has a rotation period, 24 hr., 37 min., nearly the same as the Earth's) be exposed to environmental timing different from that in which Terrestrial life evolved and developed. Although some individuals apparently exhibit unaltered performance in a drastic transferal of time zones (as would be occasioned by an intercontinental jet flight), the performance and susceptibility to various stimuli by other individuals is believed by many scientists to be altered markedly. One of the major objects of NASA's Biosatellite Program (see page 29) is to investigate the relation of these rhythms to the altered environment of space. Near ultraviolet light is only slightly more energetic than visible light. These photons, however, do have sufficient energy to break many chemical bonds which cannot be broken by the photons of visible light. Free radicals can be released in the tissue as a result of this radiation. For this reason, the ultraviolet component of solar radiation is highly efficient in the production of sunburn and the destruction of various microorganisms. Although the ultraviolet light will be sufficiently intense in space to cause severe burns, it has low penetration, and, for this reason, an individual can be shielded from the effects of this radiation by no more material than would be necessary in the construction of a space suit.

The softer x-rays also have very weak penetrating ability and therefore pose no shielding problem. The more energetic of the ionizing electromagnetic rays are more penetrating and could present a major shielding problem if they existed in space. The major source of such high-energy photons will be the secondary radiation produced as a result of beta and other ionizing rays reacting with matter. Another potential source for gamma rays will be the nuclear reactors which are now under consideration as an energy source either for nuclear rockets or for other necessary sources of power.

Action of Ionizing Radiation upon Biological Systems

At the molecular level, the biological effects of ionizing radiation are believed to be essentially the same whether the primary radiation happens to be electromagnetic rays or beams of nuclear particles. For this reason, an elementary discussion of the influence of ionizing radiation upon biological systems can serve both as an epilogue to the discussion of electromagnetic radiation and as a prologue to an elementary discussion of other types of radiation. Differences in the effects of radiation are attributed not to the type of ionization they accomplish but rather to the density and spatial arrangement of ionizations along the path which radiation traverses living systems.

The approximate times and order of biological events following exposure to radiation are indicated in Figure 9-5. A photon or a nuclear particle will react in the tissue to cause one or more ionizations. Sufficiently energetic primary ionizations can cause the release of other particles (electrons with most radiation) which in turn can set up a series of secondary ionizations. The energy accompanying the ionization can either directly break the molecular bond of a biologically sensitive molecule or it can cause the excitation of an atom with resulting bond breakage. If the broken bond is part of a biologically critical molecular structure, such as a gene, the resulting mutation can be considered a direct biological effect. The indirect effects of radiation result from byproducts of ionization-induced chemical bond breakage. The uncharged fragments of such broken molecules are referred to as "free radicals" and are highly reactive. Those resulting from water would free atomic hydrogen (H) or the free hydroxyl (OH) radicals. These are highly unstable and highly reactive. If they cannot immediately react with biological material, they will, in all probability, either recombine to form water or combine with dissolved oxygen in the tissue to form the somewhat less unstable but still highly reactive and toxic molecules of hydrogen peroxide (H_2O_2), or superoxyl (HO_2). It is probably the action of the hydrogen peroxide and the other highly reactive byproducts of radiation which are responsible for most of the biological effects of radiation which fall under the category of "indirect action."

The reader will note from Figure 9-6 that there is a wide range in the dose required to cause mortality in different types of material. The lethal dose is probably not a function of the actual amount of damage which radiation produces in an entire cell. Only one ionization is necessary to kill the smaller virus particles, and their susceptibility to radiation seems to increase as the quantity of nucleic acid increases to present a larger target for ionization. Although in some instances one ionization may produce a mutation within a cell, several properly spaced ionizations may be necessary for cell mortality. The sensitivity of a cell depends upon the critical size of a target within the cell and the number of critical targets which must be destroyed. It has been suggested that, since mammalian cells are highly specialized, destroying the specified quantity of any of a number of critical targets within the cell could

ORDER OF RADIOBIOLOGICAL EVENTS

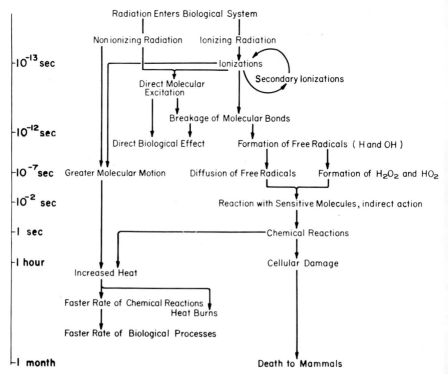

Figure 9-5. Order of radiobiological events. (Based primarily upon a modification of figures and information presented by Johns, 1961, pp. 137 and 650.)

LEVELS OF RADIATION IN RADS

NONPENETRATING RADIATION

PENETRATING RADIATION

10^7

10^6

Level of 50% Mortality for Various Viruses

Levels of 50% Mortality for Single Celled Animals

10^5

IMMEDIATE BLISTERING OF THE SKIN

Estimated Hourly Unshielded Dose in Outer Van Allen Belt

SEVERE RADIATION BURNS OF SKIN

Within 4 Hours — No Recovery Possible With Existing Methods Of Treatment — 10^4

Within 24 Hours — Level of 50 % Mortality — Level of 5 % Mortality (Man)

Dose Per Year in Space Due to Major Solar Flares is Probably Greater Than This

Dose Per Day in Space is Probably Greater Than This During a Major Solar Flare (One Which Occurs Less Frequently Than Once Per Year but Contains High Energy Particles at Relatively High Speeds

MODERATE RADIATION BURNS OF THE SKIN 10^3

Upper Limit for Recovery with Existing Methods of Treatment (Man)

OBSERVABLE DAMAGE TO DIGESTIVE SYSTEM

Level at which Radiation Could Incapacitate an Astronaut

Immediate Weakness and Vomiting (Man)
Complete Sterility
Level of 50 % Mortality (Man after 30 days)

OBSERVABLE DAMAGE TO BONE MARROW

Level of 5 % Mortality (Man)
Suggested Threshold for Leukemia (Man)

Weakness and Vomiting Within 24 Hours
Level at which Radiation Could Incapacitate an Astronaut
Tumors, Cancers and Decreased Life Span   50 % Mortality for Actively Dividing Human Cells in Tissue Culture

10^2

Suggested Maximum to Avoid Permanent Sterility (Man)
Damage to Nervous System (According to Russian Workers)
Total Natural Life Time (70 yr) Exposure on Earth at Sea Level
Total Dose From Naturally Occurring Radio-Elements (Primarily K^{40}) In Body After 1000 Years
Total Dose From Cosmic Rays At Sea Level On Earth After 1000 Years
Temporary Sterility

Yearly Soft X-Radiation From Sun Above Earth's Atmosphere

Hourly Dose Shielded by 1 gm/cm^2 In Inner Van Allen Belt

Measurable Decrease in White Blood Cells
This Can Cause an Increased Susceptibility to Infectious Disease

10

Observable Damage to Testicles

Observable Decrease In Rate of Cell Division (Mouse) Epidermis

Yearly Galactic Cosmic Radiation Above Earth's Atmosphere

Suggested Maximum Yearly Dosage (Man)

Hourly Dose Shielded by 5 gm / cm^2 In Inner Van Allen Belt

1.0

Yearly Dosage on Earth at Sea Level from Natural Sources

ESTIMATED DAILY SAFE DOSAGE

Suggested Maximum Weekly Dosage (Man)

0.1

Weekly Dose Necessary to Show Observable Change to the Blood (White Blood Cell Count)
Daily Dose Necessary to Cause More Than the Normal Incidence of Cancer

Suggested Maximum Daily Dosage (Man)
Yearly Dosage from Cosmic Rays at Sea Level
Yearly Dosage from Radio-Elements in the Body

0.01

Figure 9-6. Intensities of ionizing doses. (From various references for this chapter.) See Langham et al. (1964) for recent values. Values listed to the left are for nonpenetrating radiation while those to the right are for penetrating radiation.

prove fatal. As most single-celled animals (i.e., protozoa) display a much greater tolerance to radiation (Fig. 9-6), they presumably possess a smaller number of sensitive targets. Rapid cell division is one of the things which reduces the threshold to observable radiation damage. A number of components within a cell necessary only during the drastic developmental rearrangements which accompany cell division can be destroyed. The absence of these components would interfere with many functions of a dividing cell but not with the functions of a non-dividing cell. A man, therefore, might well survive radiation which will destroy the ability of most of his cells to divide if the affected cells are able to perform adequately other duties until they can be replaced by surviving cells still capable of division.

There is no general agreement on what would constitute safe exposure for man. Men are known to have survived 200 Roentgens (or its equivalent in rads or rem; see Table 9-2) without requiring medical attention. Although effects of radiation can be cumulative when exposure is too fast to permit adjustments by irradiated tissue, replacement of destroyed cells from others which are not destroyed can permit some recovery. This (200 r) is the suggested maximum lifetime dosage for radiological workers and space passengers; however, it is believed that space explorers could tolerate a lifetime dosage of 400 Roentgens if no acute dose exceeded 100 Roentgens (Hazel, 1964). A single exposure to 450 Roentgens can be lethal but slowly applied dosages totaling as much as 1,000 to 2,000 Roentgens can be survived. The factors which may influence tolerable dosages for astronauts have been reviewed recently by Langham *et al.* (1965).

The amount of tolerable radiation varies not only with the type of radiation but also with the material irradiated. Bone readily absorbs penetrating radiation, effecting a high sensitivity for the red-blood-cell-forming tissues of the bone marrow, so that after one month anemia can occur. Of more immediate concern during acute exposure are rapidly dividing cells, since the inhibition of cell division would first demonstrate itself with these. For this reason, white blood cells (lymphocytes), which are produced from rapidly dividing precursors, show a decreased frequency within hours. As a result, susceptibility to infection follows acute irradiation.

Reducing Susceptibility to Ionizing Radiation

It is conceivable that appropriate treatment of tissue prior to exposure could reduce the effective "target" size of critical radiosensitive areas or render these areas more subject to repair and thus reduce their sensitivity. With most procedures which decrease sensitivity, however, the mechanisms are more readily explainable in terms of reduced indirect effect (i.e., formation of free radicals or hydrogen peroxide) rather than reduced direct effect. With viable tissue, approximately one half of the radiation damage is attributable to indirect effects. This would indicate that the theoretical limit for increased tolerance would be by a factor of 2. Thus, mechanical shielding rather than treatment or conditioning remains the most promising protection.

There are several ways in which the indirect effects of radiation can be reduced by pre-treatment. *Freezing* prevents or limits the diffusion of free radicals of hydrogen and peroxide. Adequate *dehydration* would eliminate water molecules as precursors to free radicals and at the same time eliminate a liquid medium for diffusion of this toxic material. *Anoxia* reduces the presence of free oxygen required in the formation of peroxides. *Chemicals,* such as cysteamine, and other sulfhydryl compounds, probably decrease the concentration of free oxygen. It has been proposed that other materials, such as AET [5-(2-aminoethyl)-isothiuronium dibromide] (with tissue) or added protein (in virus suspensions), react with the free radicals or peroxides to "chemically shield" sensitive areas.

Low temperature (without freezing) and hibernation might not actually bring about a true reduction in radiation damage. With slower rates of metabolism and decreased requirements for active cell division, survival from some radiation damage would be longer. However, the lower body temperature might also bring about protection by tissue anoxia.

Nuclear Particles

There are two primary types of ionizing radiation. One type consists of the X-ray and gamma portion of the electromagnetic spectrum. As has already been discussed, this radiation possesses certain wave properties but at the same time consists of particle-like photons which, although they have no rest mass,[3] do behave while in motion or upon impact with matter as though they did possess mass. The other type of ionizing radiation to be considered consists of nuclear particles[4] which actually have mass even when at rest. Some of the more important ionizing radiation particles of biological interest are tabulated in Table 9-3.

Most of the energy which these particles have available for ionization of atoms is the kinetic energy of their motion. (Any remaining energy would be attributable to a particle charge.) The reader will remember that for particles moving at relatively slow speeds in comparison to that of light the kinetic energy of a particle can be described by Eq. (9-4):

$$\text{K.E.} = 1/2 \ mv^2 \qquad (9\text{-}4)$$

where m is the particle's mass and v is the velocity of the particle. These particles, however, although they cannot assume the velocity of light, can assume velocities which will approach this limit. At such relativistic speeds, the mass m is greater than the rest mass m_0 and can be described as a function of the particle's rest mass m_0 and its velocity v, by Eq. (9-5):

$$m = \frac{m_0}{\sqrt{1 - \dfrac{v^2}{c^2}}} \qquad (9\text{-}5)$$

---

[3] The rest mass for neutrinos is also zero.

[4] Physicists also consider mesons and hyperons to be particulate radiation but do not classify such particles as "nuclear particles."

TABLE 9-3. Properties of the Ionizing Radiations to Be Anticipated during Space Travel

Name of Rays	Particle	Symbol	Rest Mass* (a.m.u.)	Charge†	Absorption Properties		
					Attenuation	Path Shape	Absor Mecho
Electro-magnetic X-ray or gamma ray [γ])	Photon	hν $\rightsquigarrow$	0	0	Exponential	Straight	a. Photc electr b. Comp scatte c. Pair p ductic
Neutron beam	Neutron	n	1	0	~Exponential	Crooked (zig-zag)	a. Fast r trons Kev c collisi with a nucle b. Therm neutro (1.0 e less): sorbe nucle formi stable
Beta	Negative electron	β, β^- e, e$^-$	5×10^{-4}	$^-1$			a. Coulc scatte by pla electr b. Brem lung (ing ra tion) celera in pas throu atoms nucle
					~Exponential	Crooked (de-creasingly so with in-creased energy)	

*
†

Absorption Properties (cont.)

Best Absorber for Primary Rays	Secondary Radiation	Appropriate Shielding	RBE‡	Sources Significant to Space Travel
a. Heavy elements b. Light elements c. Heavy elements	a. β^- b. β^- + lower energy hυ c. β^- + β^+	Same mass of most materials; lead common due to low volume requirement	1	1. *Long X-rays* from Sun 2. Secondary cosmic rays 3. *Gamma rays* from radioisotope power source designed to generate heat released from absorption of isotope emission 4. Gamma rays from atomic reactor§
Protons which are available only in hydrogenous compounds	a. Accelerated, charged, atomic nuclei (more dangerous than neutrons) b. Short γ-rays from unstable atoms	1. Material of high hydro- gen content	a. 10 b. 2 to 5	1. Secondary cosmic rays 2. Atomic reactor‖
Other electrons (most common in light elements)	a. Delta rays (β of lower energy) b. hυ (X-rays)	(such as water, paraf- fin, etc.) for primary particulate rays	1	Secondary to X- or γ-rays Radiation belts Secondary cosmic rays from photon interaction

TABLE 9-3. (Continued)

Name of Rays	Particle	Symbol	Rest Mass* (a.m.u.)	Charge†	Absorption Properties		
					Attenuation	Path Shape	Absor Mech
	Positive electron	β^+, e^+		+1			Annihila upon binatic with β
Proton beam	Proton (hydrogen nucleus)	p	1	+1	Discrete depth	Almost straight	Coulom tering planet electro
Alpha	Helium nucleus (2p + 2n)	α	4	+2	Discrete	Almost straight bending at end of path	Coulom tering planet electro
Heavy cosmic primaries	Nuclei of large atoms		1.0 times (atomic mass no.)	+1.0 times (atomic no.)	a. Discrete b. ~Exponential	a. Almost straight until end of path b.	a. <Be trons move absor Ruthe scatte (With cc rays i mosp this o along "thin- path) b. >Be forma which lows a sorpti atomi clei to unsta atom

* a.m.u. = atomic mass units = multiples of 1.8×10^{-24} gm.
† Charge is expressed in negative multiples of an electron's charge or 4.8×10^{-10} electro static units.
‡ RBE = relative biological effectiveness = effect of a given amount of absorbed energy relative to that of X-rays.

Absorption Properties (cont.)

Best Absorber for Primary Rays	Secondary Radiation	Appropriate Shielding	RBE‡	Sources Significant to Space Travel
	2 hν of 0.51 Mev each	2. Above (i.e. material of high hydro-		
Planetary atomic electrons (largest quantity per mass with hydrogen)	Charged nuclei (only significant secondary radiation with very high energy primaries)	gen content for particulate radiation should be comple-	10 (.15 Mev) 2 (5 Mev) 1 (700 Mev)	Cosmic rays Inner Van Allen belt of radiation
Electrons		mented by lead or other	15 (5 Mev) 20 (1 Mev) 1 (900 Mev)	Cosmic rays (galactic)
Electrons		heavy element for secondary radiation	2 (as measured for 120 Mev carbon, and sometimes assumed without good confirmation for other particles)	Cosmic rays
Other atomic nuclei	p, n, mesons, hν (γ)	As these particles would frequently penetrate large depths of tissue before reacting, it might be best to eliminate shielding to avoid secondary radiation		

§ γ-radiation from atomic reactor (assuming 100% rather than the more likely 10% efficiency)

$$\cong \frac{0.02 \text{ rad/(min} - \text{watt of power)}}{(\text{meters from reactor})^2}$$

‖ Neutron radiation from atomic reactor (assuming 100% rather than the more likely 10% efficiency)

$$\cong \frac{0.008 \text{ rad/(min} - \text{watt of power)}}{(\text{meters from reactor})^2}$$

At speeds which come very close to the velocity of light, therefore, the mass becomes progressively greater, as is shown by a curve in Figure 9-2. For such particles, the kinetic energy would be greater than that predicted by Eq. (9-4) and would be predicted by Eq. (9-6):

$$\text{K.E.} = m_0c^2 \left\{ \frac{1}{\sqrt{1 - \dfrac{v^2}{c^2}}} - 1 \right\} \tag{9-6}$$

The more energetic particles penetrate to greater depths. Penetrating ability also decreases both with the size and the charge of a particle.

The depth to which some of the nuclear particles, particularly the protons, alpha particles, and the larger charged nuclei, can penetrate is much less than with electromagnetic energy. With electromagnetic radiation, there is a progressive absorption at a constant fractional rate, so that the thickness of a shielding material needed is expressed in terms of reduction of intensity. The penetration of nuclear particles is often described not only in terms of absorption coefficients or penetration depth but in terms of a range beyond which the primary radiant particle will not penetrate. The problem of shielding is somewhat complicated since the primary radiation produces secondary radiation resulting from the interaction with matter. Space travelers will probably be protected by a double layer of shielding. For the optimal absorption of nuclear particles, there probably will be an outer shielding layer containing hydrogen and other low molecular-weight elements, which may consist of rocket fuel, food supplies, water, and stored wastes. The secondary X-rays and gamma rays will then be absorbed by an inner shielding layer of lead.

The hazard to be expected from nuclei of less than one billion electron volts is fairly well understood. Experiments present evidence that high-speed iron nuclei (believed to possess an energy of nearly one BEV) can cause streaks of depigmentation in the hair of mice (Simons, 1960). There is also evidence that small amounts of this very high energy radiation can do serious damage to the brain. It has been suggested that no shielding be attempted for extremely energetic nuclei in the hope that they would pass entirely through a space vehicle before any absorption could occur.

Radiation Hazards in Space

Although nonionizing light will be relatively intense in space, its inability to penetrate optically opaque material results in a comparatively simple shielding problem. The big hazard comes from the much less intense but also very much more effective ionizing radiation. The Earth's atmosphere shields life from most of the dangerous space radiation. On the basis of mass per unit of area, air serves as a fairly good absorber for ionizing radiation. The pattern of collision of cosmic ray particles in the atmosphere is shown in Figure 9-7. The equivalent depth of absorbing material through which radiation must pass in penetrating to various depths within our atmosphere is shown from the graph in Figure 9-8. The anticipated hazards beyond the atmosphere are outlined in Table 9-1.

The now famous Van Allen belts of trapped radiation (Fig. 9-9) complicate the logistical problems of travel away from Earth to the Moon or to some other planet. This is particularly true for the inner belt of highly penetrating, hard radiation. Unless a very fast transit can be made through this belt, it will be necessary either to increase the payload sufficiently to carry very thick shielding or else to leave and enter Earth from the polar regions. The added difficulty of launching a heavier payload of shielding is obvious. A departure from the polar regions could not utilize the contribution to velocity which would be available from the Earth's rotation at more equatorial locations.

Once beyond the Van Allen belts, the major concern would be high-energy protons which are emitted from the Sun at high intensities almost once a year and at lesser intensities more frequently. The blast of intense radiation lasts for 2 days. It is not yet possible to know when all solar flares will take place. Probes near the sun could detect the less intense (but not the larger) outbursts several hours in advance of their travel to Earth. The more intense flares follow 11-year cycles with the next maximum flare anticipated to take place in 1969 (a time when the Apollo Moon

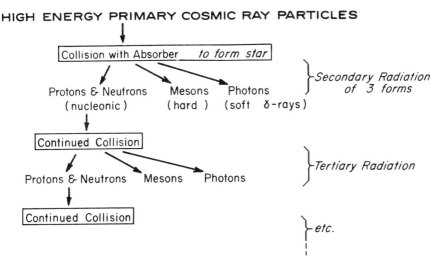

Figure 9-7.   Pattern of cosmic-ray breakdown during absorption
in upper atmosphere.

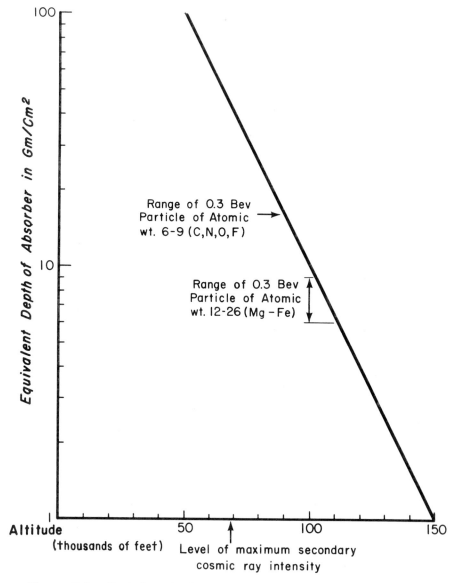

Figure 9-8. Equivalent depth of an absorber which is transversed by radiation as it passes from space into our atmosphere. (Modified from information presented by Simons, 1960.)

Project will be approaching its climax). The intensity of the larger flares is so great that completely adequate shielding for flights expected within the next decade is not practical. A possibility is to carry within a space ship small chambers of adequate shielding for short-term protection. Although a lunar trip would be of sufficiently short duration to minimize the danger of exposure, the probability of exposing an unshielded crew on a journey to Mars or Venus would be high (Waddington, 1962).

These intense blasts of high-energy protons are more properly referred to as a relativistic solar outburst accompanying a solar flare. Solar outbursts constitute one type of cosmic radiation (Table 9-1). There are also true cosmic or galactic rays. These galactic rays are believed to occur throughout our galaxy and to be oriented in no specific direction. They are believed to be released from stars other than our Sun and then to experience acceleration as they pass through various magnetic fields in space. For exposures of only a few days, they probably would not constitute a major hazard. However, the status of the large, bare, atomic nuclei (one of the constituents of this radiation) has not been completely settled from the point of view of biological hazard.

Eventually it will also be necessary to consider the hazards to be encountered when reactors must be carried as a source of energy for nuclear rockets. Although none is presently in use, the large weight costs of conventional fuels will probably require their eventual use. Their hazardous

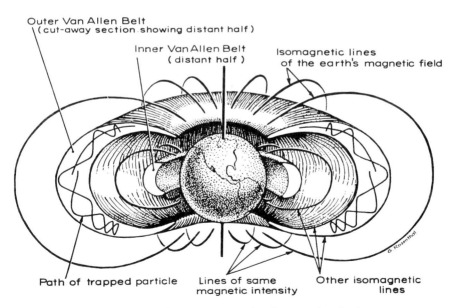

Figure 9-9.   The Van Allen belts of trapped radiation.

radiation will consist primarily of gamma rays and neutrons. The requirements for shielding will depend in part upon the distance by which it is practical to separate the reactor from the living quarters in a space vehicle.

Although not of immediate concern, the relatively sparse radiation lying between the stars could pose a problem. Due to the vast distances, any interstellar expedition would require velocities approaching the speed of light. At such speeds, a great quantity of radiation (which would be of low intensity and lower kinetic energy with respect to any stationary object) would be traversed. This would effect an immense intensity of radiation against the front of an interstellar vessel and demand heavy shielding. On a slower journey involving transport of material placed in a dormant state, transit time would be so great that this material (otherwise perfectly preserved) would be destroyed by the cumulative dose from its own natural radioactivity (see Fig. 9-6).

Prophecy of Unknown Hazards

Since ancient times, man has realized that much of his energy radiates to Earth from the Sun. Actually the energy which is radiated from the Sun is more important, more diverse, more useful, and more hazardous than ever could have been imagined by the primitive men who worshiped the Sun as a god. Perhaps we can consider the first prophecy of hazards to space travel as a result of radiation to be the story in Greek mythology of Daedalus, who, after inventing wings for manned flight, lost his son, Icarus, when heat rays from the Sun melted the wax which held his wings.

Cosmic and ionizing radiations have been known for somewhat more than half a century. The complete hazard from these rays is at best still only very imperfectly understood. It is almost impossible to predict whether or not our voyage into space will present us with still more, previously unsuspected, forms of energy.

Bibliography and References

ACKERMAN, E. (1962): "Biophysical Science." Prentice-Hall, Englewood Cliffs, N. J.

BACHEM, A., AND REED, C. I. (1931): The penetration of light through human skin. Amer. J. Physiol. 97, 86-91.

BALLINGER, E. R. (1964): New information on solar flares and space radiation. In "Lectures in Aerospace Medicine," pp. 43-49. School of Aerospace Medicine, Brooks AFB, Texas.

BARNOTHY, J. M. (1960): Biologic effects of magnetic fields. In "Medical Physics" (O. Glasser, ed.), Vol. 3, pp. 61-64. Year Book Medical Publishers, Chicago, Ill.

BAUM, S. J. (1962): Recommended ionizing radiation exposures for early exploratory space missions. Aerospace Med. 33, 1182-1186.

BEISCHER, D. E. (1963): Biomagnetics. In "Lectures in Aerospace Medicine," pp. 365-386. School of Aerospace Medicine, Brooks AFB, Texas.

BLIZARD, E. P. (1963): Shielding of man in space. In "Lectures in Aerospace Medicine," pp. 339-364. School of Aerospace Medicine, Brooks AFB, Texas.

CAMPBELL, P. A. (1961): "Medical and Biological Aspects of the Energies of Space." Columbia University Press, New York.

CASEY, E. J. (1961): "Biophysics: Concepts and Mechanisms." Reinhold Publishing Corp., New York.

CURTIS, H. J. (1961): Limitations on space flight due to cosmic radiations. *Science 133*, 312-316.

GYURDZHIAN, A. A. (1962): Radiobiological problems of space flights. *In* "Problemy kosmicheskoy biologii" [Problems of Space Biology] (N. M. Sisakyan, ed.), *Vol. 1*, pp. 29-118. As translated from Russian in NASA TT F-174, National Aeronautics and Space Administration, Washington, D. C.

HALBERG, F. (1961): Circadian rhythms: a basis of human engineering for aerospace. *In* "Psychophysiological Aspects of Space Flight" (B. E. Flaherty, ed.), pp. 166-194. Columbia University Press, New York.

HALBERG, F. (1964): Physiologic rhythms. *In* "Physiological Problems in Space Exploration" (Hardy, J. D., ed.). Charles C Thomas, Springfield, Ill.

HAZEL, J. (1964): Radiation hazards and manned space flight. *Aerospace Med. 35*, 436-439.

HOLLAENDER, A. (ed.) (1956): "Radiation Biology." (3 Vols.) McGraw-Hill, New York.

JASTROW, R., AND CAMERON, A. G. W. (1964): Space: highlights of recent research. *Science 145*, 1129-1139.

JOHNS, H. E. (1961): "The Physics of Radiology," 2nd ed. Charles C Thomas, Springfield, Ill.

KELLOGG, W. W. (1961): The upper atmosphere as observed with rockets and satellites. *In* "Lectures in Aerospace Medicine" (Paper No. 6). School of Aviation Medicine, Brooks AFB, Texas.

KLEITMAN, N. (1939): "Sleep and Wakefulness." University of Chicago Press, Chicago.

KRUSZEWSKI, E. T. (1965): Meteoroids: needs for penetration scaling—laws and potentials of simulation techniques. Paper No. 4. *In* "Proc. of Conf. on Role of Simulation in Space Technology," *Engineering Extension Series Circular No. 4, Part A*, Va. Poly. Inst., Blacksburg.

LANGHAM, W. H., BROOKS, P. M., GRAHN, D. (eds.) (1965): "Radiation Biology and Space Environment Parameters in Manned Spacecraft Design and Operations," a special report in *Aerospace Med. 36* (2), section II.

LEA, D. E. (1965): "Actions of Radiations on Living Cells," 2nd ed. University Press, Cambridge.

MORESSI, W. J. (1964): Mortality patterns of mouse sarcoma 180 cells resulting from direct heating and chronic microwave irradiation. *Experimental Cell Research 33*, 240-253.

RAGLE, J. L. (1964): On possible biological effects of magnetic fields. *Aerospace Med. 35*, 469-471.

RANDALL, J. E. (1962): "Elements of Biophysics," 2nd ed. Year Book Medical Publishers, Chicago.

ROSEN, A. (1963): Natural and man-made radiation in space. *In* "Lectures in Aerospace Medicine," pp. 301-338. School of Aerospace Medicine, Brooks AFB, Texas.

SCHAEFER, H. J. (1964): The radiation field inside space vehicles. *Aerospace Med. 35*, 104-110.

SEARLE, G. W., DAHLEN, R. W., IMIG, C. J., WUNDER, C. C., THOMPSON, J. D., THOMAS, J. A., AND MORESSI, W. J. (1961): Effects of 2450 mc microwaves in dogs, rats, and larvae of the common fruit fly. *In* "Biological Effects of Microwave Radiation," *Vol. 1*, pp. 187-197. Plenum Press Inc., New York.

SIMONS, D. G. (1960): Biologic hazard of space radiations. *In* "Medical Physics" (O. Glasser, ed.), *Vol. 3*, pp. 64-72. Year Book Medical Publishers, Chicago.

SLAGER, U. T. (1962): "Space Medicine," pp. 59-168. Prentice-Hall, Englewood Cliffs, N. J.

STONE, S. (1952): Concept of a maximum permissible exposure. *Radiology 58*, 639-661.

STRUGHOLD, H. (1963): The physiological clock in aeronautics and astronautics. *In* "Lectures in Aerospace Medicine," pp. 387-400. School of Aerospace Medicine, Brooks AFB, Texas.

STUHLMAN, O. (1943): "An Introduction to Biophysics," pp. 1-169. John Wiley and Sons, New York.

TOBIAS, A. (1959): Radiation and life in space. *Fed. Proc. 18*, 1242-1249.

VAN ALLEN, J. A. (1961): The geomagnetically trapped corpuscular radiation. *In* "Science in Space" (L. V. Berkner and H. Odishaw, eds.), pp. 275-285. McGraw-Hill, New York.

WADDINGTON, C. J. (1962): The hazard of corpuscular solar radiation to manned spaceflight. *J. Brit. Interplanetary Soc. 18*, 277-280.

WEBB, H. M., AND BROWN, F. A., JR. (1959): Timing long-cycle physiological rhythms. *Physiol. Rev. 39*, 127-161.

WHIPPLE, F. L. (1962): Dust and meteorites. *Astronautics, Vol. 7, No. 8*, 40-42.

10

Selection and Supplies: The Biologistics Problems

In previous chapters, the discussion focused upon the unique and adverse conditions which life must either encounter or be sheltered against in space. It is now appropriate to consider the best procedures for selecting the organisms and supplies to be carried into space.

General Requirements of Material to Be Taken into Space

There are a number of different general requirements and qualifications which must be weighed and examined in the preparation and selection of the final payload (see Fig. 10-1). In ventures which are not related to space travel, two requirements that frequently are considered to be almost mutually exclusive are dependability and the requirement for small space and mass. Due to the combined problem of remoteness and expense for transport, both these requirements must be met. Until less expensive and more efficient methods for leaving this planet are available, highly dependable systems which require a minimum of space will be necessary. These considerations will apply not only to the operating units themselves but also to the availability of any necessary replacement parts for essential equipment which might fail. The nature of the voyage will determine the proper balance between the size of a unit appropriate for recycling material and the amount of material which must be carried along with the rocket for the operation of a life-sustaining unit.

Every organism, individual, or unit must also be carefully screened in light of the effect it may have upon other components of the system. If there is more than one individual in the space capsule, it is important that each be of a congenial disposition. It is important that no portion of the space craft release agents or materials which might be toxic or injurious to the crew or cargo (Table 7-1). In Chapter 7, the various toxic agents which might be encountered during space flight were discussed.

Care must also be taken in order to avoid undesirable microorganisms which might cause disease and infection to the occupants of the space

223

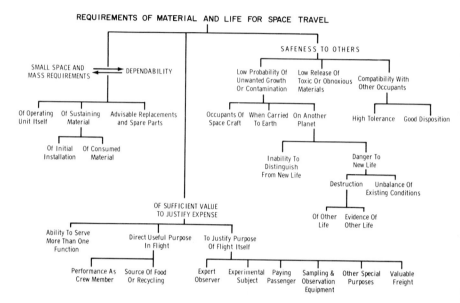

Figure 10-1. Breakdown of some of the requirements which must be considered in selecting subjects and material for space travel.

craft or which might, if carried to another planet, destroy either existing life or evidence of past life upon that planet (see pp. 283-286). Within the space craft, there will be a particular danger of spread of infectious diseases from one crew member to another during periods of weightlessness because particles containing contaminants would be unable to settle.

Due to the extreme expense involved in carrying any object into space, the value of any object should be sufficiently great to justify the expense of its transportation. If an object or crew member is able to serve more than a single function, then the cost of transporting this individual relative to his value is reduced. Dual functions might be performed by materials which can serve not only for radiation shielding but as food, water (which might also offer buoyant protection from high G), fuel, and nondisposable wastes. If a chemical is capable of absorbing carbon dioxide and at the same time of releasing oxygen for respiration, a parallel value exists. A biological system for recycling which cannot only absorb carbon dioxide and release oxygen but which is also able to recycle other waste products of human metabolism and produce food would have even greater justification on a space trip, provided its total weight is low and its dependability high. The mass within the payload will serve either a directly useful purpose for the flight (such as performance as a crew member or as a source of food or recycling) or it must serve some highly useful function which will justify the purpose of the flight itself. The living cargo that serves indirect functions is likely to be either an expert observer or experimental material. At the time of this writing (July, 1965), it is still a matter of controversy whether or not the biological samples which have been carried in space flight have been useful in obtaining any basic new biological or medical knowledge.

Requirements for Lifting Material into Space

At the present time, the only feasible way of leaving a planet is by means of a rocket, which must be accelerated to a given velocity (see Chapter 3), as described by Eq. (10-1):

$$\text{energy per unit of mass} = 1/2 \ v^2 \qquad (10\text{-}1)$$

If it is desired to place a payload in orbit, then the velocity must be such that the centrifugal force and the gravitational force are counterbalanced. This velocity for orbit near a planet's surface would be described by Eqs. (10-2) and (10-3):

$$\text{orbital velocity} = \sqrt{\mathcal{G}\,\frac{\text{planetary mass}}{\text{radius of planet}}} \qquad (10\text{-}2)$$

or

$$\text{orbital velocity} = \sqrt{(\text{surface gravity})\,(\text{radius of planet})} \qquad (10\text{-}3)$$

where $\mathcal{G}$ is equal to the universal gravitational constant (6.66×10^{-8} cm^3/gm-sec^2). The velocity necessary to lift a payload completely beyond a planet's effective gravitational field is described by Eqs. (10-4) and (10-5):

$$\text{escape velocity} = \sqrt{2\,\mathcal{G}\,\frac{\text{planetary mass}}{\text{planetary radius}}} \qquad (10\text{-}4)$$

or

$$\text{escape velocity} = \sqrt{2 \times \text{surface gravity} \times \text{planetary radius}} \qquad (10\text{-}5)$$

The velocity, required energy, and fuel necessary for lifting the payload alone from various heavenly bodies are indicated in Figure 3-2.

The fuel and energy requirements displayed in Figure 3-2 ignore the practical requirement of also lifting fuel with the rocket for progressive acceleration. (One could ignore such a practical requirement only if some presently unfeasible mechanism, such as a canon or elevator, could adequately accelerate a space vehicle without accelerating some of the fuel.) These values (in Fig. 3-2) are based upon 100 percent efficiency in a rocket using liquid oxygen and liquid hydrogen as fuel with the resultant product, water, leaving a rocket at the maximum exhaust velocity. We are forced to

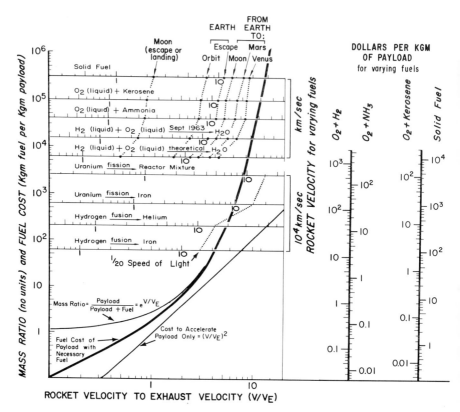

Figure 10-2. Caption on opposite page.

employ rockets which ascend almost vertically through the atmosphere, so that they may transcend the shortest path of atmospheric friction. After passing through the atmosphere, continual acceleration of a type which will permit the desired velocities is possible.

The initial stages of a rocket, however, must contain not only enough fuel for accelerating the rocket's payload itself but also for accelerating all fuel which raises the earlier stages of the rocket. The mass of fuel which would be necessary for accelerating the payload, the entire rocket complex, and the efficiency of this process is a function of the ratio of the rocket velocity to the exhaust velocity,[1] as displayed in Figure 10-3. From this figure, it is

---

[1] The exhaust velocity and cost for a number of the existing rocket fuels are displayed in Figure 10-3. Specific impulse refers to the gram of force exerted per unit rate at which grams of fuel are exhausted. Since grams of force and grams of mass are frequently and incorrectly treated as equivalent units, specific impulse is generally expressed in units of time. Even though it is expressed in inappropriate units, specific impulse can be converted into the exhaust velocity upon multiplication by the Earth's gravitational field constant of 980 gram-cm $\times$ sec^2 $\div$ (gram of force).

Figure 10-2. Mass requirements of rocket fuel as a function of the ratio of the final rocket velocity to the exhaust velocity˜of the rocket fuel. The heavy solid line represents the cost of fuel (in Kgm. on left-hand scale and in dollars on right-hand scales) which is necessary to accelerate one kilogram of payload to a given relative velocity with consideration of the amount of fuel required to accelerate the fuel employed during various stages of the rocket's acceleration. The upper horizontal scales indicate the rocket velocities for specific fuels corresponding to a fuel cost or mass ratio on the three curves as read from the vertical scales. For other fuels of known exhaust velocity, one may employ the lower horizontal scale where the rocket velocity is expressed in multiples of exhaust velocity. Mass ratio refers to the ratio of total fuel employed both for rocket and fuel acceleration to the mass of the payload. The formula shown for mass ratio can be derived from assuming that the infinitesimal gain in motion ($m_r dv$) of a rocket will be equal to the opposite motion ($-V_E dm$) of material exhausted from the rocket during the same instant.[a]

Fuel requirements would actually be somewhat greater due to the requirements not only to lift fuel but also rocket casings and fuel tanks. Fuel expended in overcoming atmospheric friction is assumed negligible as is fuel for static thrust in supporting the rocket's weight.[b] Data for chemical fuels can be obtained from Figure 10-1. Data for nuclear fuels were obtained from von Hoerner (1962). That data should indicate that, in approaching the speed of light, fuel requirements would approach extensive if not prohibitive masses, even with nuclear propulsion.

(a)

$$m_r dv = V_E dm \quad \text{or} \quad \frac{dv}{V_E} = -\frac{dm}{m}$$

which upon integration yields

$$\frac{V}{V_E} = \ln \frac{M}{M_o} \quad \text{or} \quad \frac{M}{M_o} = e^{V/V_E}$$

where M is the final mass of the accelerated payload and M_o that of the initial combined weight of the payload and fuel.

(b) Actually to correct for this fuel loss for static support in escaping a planet's gravity the following relationship applies:

$$(\text{Corrected Rest Mass}) = (\text{Uncorrected Rest Mass})^{(a + g) \div g}$$

where a is the rocket's effective acceleration and g is a planet's surface gravity. In determining the corrected rest mass by means of the values in this figure one could use the following relationship:

Effective velocity (for reading corrected mass ratio from the figure)

$$= (\text{desired velocity}) \times \frac{a + g}{a}$$

Note that no correction is necessary when $a >> g$.

obvious that the mass ratio (i.e., the ratio of the total initial mass of the rocket to that of the payload) is many fold greater than the ratio of the payload's mass to the amount of fuel representative of the payload's kinetic energy (in other words, the amount of fuel that would be necessary in raising the payload by itself without the supporting fuel).

Typical values and procedures for calculation of the fuel requirements and fuel costs with rockets are indicated in Figure 10-2. In practice, somewhat greater fuel requirements than those indicated here would be necessary because these relatively simple computations do not consider the weight of the rocket hulls themselves, the fuel expended in overcoming atmospheric friction, or the fuel consumed in statically counterbalancing planetary gravity. Frequently it is less expensive to use a more costly fuel due to a greater efficiency possible with certain fuels. At the present time, only chemical fuels are operational.[2]

The reader will note that substantially lower fuel requirements would be necessary in lifting material from the Moon. If appropriate sources for fuel are obtainable on the Moon, it is likely that it would serve as a suitable base either from which to launch expeditions to other parts of the Solar System or from which to obtain the fuel to be utilized in launching expeditions from a station in space. For this reason, if extensive space explorations are pursued in the coming generations, it might prove desirable to colonize the Moon.

By similar logic, landings on a satellite or planet (unless that body serve as a source of supplies) will probably involve carrying only enough fuel for landing and reorbiting. Fuel needed for return to Earth will be conserved by retaining it within the primary space vehicle in orbit about a satellite or planet

---

[2] A venture beyond our Solar System into deep space would require velocities approaching the speed of light. The reader will note from Figure 10-2 that approaching this velocity the requirements would be beyond the most fanciful dreams. Highly efficient nuclear fuels offer the only possibility, although it has been computed that nuclear units of sufficiently small mass to utilize the relatively small thrust which is anticipated from nuclear engines is extremely unlikely (von Hoerner, 1962). On the other hand, once a rocket has been lifted beyond the Earth's gravitational pull, some sort of nuclear, electrostatic, or ion drive might be feasible in traveling from one portion of the solar system to another.

Sagan (1963), in contending that von Hoerner is overly pessimistic, cites the suggestion of Bussard (1960) that an interstellar space vehicle might not require sufficient initial mass to provide the entire fuel load. It is proposed that propulsion be achieved by a so-called "thermonuclear ramjet" feeding upon interstellar particles. Although much time would elapse on Earth awaiting the return of such a vessel, relativistic time dilation might allow a shorter interval to be experienced by the voyagers. This shorter time t, as measured on a space vehicle, uniformly accelerated at a to the midpoint of a voyage and then decelerated at $-a$, would, according to Sagan, for a trip distance of S be

$$t = \frac{2c}{a} \text{ arc cos } h(1 + aS/2c^2),$$

where c is the speed of light. With an a of one G this would yield slightly less than 4 years for the 4 light years to the nearest star, Alpha Centuri, 21 years for the 30,000 light years to the center of our own galaxy, and 28 years to reach the two million light years to the nearest galaxy beyond our own.

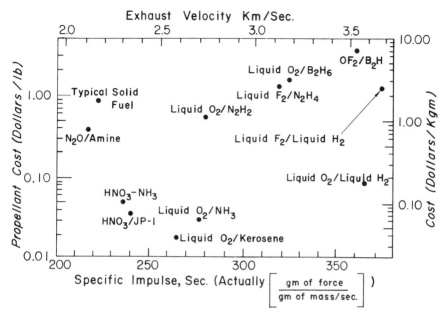

Figure 10-3. Cost and exhaust velocities of various rocket fuels. This is a modification of a figure in *Chemistry and Engineering News* (Sept. 3, 1963, p. 74). Note that the exhaust velocity is proportional to the specific impulse and can be computed from the following equation:

$$\text{Specific Impulse} = \frac{\text{gm of force}}{(\text{gm of fuel exhausted})/\text{time}}$$

and

$$\text{exhaust velocity in cm/per sec} = \text{specific impulses in secs} \times \frac{980 \text{ gm-cm/sec}^2}{\text{gm of force}}$$

without being carried down from and back into orbit. Landing and departure would be achieved in a smaller auxiliary vehicle. Such a procedure has been planned for the Apollo expedition to the Moon. Similar approaches to Mars (possibly involving its tiny moon Phobos as an orbital station) have been proposed.

In landing, an amount of deceleration equivalent to escape velocity (or orbital velocity if descending from orbit) must be executed. If no other means presents itself (as will be the case for a soft landing on the airless Moon), additional fuel, equivalent to that for escape, must be expended for proper deceleration. With the Earth and probably also with Mars and Venus, the atmosphere can serve to decelerate the space craft. Although this will reduce fuel requirements, tremendous reentry heat (pp. 76-79) will be generated, necessitating massive heat shielding.

Traveling to other planets will not only involve fuel expenditures for escape and reentry, but fuel must also be utilized in raising or lowering the vehicle to a different orbital level in the Sun's gravitational field. The greatest fuel savings can be achieved if this transition utilizes the planet's orbital velocities, so that acceleration is only to a velocity equivalent to the difference between planetary velocities (Fig. 10-4). Such maneuvers, although conserving rocket fuel, will necessitate long journeys and consequently greater supplies for life support.

Selecting and Changing the Organism for Space

At the beginning of this chapter, some of the general requirements for any constituent of a space rocket's payload, be it living or nonliving material, were discussed. Whether or not it is necessary that space vehicles carry men, particularly during the early stages of space exploration, is a matter of debate. Some scientists feel that many observations can be made in a more satisfactory manner by use of highly automated instruments. There is general agreement, however, that if landings are actually to be made upon the Moon or other heavenly bodies the presence of man as a qualified observer is extremely desirable. The controversy persists as to whether or not carrying a man to another heavenly body in the near future is justified unless such a man is a qualified scientific observer.

Our government has started to recruit a limited number of scientists for its "Scientist-Astronaut" training program. These individuals will not exceed 35 years of age at the onset of training and will be expected to possess the equivalent of a doctorate in the natural, medical or engineering sciences. At this writing (July, 1965) the selection of six individuals for this program has been announced. Among these scientists are two physicians, Duane Graveline and Joseph P. Kerwin; three physicists, Edward G. Gibson, Curtis Michel, and Owen Garriott; and an astrogeologist, Harrison Schmitt. During later phases of the Apollo Project a scientist (probably a geologist) will be carried to the Moon. He will be preceded by trained astronauts, who, on previous journeys, have tested equipment reliability and placed an advance supply of equipment for the scientist. Even though this individual will not have the rigorous astronaut training of regular astronauts, he will undoubtedly receive a certain minimum of training in this area. Thus far (July, 1965), manned American flights have carried only occupants whose backgrounds were essentially that of test pilot rather than that of a scientist. The Russians have already orbited in one single-passenger vessel a woman without pilot training. In a more recent voyage (Oct., 1964) a three-man Soviet vessel included as occupants not only a trained pilot but also an engineer and a physician. The crew size and possible duration of future American explorations are indicated in Table 10-1.

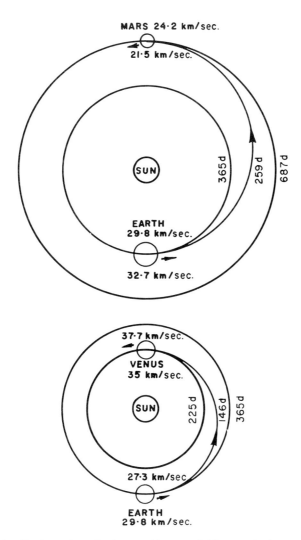

Figure 10-4. Trajectories of trips to Mars and Venus which would conserve available centrifugal velocities (Figure "Cotangential Orbits to Mars and Venus" from INTERPLANETARY FLIGHT, Rev. Ed., by Arthur C. Clarke [Harper & Brothers, 1960]).

The general requirements for astronauts during the Mercury Project, as described in a recent NASA publication (Voas *et al.*, 1963), are listed in Table 10-2. The reader will note that knowledge of aircraft and missile operation, together with engineering knowledge, was emphasized, with the requirement that scientific and research ability merely be at the general level.

TABLE 10-1.   Estimated Crew Size and Duration of Space Mission*

Number of Crewmen	Days of Duration				
	3-14	10-20	25-50	60-90	100-
2-5	Gemini, Apollo	Advanced Apollo		Apollo Emergency	Beyond Moon
5-10	Unlikely	Space Laboratory Development	Space Laboratories		Missions to Other Planets
10-20	Training	Lunar Exploration	Lunar Construction	Operation of Facilities in Space	Exploration of Other Planets
20-		U n l i k e l y		Operation of Facilities on Moon	Extra-Terrestrial Colonies

* Modified from Hartman and Flinn, 1964.

TABLE 10-2.   General Requirements for Astronauts during Mercury Project*

1. Aptitude and ability
   a. Good engineering knowledge
   b. Good knowledge of aircraft and missile operation
   c. General scientific and research ability
   d. High intelligence
   e. Psychomotor skills similar to aircraft pilots

2. Personality factors
   a. Good tolerance to "psychological stress"
   b. Good decision-making ability
   c. Ability to work with others
   d. Emotional maturity
   e. Strong motivation

3. Physical requirements
   a. Freedom from disease or disabilities
   b. Resistance to the physical factors in the space environment likely to
      act as "physiological stressors"
   c. Medium size

* Based on tabulation by Voas et al., 1963.

The astronaut must function as an integral part of the space vehicle with a close meshing of the human and machine operations. At the same time one should recall that the Soviet woman cosmonaut, without aircraft-pilot experience, performed satisfactorily. The items which would enhance the necessary performance were emphasized in the early American orbits at the expense of the type of scientific background which would produce the best qualified scientific observer (see Table 10-2). The purpose of the early manned flights, however, has not been primarily to obtain basic scientific information. They have been intended fundamentally, at least from the scientific and technological point of view, for the purpose of developing techniques which will permit future space exploration of a more scientifically significant nature.

It is interesting to note that the astronauts should be of medium size. If an individual were satisfactory in all other respects, his mass, together with that of supporting materials in the payload, would be less the smaller his size. Perhaps only individuals of medium size have the opportunity to obtain adequate experience with aircraft and rockets.

There are certainly many reasons why a larger experimental organism (such as a primate) is likely to yield data from satellite experiments of more immediate application to manned flight. However, somewhat smaller animals could more easily be carried with sufficient supplies and in sufficient numbers to yield statistically significant data. Very small organisms are not so likely to be affected by the unique nature of the space environment (particularly with respect to weightlessness [see pp. 133-135]). Animals the size of mice, young turtles, and insects are of a sufficient size for the effects of weightlessness to be expected.

The physical conditioning and preparation of subjects for the current space flights have been of a conservative nature (see Table 10-3). On the other hand, serious scientific articles (Kline and Clynes, 1961) have proposed changes and special preparations for men or some other subjects for space

TABLE 10-3. Preparations of Subject for Mercury Flights*

1. Formal lectures in space science .... 42 hr.
2. Training time
   a. Simulator training experience .... 160 hr.
   b. Proficiency airplane flights .... 460 hr.
   c. Centrifuge experiments .... 48 hr.
   d. Slow rotation room .... 1 hr.
   e. Zero-G airplane flights .... 1 hr.
   f. Star recognition .... 28 hr.
3. Diet
   a. Balanced diet .... 1 wk. prior to flight
   b. Low residue diet to prevent defecation during flight ...... 3 days prior to flight
4. Drugs
   a. To be used routinely .... none
   b. To be available for use
      1) A pain-relieving drug   ⎫
      2) A motion-sickness drug   ⎪ emergency
      3) A stimulant (only with early flights) ⎬ use
      4) A vasoconstrictor for shock   ⎪ only
         (only with early flights)   ⎪
      5) Antihistamine tablets   ⎭
   c. Dextro-amphetamine to overcome fatigue .... just prior to reentry

* Based on discussion by Berry, 1963.

travel which are of such a drastic nature that many of our science fiction writers would be considered by comparison almost reactionary. It is suggested that altering metabolism by appropriate drugs would permit men to survive otherwise impossible rigors in space exploration. In order to save space and mass, the lungs and mouth would be eliminated. Necessary nutrients would be ingested by means of injection, and the blood would be oxygenated as it perfused through special chemical devices. Man and machine would be amalgamated into one inseparable unit referred to as a "Cyborg."

Requirements for Men

The exact environmental requirements which would be tolerable for man during extended space voyages have not been completely resolved. Certain environments which have been proposed as the most efficient for space flight have never before required prolonged testing. Although various industrial situations have required the exposure of man to somewhat adverse conditions for as long as 8 hours per day and 5 days per week, very few of these extreme situations have been required for continuous exposure throughout 24 hours a day for 7 days a week over a number of weeks without interruption.

With very few exceptions, essentially all of the known metabolic requirements for any organism are based upon measurements performed at the Earth's normal gravity of 980 dynes per gram. It has been suggested, but not rigorously substantiated, that if no artificial gravity is employed in a space vehicle the metabolic requirements may be reduced by as much as one third. On the basis of measurements at the School of Aerospace Medicine (Myers, 1960), it has been proposed that men in space have a metabolic requirement of 2,900 kcal a day with a turnover which involves an intake of 2.2 kilograms of water, 520 grams of food, and 860 grams of oxygen (Fig. 10-5). This would be somewhat less than the requirement of an active soldier at 22° C who would consume somewhat closer to 3,600 kcal per day with a total turnover of about 4 kilograms per day. Values computed in this and other portions of the book are based upon the latter metabolic requirement with proportionate increases in other materials.

Atmospheric Considerations

The recent American manned space flights as well as those proposed for the near future have involved atmospheres of 100 percent oxygen with a partial and total pressure of approximately ⅓ of an atmosphere. The advantages of this and other types of atmospheres are listed in Table 10-5. The arguments for and against various types of atmospheric environment are based upon the relative merits of simplicity of operation, avoidance of adverse effects of decompression, mass of payload, fire hazards, the supposedly nonessential nature of nitrogen as a respiratory gas, and the auditory properties of various gases. Men have tolerated exposure to such atmospheres for

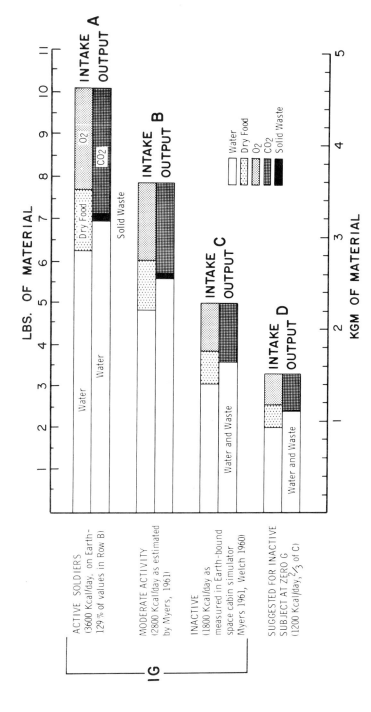

Figure 10-5. Grams of material turned over by man per day. Values for parts A and C are based upon the assumption that magnitude would be proportional to those indicated in Column B. A more complete breakdown of part A is shown in Figure 7-2.

TABLE 10-4. Life Support Requirements for Man during Space Flight

	Range as Tabulated by Welch, 1963	Turnover per Day in Grams per Man (3600 Kcal) as Tabulated in Fig. 10-5: Intake	Output	Possible Sources	Remarks
Pressure	760-180 mm Hg				
O_2	425-100 mm Hg	1100		Could be stored in cylinders at high pressure to reduce volume. Storage in liquid form (at $-183°$) would reduce volume requirement further. Release from oxygen-containing compounds. Recycling from water (which might exceed intake due to metabolic water) by electrolysis.	Essential that systems be balanced such that ratio of CO_2 absorption and O_2 release by control system be equal to the respiratory quotient (R.Q. = volume ratio of CO_2 release to O_2 consumption by the organism). R.Q. varies with the metabolic state and diet of the organism but for a normal individual with mixed diet it would have a value of approximately 0.82
CO_2	8-0 mm Hg		1260	Could be removed by chemical absorbents such as Baralyme [mixture of $Ca(OH)_2$ and $Ba(OH)_2$] and soda lime [mixture of $Ca(OH)_2$ and NaOH, LiOH, NaOH, KOH], reaction with Na_2CO_3 or K_2CO_3	
Temperature	16-18° C (wet bulb) 21-24° C (dry bulb)				
Relative humidity	60-40%				

Water	2830	3260	1) Storage; 2) supply as byproduct of other systems in spacecraft; 3) recycling by: freeze drying (lyophilization), distillation, and chemical treatment. Moisture might be removed by such absorbents as silica gel. Might also be removed by molecular sieves
Microcontaminants	Nontoxic (see Table 7-1)		
Food	670		
Solid waste		80	Reconversion into food not practical until a better closed ecological system is developed. Major problems of keeping associated gases from cabin atmosphere. If stored would occupy approximately 600 cc/day (150 cc dry). Might be expelled overboard or incinerated
TOTAL	4600	4600	

as long as 17 days (Morgan *et al.* 1963). However, this exposure was accompanied by mild symptoms generally associated with oxygen toxicity (respiratory irritation, ear discomfort, and eye irritation), which suggested that some nitrogen might be necessary during extended voyages. The absence of molecular nitrogen is reported to arrest development of chicken embryos (Allen, 1963). Other workers (Wright *et al.,* 1965) however report that, although the absence of nitrogen results in an altered oxygen metabolism and greater water loss from chicken embryos, they could not detect the detrimental developmental effects reported by Allen. Whether or not nitrogen itself serves

NASA-S-64-837

PORTABLE LIFE SUPPORT SYSTEM SCHEMATIC

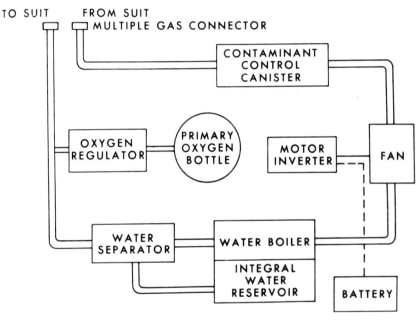

Figure 10-6. Schematic of portable life support system for use with Apollo Lunar Space Suit (Kincaide, 1964, NASA-S-64-837). The contaminant control canister will contain lithium hydroxide for CO_2 removal and activated charcoal for odor control. The water boiler will serve as the air-conditioning unit to dissipate 400 k cal/hr by conversion of liquid to gas. This process will also serve as a heat sink to remove moisture (originating from sweat or evaporation in the lungs from the circuit by condensation. Unit will attach as a back-pack to the suit shown in Figure 4-3. The unit will weigh 23 kgm and remain operational for 4 hours. A more recent design (not shown in the figure but presently under development) will involve cooling of the body with a liquid pumped through tubes in the space suit. This has been described by Goodman and Radnofsky (1965).

some essential purpose is unknown. It has been suggested that free nitrogen merely serves physically to dampen diffusion of oxygen down to safe levels of activity (Clamann, 1964).

A space suit to be pressurized at ¼ atmosphere of pure oxygen is being developed for use on the lunar surface during the Apollo Project (see Fig. 4-3). In design, it will be quite similar to the pressure suits employed in the Mercury flights. A 22-kgm portable life support system for use with this suit will be in a pack which attaches to the back of the suit (see Fig. 10-6).

TABLE 10-5. Various Types of Artificial Atmospheres for Space Craft*

Type	Advantages	Disadvantages	Remarks
100% O_2 with a partial pressure of 260-175 mm Hg	1. Only one control mechanism needed both for O_2 concentration and total gas pressure 2. With no inert gases dissolved in tissue, no bends would accompany decompression	1. Potential biological effects of chronic N_2 lack not known 2. Possible atelectasis of lungs has been suggested 3. Fire hazard due to less inert gas to conduct and absorb heat from hot points such as electrical wiring	Employed with past and proposed American flights
O_2 with N_2 as inert gas	As this is the natural environment on Earth, one can be assured of no adverse biological effects	1. Would add additional payload unless there is no loss or leakage of this gas 2. Increased hazard for bends	Believed to be employed with Russian flights
O_2 with helium as inert gas	1. Good for fire prevention due to very high heat conductivity 2. Due to high heat conductivity less circulation of gas would be needed for cooling of personnel 3. Due to low density would impose a lower payload requirement	1. Potential biological effects of chronic exposure not known 2. Increase pitch of sounds as result of lower density of N_2 3. Due to greater heat conductivity, it could alter thermal equilibrium of a living body	Has been used for underwater diving

* Based primarily upon a discussion by Welch, 1963.

TABLE 10-6.   Systems for Supply, Removal, or Recycling of Respiratory Gases*

	a Mass of Material Consumed	b	c	d Accessory Equipment or Supplies	e
	Kgm per $Kgm\ O_2$	$Kgm\ per$ $Man\ per$ Day $(3600$ $Kcal/$ $day)$	$For\ Storage$ $Kgm\ per$ $Kgm\ O_2$	$Storage$ $Kgm\ per$ $Man\ per$ Day	$Other\ Equipment$ $Needs$
I. **Non-regenerative systems** A. O_2 release without CO_2 absorption					
1. O_2 gas in pres- surized cylinders	1	1.05		1.10(a+c)	
Voyage of 8 man-hr			5	6.6	
Voyage of 10 man-days			2	3.3	
2. O_2 liquid at low temperature	1	1.1			
Voyage of 25 man-days			.77	1.95	
Voyage of 50 man-days			.66	1.73	
3. Sodium chlorate candles ($NaClO_3$)	2.5	2.8	0.5	3.3	

4. Lithium perchlo-
     rate candles
     ($LiClO_4$)
	1.67	1.74			

5. Hydrogen perox- ide (H_2O_2)	2.1	2.3	.9	3.3	
6. Hydrogen super- oxide (H_2O_4)	1.38	1.52			

* Values are based upon the assumption of a metabolic rate of 3600 kilocalories per day with a turnover of the type indicated in Figure 10-4, Part A. Values are based primarily upon articles by Bongers (1964), Bongers and Kok (1964), Petrocelli and Capotosto (1964), Welch (1963), Keller (1960), and Kammermeyer (1964).

f	g	h	i	j	k	l
		Extra Material for CO_2 Absorption				
...gm Compound Required per Kgm of CO_2 Absorbed	*Kgm Other Material and Equipment per Kgm CO_2 Absorbed*	*Kgm/Kgm CO_2*	*Total Kgm/Man/Day (Assuming 1.1 Kgm CO_2/Day/Man)*	*Advantages*	*Disadvantages*	*Remarks*
			1.2b(e+g)			Some CO_2 can be flushed out with a continuous stream of O_2 Procedure for American Mercury flights
					Requires low temperature ($-183°$ C)	Procedure for Gemini and Apollo flights
				1. Has been widely used as emergency O_2 source 2. Supply heat	1. Gives off Cl_2 gas (unless barium peroxide is added) 2. Rate of O_2 release cannot be varied once reaction begins	Candles contain fiber glass for structural strength
				Lower weight of Li	Not yet in usable form	
				1. Supplies heat 2. Supplies H_2O during reaction	1. Difficulty in removing H_2O from O_2 2. Liquid solutions would cause difficulty at zero-G	
				Probably not stable enough under conditions appropriate for respiratory O_2 source in space craft		

TABLE 10-6.   Continued

| | a   b *Mass of Material Consumed* | | c | d | e |
| | | | | *Accessory Equipment or Supplies* | |
	Kgm per Kgm O_2	*Kgm per Man per Day (3600 Kcal/ day)*	*For Storage Kgm per Kgm O_2*	*Storage Kgm per Man per Day*	*Other Equipment Needs*
7. Electrolysis of water	1.12	1.23			6 Kgm fixed mass per man continuously – power source required of 6kwatt-hr/man/day
B. CO_2 removal without O_2 release Chemical absorption					
1. Lithium hydroxide (LiOH)					Blower
2. Baralyme [Ca(OH)$_2$ and Ba(OH)$_2$]					Blower
3. Soda lime (CaOH$_2$ and NaOH)					Blower
4. Potassium hydroxide (KOH)					Blower
5. Reduction of CO_2 with hydrogen					
C. Combined O_2 release and CO_2 removal					

f	g	h	i	j	k	l
		Extra Material for CO_2 Absorption				
Kgm $Compound$ $Required$ per Kgm of CO_2 $Absorbed$	Kgm $Other$ $Material$ and $Equipment$ per Kgm CO_2 $Absorbed$	Kgm/Kgm CO_2	$Total$ $Kgm/Man/Day$ $(Assuming$ 1.1 Kgm $CO_2/Day/Man)$	$Advantages$	$Disadvantages$	$Remarks$
				Could use H_2 for reduction of CO_2	Might be awkward at zero-G	
						Cabin air forced through granular material packed in columns
		1.7		Low weight requirement	1. Dusts of this compound can cause irritation but dust can be filtered out with glass wool 2. Gives off water vapor	Acts well at low temperature
		4.7		Little dust	Gives off water vapor	
				1. Could use H_2 from dialysis of H_2O for O_2 2. Solid carbon produced can be used as an absorbent	Carbon monoxide can be produced in a side reaction	Steel wool as catalyst
				Lower weight requirement if 2 jobs in one	Extra systems possibly necessary for exact O_2 and CO_2 rates	Soviet flights believed to have employed some superoxide

TABLE 10-6. (Continued)

	a	b	c	d	e
	Mass of Material Consumed			*Accessory Equipment or Supplies*	
	Kgm per Kgm O_2	*Kgm per Man per Day (3600 Kcal/ day)*	*For Storage Kgm per Kgm O_2*	*Storage Kgm per Man per Day*	*Other Equipment Needs*
1. Potassium superoxide (KO_2)	3.00	3.3	2.50	6	Blower
2. Calcium superoxide $[Ca(O_2)_2]$	2.2	2.4			
3. Lithium peroxide (Li_2O_2)	3.1	3.4			
II. Regenerative systems A. Those that remove only CO_2 1. Physical adsorption of CO_2 by activated charcoal					
2. Solidification by cooling					
3. Molecular sieves					15 kgm fixed mass per man indefinitely plus 9 kwatt hr per man per day

f	g	h	i	j	k	l
				Extra Material for CO_2 Absorption		
Kgm Compound Required per Kgm of CO_2 Absorbed	*Kgm Other Material and Equipment per Kgm CO_2 Absorbed*	*Kgm/Kgm CO_2*	*Total Kgm/Man/Day (Assuming 1.1 Kgm CO_2/Day/Man)*	*Advantages*	*Disadvantages*	*Remarks*
3.2	4.0	.4	4.5	1. Commercially available 2. Has been used for similar purposes 3. Dehumidifier 4. Odor remover 5. Heat source	In some existing uses (fire-fighting and mountain-climbing) get only 50% utilization	
2.4	3.0			1. Thought to be more efficient than CO_2 2. Less mass of compound required	1. Not presently available in high purity	
1.04	1.31			Low mass requirement for O_2 removal	More research and development necessary before usable	
						Believed necessary for longer flights
				CO_2 could be disorbed from charcoal by vacuum of space	Believed to have low capacity requiring frequent regeneration	
				Might be possible to do by thermal radiation on dark side of satellite with vaporization into space of sunlit side		

TABLE 10-6.   Continued

	a b *Mass of Material Consumed*	c	d	e
			Accessory Equipment or Supplies	
	Kgm per Kgm O₂	*Kgm per Man per Day (3600 Kcal/ day)*	*For Storage Kgm per Kgm O₂*	*Storage Kgm per Man per Day*	*Other Equipment Needs*
4. Selective perme- ability of plastics					
5. Electrodialysis of carbonate ion				7 kgm fixed mass per man indefinitely plus 30 kwatt hr per man per day
6. Silver oxide					

B. Combined recycling
of CO₂ and O₂
 1. Non-biological
  a. Electrolysis of
   water combined
   with reduction
   of CO₂
				Fixed mass of 45 kgm
				per man continu-
				ously plus source
				of 15 kwatt hr per
				man per day

2. Biological re- cycling					

f	g	h	i	j	k	l
Kgm Compound Required per Kgm of CO₂ Absorbed	*Kgm Other Material and Equipment per Kgm CO₂ Absorbed*	*Extra Material for CO₂ Absorption* *Kgm/Kgm CO₂*	*Total Kgm/Man/Day (Assuming 1.1 Kgm CO₂/Day/Man)*	*Advantages*	*Disadvantages*	*Remarks*
				Might become practical at some future date when compact nuclear power sources are practical in space craft	1. Requires too much power to be practical at the present time 2. Requires improved compression systems	
				Can be regenerated by decomposition of silver carbonate to silver oxide and CO₂	1. Might be limited by requirements for large surface 2. Regeneration might decompose silver oxide	
				1. Consume CO₂ and produce O₂ without consumption of stored products 2. Might represent lowest mass requirements for extremely long voyages 3. Possibly produce food 4. Performs at room temperature	Most systems have not been tested in weightless environments	

TABLE 10-6. (Continued)

| | a b
*Mass of Material
Consumed* | c | d | e |
| | | *Accessory Equipment or Supplies* | | |
	Kgm per Man for Contin- uous Opera- tion	*Power (exclu- sive of Sun- light) Re- quired in Kwatt Hr per Man per Day*	*For Storage Kgm per Kgm O$_2$*	*Storage Kgm per Man per Day*	*Other Equipment Needs*
a. Photosynthetic recycling					
(1) Algae (many different species con- sidered but most work has probably been with *Chlorella*)					
With artifi- cial illumi- nation	230	250			
With solar illumination	150	6			
(2) Higher green plants such as Duckweed or larger non- aquatic seed- plants					

f	g	h	i	j	k	l
		Extra Material for CO₂ Absorption				
Kgm Compound Required per Kgm of CO₂ Absorbed	*Kgm Other Material and Equipment per Kgm CO₂ Absorbed*	*Kgm/Kgm CO₂*	*Total Kgm/Man/Day (Assuming 1.1 Kgm CO₂/Day/Man)*	*Advantages*	*Disadvantages*	*Remarks*
						Requires light
				1. Appropriate growth medium can closely balance man's respiratory quotient 2. Might be able to utilize human waste such as urea 3. High O₂ output per mass of algae	1. Little known of biochemistry and physiology of algae 2. Large mass of supporting material required 3. Large power requirement if solar illumination cannot be employed. Low efficiency of converting power into light (10%) and 10% efficiency for conversion of light into plant energy	
						Require large surface area (9 m²/man at Earth distance from Sun)
				Less supporting equipment needed than with algae	Lower rate of O₂ produced per gram of plant material	

TABLE 10-6. Continued

	a *Mass of Material Consumed*	b	c	d *Accessory Equipment or Supplies*	e
	Kgm per Man for Continuous Operation	*Power (exclusive of Sunlight) Required in Kwatt Hr per Man per Day*	*For Storage Kgm per Kgm O_2*	*Storage Kgm per Man per Day*	*Other Equipment Needs*
b. Hydrogen-oxidizing bacteria (*Hydrogenomonas eutropha*)					
$CO_2 + 6H_2O + O_2 \xrightarrow{\text{bacteria}}$ $[CH_2O] + 5H_2O)$					
Combined with electrolysis of water	52	26			
If also combined with waste processing by means of electrochemical treatment and waste processing	64	31			

f	g	h	i	j	k	l
Kgm Compound Required per Kgm of CO_2 Absorbed	*Kgm Other Material and Equipment per Kgm CO_2 Absorbed*	*Kgm/Kgm CO_2*	*Extra Material CO_2 Absorption* *Total Kgm/Man/Day (Assuming 1.1 Kgm CO_2/Day/Man)*	*Advantages*	*Disadvantages*	*Remarks*
					1. Excretion of organic material might poison system 2. Little known of this organism's metabolism	

This unit will supply oxygen and provide for CO_2 removal and air conditioning (for removal of metabolic and environmental heat) over a 4-hour period.

The methods of maintaining an adequately high level of oxygen and an adequately low level of carbon dioxide in the atmosphere of the space capsule might involve separate agents for the storage and release of oxygen and for the absorption of carbon dioxide (see Table 10-6). For relatively short voyages, the release of oxygen, either from storage in pressurized cylinders, liquid at low temperatures, or from various chemicals, particularly the superoxides, such as potassium superoxide, would appear quite attractive. Potassium superoxide is one of the chemicals which has the advantage of functioning both as an oxygen source and as a carbon dioxide sink. Moreover, it has proven acceptable for some time as a portable oxygen source for men.

For extended space voyages, some method of recycling the expired carbon dioxide into breathable oxygen is highly desirable. This would probably involve a closed ecological system mimicking on a microscopic scale that of our own planet. Should this become feasible in space craft (Fig. 10-7),

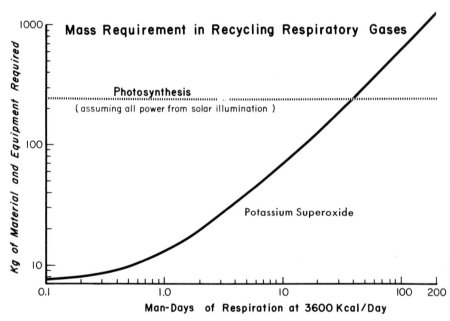

Figure 10-7. Example of mass requirement with regenerative and nonregenerative systems: release of O_2 and absorption of CO_2. Curves are based upon data displayed in Table 10-6. Figures are based upon the assumption that there is no leakage or loss of gas, and upon the assumption that fixed equipment for storage and use of potassium superoxide is negligible. This figure illustrates that with increasing duration of a space flight the completely regenerative system for recycling metabolic material becomes more attractive.

biological recycling of oxygen would be preferable to sodium superoxide after 40 man days of flight. More research and development are necessary before we can be assured of a workable photosynthetic gas exchange unit which would be feasible for a space craft, particularly in the absence of a gravitational field.

Should a photosynthetic plant be employed for the recycling of gases, some single-celled algae, such as *Chlorella,* would have the advantage of producing the largest amount of oxygen per unit mass of plant material. It is entirely possible, however, that one of the vascular plants, although producing less oxygen per mass of living material, might, as a result of its better vascular and supporting structures, be able to produce more oxygen per unit mass of accessory equipment.

Green plants have the added advantage that they act as a source of food while recycling man's excretory and solid wastes. Certainly some of the vascular plants have a history of supplying highly nutritious and palatable foods. As a major constituent of the human diet, algae have less proven value. Although their palatability and long-term nutritional or toxic effect upon man is essentially unknown, experiments have shown that the single-celled algae *Chlorella* can serve as a major dietary constituent for the growth of rats (Lubitz, 1963). Perhaps a cycle which interjects other intermediary organisms and more closely approximates the complex ecological cycles of Earth would be necessary for complete recycling. Tiny crustacea (such as Daphnia and brine shrimp) of the type found as zooplankton in seas or lakes and which are known to live on algae have been suggested. Russian workers (Akhlebininskiy *et al.,* 1962; Ushakov and Bychkov, 1962) contend that the chicken is the most promising of the animals which are known to rapidly and efficiently produce large quantities of human food and for which culture methods are well established.

A new approach to the problem of biologically recycling respiratory gases has recently been proposed (Bongers and Kok, 1964; Bongers, 1964) involving the use of the hydrogen-oxidizing bacteria, *Hydrogenomonas eutropha,* in combination with a process involving the electrolysis of water. Oxygen and hydrogen would be produced from the electrolysis of water. Water and a portion of the electrolytically produced oxygen would combine with carbon dioxide as a result of the action of this bacteria to yield water and carbohydrate. The remaining oxygen would be utilized in man's respiration. It is claimed that this process would have a lower requirement with respect to the mass of fixed equipment and with respect to the requirements for electrical power than would be the case for algae (particularly if solar illumination is not available).

One consideration that must not be overlooked in any process which recycles oxygen is the respiratory quotient (or R. Q.), i.e., the volume ratio of carbon dioxide release to oxygen consumption of the occupant must equal the volume ratio of the carbon dioxide absorption to oxygen release from the recycling system (Green, 1963). A considerable turnover of gas in the space craft due either to leakage or to flushing might become a concern.

TABLE 10-7. Water Sources for Space Flight*

| Source | Mass Requirements in Supplying Water Necessary in Food and Drinking (Assuming No Water for Washing, Cleaning, etc., and Ignoring Mass of Fuel Required for Recovery Processes) | Kgm of Fixed Mass per Man for Recovery Equipment | Advantages | Disadvantages | Remarks |
| | Kgm of Substance Consumed per Man per Day for Water Supply | | | | |
	a	b	c	d	e
Storage	2.5				
Recycling or recovery from urine (1.5L/day/man) evaporation, respiration and sweat (1.8L/day/man)—water with solids (.2L/day/man) 1. Freeze sublimation (lyophilization)		8	1. Believed to be operable in absence of gravity 2. Best quality of water	1. Some authorities (Wallman & Barnett, 1963) feel that space and mass requirements would be greater than with distillation	
2. Distillation			1. Less space and mass required than with freeze dryers	1. Requires treatment of water with activated charcoal for adequate purity 2. Most systems would require generation of artificial gravity	

a. By means of space radiator as heat sink for condensation of distillate and cabin heat as energy source for evaporation into vapor	.09	13	1. Could employ sponge to contain water by capillarity in absence of gravity 2. Could be hand-operated as source of power 3. Requires no electrical power 4. More dependable due to simplicity	1. Continuous operation would require rotation of vehicle to keep radiator facing away from sun	1. Recommended for crews of one or two men for voyages exceeding 6 days
b. Vapor compression with centrifugal condenser where suction from compressor enhances boiling of water	.08	8	1. Could be hand-operated as source of power 2. Suitable for any size of crew		1. Recommended for large crews (3-20 men) for flights in excess of 4 days
c. Centrifuged evaporator with heat transfer from evaporative surface to condensing surface	.07	8	Low consumable mass	1. Must have high efficiency of heat transfer 2. Could not depend upon hand power	
3. Osmosis across semipermeable membranes into dehydrated food			1. Low requirements for space and volume if food is not to be recycled	1. Could only supplement water supply but probably not supply water of sufficiently low osmotic pressure to prevent desiccation	

* Information is based primarily upon values discussed by Wallman and Barnett (1963), and Kammermeyer (1961, 1964).

Some additional control procedures would be necessary, possibly in the form of an auxiliary chemical oxygen source or carbon dioxide absorbent to assure optimum levels of the respiratory gases. It is believed that with an algal system this might be controlled by minor modifications of the growth medium of the algae.

Water and Food

The requirement for food probably would amount to slightly less than 0.6 of a kilogram (dry mass) per man per day. Recycling of this material for metabolic requirements does not seem to be highly practical during voyages within the near future. Eventually food production might be feasible with algae or with a system utilizing vascular plants (particularly one which involves use of hydroponics in a lunar station or in a large manned orbiting laboratory). Should adequate water be available, the use of dehydrated products will probably be the most convenient form of food storage and transportation within the coming decade. There are some investigators, however, who contend that complete dependence upon dried food might result in a high incidence of cancer (Generales, 1963).

At the present time, the practicality of recycling water is somewhat greater than it is for food. Not only is its daily required mass approximately 4 times that for dried food, but it is released from the body [either in the urine (60 percent), by evaporation (30 percent), or with solid waste (10 percent)] in a form which is suitable for reuse (with respect to chemical structure although not with respect to purity). Water which could be extracted from the solid wastes would probably contain too many impurities to permit suitable reuse. On the other hand, if the water which has evaporated from the body either from perspiration or across the surfaces of the lung could be condensed, it should yield water of relatively high purity. Water which has been sublimated from frozen urine and then condensed upon appropriate collecting surfaces has been found to be highly palatable (Vetter and Kammermeyer, 1963). Distillation of the liquid would require the use of either centrifugal forces or capillary forces within a sponge or similar body to replace the gravitational field. This water, moreover, would require additional purification by treatment with activated charcoal. Some of the properties and estimated specifications for the different methods of recycling water are tabulated in Table 10-7.

Advance Testing

Most of the equipment and organisms which have been proposed for flight study and life support during extended space trips have not yet been adequately tested under appropriate environmental conditions. Certain properties, particularly the effects of isolation upon human subjects, have been studied by confining men and some types of life-support equipment for extended periods of time in enclosed chambers. The U. S. Air Force has proposed plans to construct and orbit a large manned orbiting laboratory (MOL) which should be operational by 1968. In such a laboratory, much testing will be necessary before advanced space craft can be designed (Fig. 2-5). Before a manned interplanetary voyage is undertaken, the utilization of an orbiting laboratory will be necessary for the testing of any proposed space craft and of the interaction between all of its components.

Bibliography and References

AKHLEBININSKIY, S. S., BYCHKOV, V. P., IL'INA, I. A., KONDRAT'YEV, YU. I., AND USHAKOV, A. S. (1962): On the problem of supplying the crews of spaceships with animal foodstuffs. *In* "Problemy Kosmicheskoy Biologii" [Problems of Space Biology] (N. M. Sisakyan, ed.). *Vol. 1,* pp. 161-168. As translated from Russian in NASA TT F-174, National Aeronautics and Space Administration, Washington, D. C.

ALBRIGHT, G. A. (1965): Closed atmospheres. Paper No. 25. *In* "Proc. of Conf. on Role of Simulation in Space Technology," *Engineering Extension Series Circular No. 4, Part D,* Va. Poly. Inst., Blacksburg.

ALLEN, S. C. (1963): A comparison of the effects of nitrogen lack and hyperoxia on the vascular development of the chick embryo. *Aerospace Med. 34,* 897-899.

ANON. (1963): U. S. in space. *Chem. and Eng. News, Sept. 23 and Sept. 30,* 98-128; 70-100.

BERRY, C. A. (1963): Aeromedical preparations. *In* "Mercury Project Summary Including Results of the Fourth Manned Orbital Flight," pp. 199-209. NASA SP-45, National Aeronautics and Space Administration, Washington, D. C.

BONGERS, L. H. (1964): Sustaining life in space—a new approach. *Aerospace Med. 35,* 139-144.

BONGERS, L. H., AND KOK, B. (1964): Life support systems for space missions (paper presented at AIBS Meeting, Amherst, Mass., September 1963). Submitted for publication *in* "Developments in Industrial Microbiology."

BUSSARD, R. W. (1960): Galactic matter and interstellar flight. *Aastronautica Acta 6,* 179-194.

CLAMANN, H. G. (1964): Hazards in oxygen environments. *In* "Lectures in Aerospace Medicine," pp. 209-224. School of Aerospace Medicine, Brooks AFB, Texas.

CLARKE, A. C. (1960): "Interplanetary Flight." Harper & Bros., New York.

GENERALES, C. D. J., JR. (1963): Weightlessness: its physical, biological, and medical aspects. *In* "Medical and Biological Problems of Space Flight" (G. H. Bourne, ed.), pp. 123-187). Academic Press, New York.

GOODMAN, I. R., AND RADNOFSKY, M. I. (1965): Lunar surface and free space hazards relating to space suite design. J. Environmental Sciences 8 (3), 26-31.

GREEN, C. D. (1963): Biomedical capsules. *In* "Physiology of Man in Space" (J. H. U. Brown, ed.), pp. 257-285. Academic Press, New York.

HARTMAN, B. O., AND FLINN, D. E. (1964): Crew structure in future space missions. *In* "Lectures in Aerospace Medicine," pp. 51-72. School of Aerospace Medicine, Brooks AFB, Texas.

KAMMERMEYER, K. (1961): Review and evaluation of available literature on conversion of human waste materials to potable water (as modified in A. R. Slonim, A. P. Hallam, D. H. Jensen, and K. Kammermeyer, 1962, Water recovery from physiological sources for space applications, *in* "Technical Documentary Report No. MRL-TDR-62-75").

KAMMERMEYER, K. (1964): "Space Technology—A Challenge to the Chemical Engineer." Manuscript in press.

KELLER, D. M. (1960): Cabin atmospheres: their physical and chemical control. *In* "Lectures in Aerospace Medicine" (Paper No. 13). School of Aviation Medicine, Brooks AFB, Texas.

KINCAIDE, W. C. (1964): Development of the Apollo portable life support systems. *In* "Lectures in Aerospace Medicine," pp. 183-192. School of Aerospace Medicine, Brooks AFB, Texas.

KLINE, N. S., AND CLYNES, M. (1961): Drugs, space, and cybernetics: evolution to cyborgs. *In* "Psychophysiological Aspects of Space Flight" (B. E. Flaherty, ed.), pp. 345-371. Columbia University Press, New York.

LAMB, L. E. (1964): Aeromedical evaluation of space pilots. *In* "Lectures in Aerospace Medicine," pp. 120-142. School of Aerospace Medicine, Brooks AFB, Texas.

LUBITZ, J. A. (1963): Growth and toxicity studies on rats fed Chlorella 71105. *In* "Medical and Biological Problems of Space Flight" (G. H. Bourne, ed.), pp. 245-259. Academic Press, New York.

MORGAN, T. E., JR., ULVEDAL, F., CUTLER, R. G., AND WELCH, B. E. (1963): Effects on man of prolonged exposure to oxygen at a total pressure of 190 mm. Hg. *Aerospace Med. 34,* 589-592.

MYERS, J. (1960): Space logistics II. biosynthetic gas exchanges. *In* "Lectures in Aerospace Medicine" (Paper No. 15). School of Aviation Medicine, Brooks AFB, Texas.

PETROCELLI, A. W., AND CAPOTOSTO, A., JR., (1964): Some notes on the use of superoxides in non-regenerative air revitalization systems. *Aerospace Med. 35,* 440-443.

POPMA, D. C. (1962): Life support for space stations. *Astronautics, Vol. 7, No. 9,* 44-47.

SAGAN, C. (1963): Direct contact among galactic civilizations by relativistic interstellar space flight. *Planet. Space Sci. 11,* 485-498.

SISAKYAN, N. M., GAZENKO, O. G., AND GENIN, A. M. (1962): Problems of space biology. *In* "Problemy Kosmicheskoy Biologii" (Problems of Space Biology) (N. M. Sisakyan, ed.). *Vol. 1,* pp. 17-27. As translated in NASA TT F-174, National Aeronautics and Space Administration, Washington, D. C.

STEINHOFF, E. A. (1964): Use of extraterrestrial resources for Mars basing. *In* "Lectures in Aerospace Medicine," pp. 273-297. School of Aerospace Medicine, Brooks AFB, Texas.

STEINMETZ, C. H. (1963): Apollo. *In* "Lectures in Aerospace Medicine," pp. 175-184. School of Aerospace Medicine, Brooks AFB, Texas.

SUTTON, G. P. (1956): "Rocket Propulsion Elements: An Introduction to the Engineering of Rockets," 2nd ed. John Wiley and Sons, New York; Chapman and Hall Ltd., London.

USHAKOV, A. S., AND BYCHKOV, V. P. (1962): Nutritional problems under space flight conditions. *In* "Problemy Kosmicheskoy Biologii" (Problems of Space Biology) (N. M. Sisakyan and V. I. Yazdovskiy, eds.). *Vol. II,* pp. 51-55. As translated in OTS: 63-21437, U. S. Department of Commerce, Washington, D. C.

VETTER, A. F., AND KAMMERMEYER, K. (1963): "Water Recovery by Freeze Drying Using Microwave Energy." *Tec. Doc. Rep.* No. AMRL-TDR-63-130.

VOAS, R. B., JOHNSON, H. I., AND ZEDEKAR, R. (1963): Astronaut training. *In* "Mercury Project Summary Including Results of the Fourth Manned Orbital Flight," pp. 171-198. NASA SP-45, National Aeronautics and Space Administration, Washington, D. C.

VON HOERNER, S. (1962): The general limits of space travel. *Science 137, No. 3523,* 18-23.

WALLMAN, H., AND BARNETT, S. M. (1963): Evaluation of water recovery systems for space vehicles. *In* "Medical and Biological Problems of Space Flight" (G. H. Bourne, ed.), pp. 225-235. Academic Press, New York.

WELCH, B. E. (1963): Ecological systems. *In* "Physiology of Man in Space" (J. H. U. Brown, ed.), pp. 309-334. Academic Press, New York.

WELCH, B. E., CUTLER, R. G., HERLOCHER, J. E., HARGREAVES, J. J., ULVEDAL, F., SHAW, E. G., SMITH, G. B., McMANN, H. J., AND BELL, L. (1963): Effect of ventilating air flow on human water requirements. *Aerospace Med. 34,* 383-388.

WHITE, S. C., AND SMITH, G. B., JR. (1963): Project Gemini. *In* "Lectures in Aerospace Medicine," pp. 157-172. School of Aerospace Medicine, Brooks AFB, Texas.

WILKS, S. S. (1963): Biological recycling processes in closed systems. *In* "Lectures in Aerospace Medicine," pp. 273-280. School of Aerospace Medicine, Brooks AFB, Texas.

WRIGHT, R. A., LESSLER, M.A., WEISS, H. S., AND HIATT, E. P. (1965): Metabolism and x-ray sensitivity of chick embryos incubated in a helium-oxygen atmosphere. *Aerospace Med. 36,* 311-314.

11

Life on Other Planets

Probability and Information Content of Life

No absolutely satisfactory criteria for life have been established (see Chapter 1). Nor does any idea exist as to which of the properties common to all life found on this planet are adequate to describe the various types of life which might be encountered throughout the universe. There is one criterion which appears the most likely to be applicable to both Terrestrial and possible extra-Terrestrial life: the ability to maintain within itself and to transmit to less organized systems such a complex arrangement of constituents that the probability of frequent accidental origin would be extremely low. The molecules of nucleic acid in genes, for example, are believed to replicate new genes and other nucleic acids by arranging simpler molecules (organic bases, such as adenine, guanine, thymine, and cytosine and sugar molecules or combinations of these bases and sugars in the form of nucleosides) into arrangements of similar nucleic acids. As this new arrangement would be more complex (i.e., possesses more information), the replication of nucleic acids would involve information transfer.

The most random array of molecules or other particles would have the highest probability of occurring and therefore would be indicative of the lowest information state. The more information a system contains, the lower the probability that such a configuration could have arisen accidentally. Living material would thus have a less probable arrangement (higher information content) than would the non-living material from which the living material is synthesized. It would have the ability to convert other non-living material into a low probability configuration similar to its own.

Since the introduction of the term "information theory," quantitative description of the complexity of various coded systems, such as messages or life itself, in terms of the "information content" has become increasingly popular among many life scientists. Very simply, a quantitative value for the information content of a system expresses the number of yes or no decisions which must be made in describing the situation. As this implies a dichotomous or binary system of decision, these units of information are referred to as "binits" or simply as "bits." It can be shown that the number

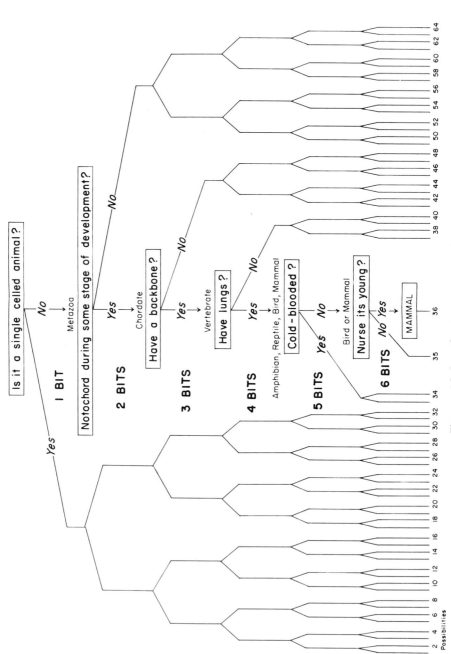

Figure 11-1. Caption on opposite page.

Figure 11-1. Quantification of information content as illustrated by use of a dichotomous key. It will be noted that 6 individual decisions, that is, 6 bits of information, are required in separating the mammal from 64 alternate possibilities. Substituting this value of 64 for the number of possibilities into Eq. (11-1), we arrive at the following relationship:

$$Information = [\log_2 64] \text{ bits}$$

or

$$Information = 3.32 [\log_{10} 64] \text{ bits} = 6 \text{ bits}$$

Obviously something so complex as the human body is so involved that at this time it would be essentially impossible to quantitate the number of bits or yes and no decisions necessary in completely describing all details of human function and structure. It is difficult as yet to give the number of bits required for the description of relatively simple chemical compounds. For this reason, the information content of organisms and molecules is more likely to be described in terms of information difference between it and some other system rather than the absolute or total amount of information involved.*

---

* Thus, the difference between the information of two systems would be described by:

$$\triangle \text{ information} = \log_2 (\# \text{ possibilities}) = \log_2 \frac{\text{possibilities}_2}{\text{possibilities}_1}$$

or since the number of possibilities

$$= \frac{1}{\text{probability}} = \frac{1}{p} \text{ , then } \triangle \text{ information} = \triangle\log_2 \frac{1}{p} = -\triangle \log_2 p$$

The merit in stating that the number of possibilities is equal to the reciprocal of the probability will be understood when one considers that the possibility of a coin landing with heads up is equal to one half and that there are two possibilities, either heads or tails. With dice, there is a probability of one sixth, for each of the six separate sides is a possibility.

---

of these alternate yes and no decisions can be expressed in terms of the binary logarithm (i.e., the logarithm to the base of 2), as indicated by Eq. (11-1)[1]:

Information (as expressed in bits)

$$= [\log_2 (\text{number of possibilities})] \qquad (11\text{-}1)$$

As an illustration of the quantification of information, the reader is referred to the example in Figure 11-1 of the quantity of information required by a taxonomist in using the dichotomous keys employed as guides in the identification of plants and animals.

The concept of information theory was originally introduced primarily for use by engineers. For a number of years previous to the introduction of this

---

[1] A more rigorous discussion of information theory would also include details of the weighting factors and other considerations which must be employed when decisions are not of a simple yes or no variety but involve more than two decisions or unequal probabilities for two alternate possibilities.

concept, physicists and chemists had thought of the probabilistic configurations of various systems in terms of entropy.[2] Using logic of this nature, the physicist Schrödinger (1947) popularized the thinking of life in terms of a process which increases the negative entropy of a system. He first spoke of negative entropy in 1943, which was prior to the introduction of information as a quantitative description of the order of a system. Since the nineteenth century, the term "entropy" has been used as a description of the disorder of a system.[3]

Alternate Types of Life

If the restriction of similarity to "life as we know it" is removed, it is then possible for an unleashed imagination to conjure up many alternate types of self-replicating information systems. Some of the suggested possibilities are shown in Figure 11-2. We know that the primary category of life which exists on the Earth today is "organic" life, by which we mean forms of life (such as plants and animals in the case of the Earth) which arose or evolved from simpler forms (which presumably also originated on the same planet). This is one type of life which may be encountered on arriving on another planet.

Another type of self-replicating intelligence would be what might be called "mechanical" life—a form of intelligence which, although capable of reproducing or replicating itself, was originally created or produced by organic intelligence (MacGowan, 1962). We are living in an age of automation. Whether or not computers will ever be able to do creative thinking is a matter of debate. We know that at the present time they are able to perform many tasks which previously could be accomplished only by the human mind. Some authorities feel that the time is not far distant when these machines (which do possess a certain type of intelligence) will be perfected to the stage where they themselves will be able to construct similar or improved computers. If such improvement continued, a stage might be arrived at which would no longer require human intelligence for maintenance or servicing of the machine. A mechanical form of life could then proceed to evolve with independence from human or other organic intelligence. Some scientists doubt if such advanced computers could ever exist.

---

[2]
$$\triangle \text{ Information} = 1.443 \ \frac{-\triangle S}{R} \ \text{bits}$$

where R is the Ideal Gas Constant. One can see that the change or difference in information is proportional to the change in entropy ($\triangle S$) but of opposite sign.

[3] In a thermodynamic system, it is equal to the ratio of the absolute temperature to the amount of energy which is rendered unavailable due to disorder. This unavailable energy is energy which is present in a system but which cannot be utilized due to the random configuration. The amount of entropy in a system increases as randomness increases or as the probability p increases, as indicated by the relationship $\triangle S = R \triangle (\ln p)$; where S is the molar entropy and R is the Ideal Gas Constant (equal to 1.98 calories per mole per degree Kelvin).

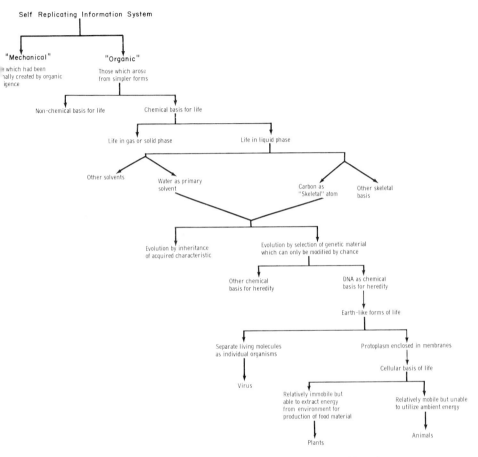

Figure 11-2. Some of the alternate types of living or self-replicating systems which might be encountered.

It is generally assumed that the existence and evolution of any organic intelligence or life is dependent upon unique chemical arrangements at the molecular level. Only molecules constantly moving due to thermal kinetic energy (and thus constantly changing their orientation with respect to one another) would be considered likely to arrive eventually at one of the relatively improbable states which would be capable of replication. Perhaps there is the remote possibility that some other system, such as combinations of planetary bodies or of subatomic particles, could at one time or another have arrived at a highly organized state in which there was a capability for replication or reproduction. There has been little or no publication of serious discussions considering life which does not possess a chemical basis.

Essentially all of the life processes with which we are familiar on this planet occur within the liquid phase. This permits sufficient movement of the molecules, so that random events will occasionally permit assemblage of a highly improbable molecular configuration (i.e., one of high information content). At the same time, the existence of a liquid phase permits sufficient buoyant support and restriction of movement to permit stability of these complex molecular configurations. It is extremely difficult to visualize chemical processes of a vital nature which could occur either in the gaseous or solid phase. Sagan (1964), however, has proposed that on the Jovian planets (i.e. Jupiter, Saturn, Uranus, and Neptune) the surface atmospheric densities ($\sim$ 0.1 gm/cm^3) might be dense enough to permit sufficient molecular interaction for life to exist.

Most serious discussions of the chemical nature of life as it could exist on another planet assume that it is quite similar to our own in two important respects. It is generally assumed that (1) water will be the primary solvent in which vital processes are pursued and (2) that the principal atom that will permit a chemical or molecular skeleton of large, complex molecules will be the carbon atom. Scientists are familiar only with the Terrestrial type of life, which is itself of an extremely intricate nature. Most of these scientists do not feel qualified to consider the possibilities of extra-Terrestrial forms which might be of a drastically different chemical nature. Any predictions based on our present knowledge would be extremely premature. There have been certain semipopular discussions (Asimov, 1963; Jackson and Moore, 1962) which consider the possibility that life could have either the silicon atom or a combination of silicon and carbon atoms as the skeletal basis for biological molecules. Ammonia has been considered as the liquid solvent for biological processes which on some other planet would occur at temperatures below those on this planet. (It, like water, is a polar compound, and therefore able to permit the existence of many ions considered essential to life processes.) Sulfur rather than oxygen has been considered the primary chemical to be consumed from the environment during respiration. Some of these possibilities are listed in Table 11-1.

Although many scientists are willing to predict extra-Terrestrial life which, like our own, has carbon as the primary atom in the molecular skeleton, oxygen as the primary respiratory gas, and water as the basic solvent, they are less dogmatic in suggesting that these new organisms would bear other resemblances to Terrestrial life. Probably it is too early to state definitely whether or not life which arose on another planet would necessarily have to pursue a Darwinian path of evolution, with a genetic basis and selection by natural processes rather than some form of life which proceeds by evolution of acquired characteristics. Life capable of altering the characteristics of its progeny by acquired attributes would seem to be more improbable for organic forms but at the same time most probable for a mechanical type of intelligence. Most biochemists and geneticists do not insist that some entirely different organism of non-Terrestrial origin would necessarily possess genetic material of exactly the same nature as deoxyribonucleic acid (DNA) which is believed to be the primary chemical structure for all Terrestrial hereditary mechanisms.[4]

Our own planet abounds with organisms displaying diverse and contrasting types of anatomical structure. New planets would permit an even greater contrast. Perhaps within a few centuries organisms transplanted from the Earth to new worlds will adjust and evolve in a new planetary environment. We know that men and other animals which live in the rarefied atmosphere of our higher mountains develop larger chests and possess blood with a greater capacity for oxygen than do those living in lower altitudes. Would descendants of colonists on Mars someday possess barrel-like chests and altered circulatory systems in order to exist in the lower oxygen tension on Mars? (Recent data on Mars suggests that even this change would be inadequate.) Would these new generations also possess decreased musculature and altered neural characteristics in response to the lower gravitation to be encountered upon smaller planets?

Previous to the time of Darwin and Pasteur, there were many people who believed that, given relatively simple conditions and materials, complex organisms could arise spontaneously. Had these concepts not been disproven, it would be quite reasonable to assume that any habitable planet would have its own life and that this life would probably be comparable to that found on this planet (since all life on Earth is itself quite similar at the chemical level). On the other hand, if the probability that living material can undergo spontaneous generation is extremely remote, then the origin of life might be unique to our own planet (du Noüy, 1949). If, moreover, contrary to the suggestions of Arrhenius, spores for life could not pass from one planet to another, then the likelihood of finding life elsewhere would be quite low. It is conceivable that life might have been carried within the meteors originating from exploding planets.[5]

Arrhenius (1908), in his *panspermia* hypothesis, suggested that life need not undergo new creation or chemical evolution on every planet. He proposed that tiny spores for primitive life could drift through space from one star to another, germinating and evolving higher life on the habitable planets. With a common origin, life might be expected which chemically is quite similar throughout the universe.

The panspermia hypothesis has recently been critically examined by Sagan (1961b). Assuming that a net force would push spores away from a star

---

[4] Deoxyribonucleic acid (DNA) is found primarily in the nucleus of all known forms of cellular life and serves as the template for production of more DNA or of ribonucleic acid (RNA), which is found primarily in the cytoplasm and is the primary template for production of proteins.

[5] The origin of meteors from an exploding planet is an old idea which is not readily accepted by most modern astronomers. Present theory suggests that meteors and asteroids were formed independently and simultaneously during the formation of the rest of the solar system. Moreover, some meteors might have originated from outside of the solar system. However, even if they carried life from beyond our Solar System, transit time from star to star would probably be of such long duration as to dictate destruction of all living material due to natural radioactivity.

TABLE 11-1. Conceivable Types of Life with a Different Chemical Basis*

New Material	Rather Than	Function	Similarities	Dissimilarities	Implications

Silicon atoms	Carbon atoms	Structural basis or "backbone" of biological molecules	1. Form long-chain molecules by bonding together
			2. Four electrons in outside electron shell
				1. Carbon forms longer, more stable chains
				2. Larger atom
				  a. Greater atomic radii permit weaker hold on valence electrons allowing easier rearrangement of Si-O-Si bonds than with C-O-C bonds, thus more bonding of molecules together into crystalline solids (rocks and stones)
				  b. Outer valence shell (M) can accommodate up to 18 electrons rather than 8 as in the case for carbon (L shell)
					1. Reduced likelihood of sufficiently stable chemical basis for life
					2. Permits similar valences reactions and compounds (CH_3 vs SiH_4; C_2H_6 vs Si_2H_6; CH_3OH vs SiH_3OH; and CH_3CH_2OH vs CH_3SiH_2OH)
					3.
					  a. Higher temperature required for similar compounds to exist in a liquid or gaseous state (2500° C for SiO_2 to be gaseous)
					  b. Silicon can be more readily oxidized and its compounds would be therefore less stable

Ammonia (NH_3)	Water (H_2O)	Primary solvent for reaction of life processes	Polar compounds permitting ionization of dissolved electrolytes	Lower melting and boiling temperature than water	1. Both good solvents 2. Might permit life process to occur on planets which are cooler than Earth

Sulfur atom			Outer shell of electrons (M) of sulfur can hold up to 18 electrons rather than 8 as is the case for oxygen (L shell)	1. Permits similar valences, reactions, and compounds 2. Reactions although similar would not be identical 3. Sulfur is an important compound in life on Earth and could therefore be expected to be even more important with the appropriate type of life 4. Molecular oxygen is not essential for all known forms of Terrestrial life. This gas is believed to have become a major atmospheric constituent only after life was well established on Earth.
Oxygen atom	Primary respiratory chemical	6 electrons in outside electron shell		

* Based primarily upon a discussion in the book by Jackson and Moore (pp. 118-121, 1962).

when the force of radiation exceeds gravitational attraction and toward a star when the reverse is true, he concluded that tiny particles once ejected from one planet could travel to another. Sagan concluded that particles varying in size from 0.2 to 0.6 microns (which would include some viruses, fungal spores, and bacteria) would not be attracted by the Sun toward the Earth from another star but could be forced away from the Earth toward the outer planets and other stars. He calculated that such particles would be accelerated to Mars within weeks, to Jupiter within months, to Neptune within years, to the nearest star after more than 10,000 years, and across the galaxy in less than a billion years. It was noted by Sagan that by the time spores reached Mars they would have been inactivated (assuming the properties of Terrestrial life) by solar ultraviolet light. On the other hand, he does suggest that with the lower radiant intensities further from the Sun, spores might travel between Uranus or Neptune and outer planets of another star without receiving a lethal dosage of incident radiation. The time he computes for interstellar transit would, however, permit inactivation by natural radiation from isotopes within the spore.

Even before the possibilities of persistent spontaneous generation of life had been completely disproven, the belief developed that various organic materials could be synthesized from non-living chemicals. Darwin recognized that, under conditions very similar to those believed to have occurred upon the surface of the primitive Earth, highly complex molecules could have formed which eventually evolved into various living organisms (Calvin, 1962a). Some of the organic materials which have been synthesized from non-living sources in laboratories are tabulated in Table 11-2. Fox and Harada (1963) have synthesized protein-like materials referred to as "proteinoids" and from this have formed, by means of appropriate treatment, tiny spheres which possess certain of the chemical and physical properties of bacteria.

The likely stages in the creation of any life involve the assemblage of various types of unspecialized material in the presence of appropriate energy into primary units. As we can see from Table 11-3 some of the relatively simple chemical reactants believed to have been present in the Earth's early atmosphere, such as water, carbon dioxide, methane, hydrogen, and ammonia, are thought to have been combined upon the appropriate application of energy available in the Earth's primitive atmosphere from lightning, natural radioactivity, ultraviolet light, cosmic radiation, and volcanic heat. Similar syntheses have been accomplished in laboratory experiments (Table 11-2). The products of these reactions were the amino acids, organic acids, sugars, and organic bases. These primitive organic compounds were the primary units or building-block compounds from which the more complex molecules arose. Appropriate chance alignment of the amino acids would permit their condensation into proteins. Appropriate condensation of the sugar molecules would result in long molecules of cellulose and starch. Both the proteins and the larger carbohydrates (cellulose and starch) could serve as the molecular skeletons for the support of life at the cellular or subcellular level.

The probability that any relatively small sample of molecules initially could have arrived at the appropriate orientation for the spontaneous generation of proteins, of lipids, or of large carbohydrate molecules must have been relatively small. There were so many molecules or systems of molecules throughout the surface of the Earth, however, that the probability of adequate configurations occurring in at least one place was much higher. Expediting devices referred to as "catalysts" (more specifically referred to as "enzymes" with most biochemical reactions) formed at some stage. Once the enzymes were present, the synthesis or change of further material was enhanced.

Eventually certain replicating devices or agents appeared due to the chance interaction of various simpler systems of lower information content. In a chemical system, these replicating devices, such as DNA, would act as template molecules which would greatly enhance the incorporation of more molecules into the complex structures. This would render less remote the possibility that further complex molecules of high information content would occur. The steps whereby relatively simple chemical compounds were eventually converted into complex molecules of high information content which were able to cause other molecules to be arranged in the same or similar configurations comprised the steps referred to as "chemical evolution."

Consideration of Life on Other Planets

At the time of this writing, there is no clear-cut proof that life either does or does not exist on any planet other than Earth. Yet there are a number of astronomical and other observations or reports which are compatible with suggestions of life beyond this planet. Certain of these observations are tabulated in Table 11-4. A conservative astronomer, however, would remind us that since such reports are so highly selective and sufficiently amenable to other interpretations, one should be conservative in even considering these reports to be evidence for the probability of new life. One must realize that when a number of possible explanations are proposed for astronomical observations, the one suggesting extra-Terrestrial life is most likely to attract popular interest. Other more reasonable explanations, requiring greater technical competence by the public or popularizer of space science, are neither understood nor remembered.

If any of the other planets in the Solar System do possess life which is remotely similar to that found on Earth, the most promising candidate is the planet Mars. Although this planet's average temperature is colder than the Earth's and although there is no evidence that its atmosphere possesses oxygen, certain microorganisms have been cultured under laboratory conditions which approximate those to be expected upon Mars (assuming an atmosphere tenfold denser than detected by Mariner IV). Due to the very limited quantity of water on this planet, any elaborate organism would require rather extensive mechanisms whereby water could be conserved. If not present in the atmosphere oxygen might be extracted from rocks or other minerals and stored in the organisms which consume it (Salisbury, 1962).

TABLE 11-2.   Artificial Production of Organic Material Pertinent to Origin of Life*

Worker	Date of Report	Reactants	Energy Source
Scheele	1776	Nitric acid on cane sugar	
Wöhler	1828	Ammonium sulfate and potassium cyanate	
Loeb	1913		Electrical discharge
Miller	1953	Methane + hydrogen + ammonia + water	Electrical discharge at 100° C
Abelson	1956	Carbon dioxide + hydrogen +methane + ammonia	
Bahadur	1954	Water + paraformaldehyde + potassium nitrate + ferric chloride	Sunlight
Hasselstrom *et al.*	1957	Ammonium acetate	Beta rays
Paschke *et al.*	1957	Ammonium carbonate	Gamma rays
Dose and Rajewsky	1957	Methane, ammonia and other gases	X-rays
Fox	1960	Hydroxy acids and ammonia or urea	Heat
Heyns and Pavel	1957	Glycine	Heating with quartz sand
Oro *et al.*	1959	Formaldehyde and hydroxylamine	Thermal reaction
Balbiano and Trosciatti	1901	Glycine	Heating
Fox and Meadowbrook	1954	Amino acids	Heating

* Information listed in this table is based primarily upon the discussions by Fox and Harada (1963) and by Sagan (1964). The reader should refer to those articles for most of the original references and for a more complete discussion of these and other syntheses.

Oxalic Acid	Urea	Amino Acids	Glycine	Alanine	Aspartic Acid	Glutamic Acid	Diaminosuccinic Acid	Serine	Threonine	Peptides (Proteinoids or at Least Polymers of Amino Acids)	Microspheres Which Have Some Chemical and Physical Similarity to Boderial Cells	Adenosine Triphosphate (ATP, an Energy Intermediary for All Terrestrial Life and a Supposed Precursor for DNA Synthesis)	Deoxyribonucleic Acid (DNA)
												Products	
X													
	X												
			X										
			X	X	X	X							
		X											
		X											
			X		X		X						
			X										
		X											
			X	X	X	X							
				X	X								
			X	X	X			X	X				
										X			
										X			

TABLE 11-2. Continued

Worker	Date of Report	Reactants	Energy Source
Otozai *et al.*	1954	Glycine	Electrical discharge
Bahadur	1958	Glycine and glucose in water	Heat
Kovacs and Nagy	1961	Asperine in water	Heat
Fox *et al.*	1959	Proteinoid	Heat by boiling water followed by cooling
Ponnamperuma *et al.*	1963	Adenine, ribose, and ethyl-metaphosphate; or Adenosine and ethylmeta-phosphate	Ultra-violet light
Kornberg *et al.*	1958	Triphosphates of the four deoxynucleosides (thymidine, deoxycytidine, deoxyguanosine, and deoxyadenosine) found in DNA	ATP with some DNA as a primer, Mg^{++}, and DNA polymerase as a catalyst to make the reaction fast enough for observation

										Products			
Oxalic Acid	Urea	Amino Acids	Glycine	Alanine	Aspartic Acid	Glutamic Acid	Diaminosuccinic Acid	Serine	Threonine	Peptides (Proteinoids or at Least Polymers of Amino Acids)	Microspheres Which Have Some Chemical and Physical Similarity to Boderial Cells	Adenosine Triphosphate (ATP, an Energy Intermediary for All Terrestrial Life and a Supposed Precursor for DNA Synthesis)	Deoxyribonucleic Acid (DNA)
										X			
										X			
										X			
											X		
												X	
													X

TABLE 11-3. Probable Stages in Creation of Life on Earth or Earth-Like Environment*

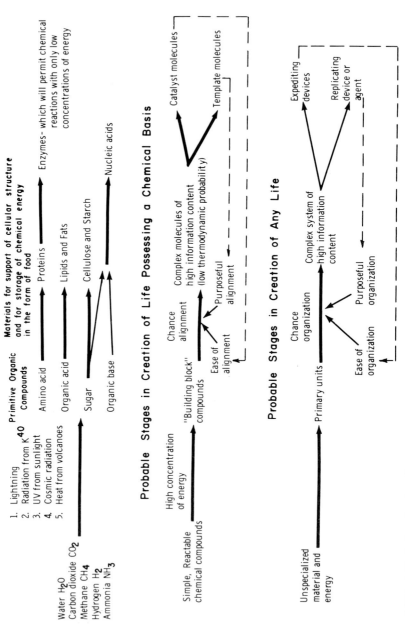

* This table is based primarily upon material discussed by Calvin (1962a, b).

The best-known argument for intelligent life on Mars is the existence of a number of lines, more commonly referred to as "canals." Proponents of a theory of intelligent life on Mars originally suggested that these are artificial waterways which were dug by some intelligent form of life to channel the planet's sparse quantity of water from the polar regions to other sections of Mars. Modern proponents of "canals" as evidence for life on Mars do not consider the visible lines to be waterways. Rather they suggest that the visible lines represent stripes of "vegetation" in the proximity of waterways which are themselves not visible from Earth. The existence or nature of these lines has remained a matter of controversy for almost a century. Although they are described as being readily visible by means of direct observation through a telescope, constant fluctuations in the refractive property of the Earth's atmosphere render photographic documentation of the existence or nature of these lines extremely difficult. Recent photographs from the Mariner IV space probe were not influenced by the Earth's atmosphere, but did not confirm the presence of canals.

There are seasonal changes in the coloration of the planet's surface which could be associated with the climate-dependent growth of organisms. There are also the spectrographic studies of the optical absorption by portions of the planet, which could indicate the presence of organic compounds.

Probably the most intriguing of the arguments for intelligent life on Mars are those based upon observations of the two moons of the planet. Both moons were observed almost simultaneously by many observers in 1877 after numerous previous attempts to locate satellites about this planet had failed (Rudaux and de Vaucouleurs, 1959, p. 205). This has led some people to suggest (in popular articles [Zigel, 1961] and other articles cited by Briggs [1962]) that these two moons are actually artificial satellites which were launched into orbit in the year 1877. The more competent proponents of these moons as being artificial satellites feel that these moons may have been launched in ancient times rather than in 1877. Such workers base their arguments upon the peculiar orbital properties of these satellites.

Although the present surface of our Moon would be uninhabitable to any of the known forms of life, it is not inconceivable that at an earlier time in the Moon's history it did possess an atmosphere, oceans or seas, and a temperature comparable to that of the Earth (Sagan, 1960; Gilvarry, 1960). The darkened surface on part of the Moon (the maria) has been proposed as the remains of organic carbon deposited as bodies of water receded.

Until interplanetary flight becomes a reality, the investigation of material from meteors will no doubt continue to be the most promising approach to the investigation of extra-Terrestrial life. Some materials reported to have been extracted from meteors possess chemical and physical characteristics of a type to be expected from the remnants of past life (Nagy et al., 1962; Briggs, 1962 [see Fig. 11-3]). Although natural radioactivity would have been expected to destroy any material which had remained in the meteors over a period of thousands or millions of years (Chapter 9), some of this

TABLE 11-4. Reported Observations Which Some People Have Considered Suggestions of Extra-Terrestrial Life*

Body Observed	Nature of Reported Observation	Reason Suggesting That Such Might Indicate Life	Alternate Explanations
Mars	Canals	Thought to be water channels dug by intelligent forms	Cracks in surface or series of spots along surface; optical illusions
	Darkening of canals and areas over the planet's surface in spring	Seasonal growth of vegetation as water melts at poles and flows through ground	Color changes in chemical compounds caused by water of hydration; temperature-dependent, radiation-induced color changes in rhyolites on the Martian surface (Smoluchowski, 1965); other chemical changes; or dampness of the soil.
	Occasional bright flashes (observed in 1937, 1951, 1954)	Atomic explosions by intelligent creation	Natural explosions
	Spectroscope patterns characteristic of organic material (infrared at 3.45, 3.58 and 3.69 μ)	Organic material in or produced by living organisms (supposedly carbohydrates)	This has recently been shown to be an artifact due to heavy water in the Earth's atmosphere (Rea et al. 1965). Moreover, organic compounds are known to be produced by non-biological processes
Satellites of Mars	Seen by many observers in 1877 but never seen before	Placed in orbit as artificial satellite	Previous telescopes were not of adequate quality
	Irregular orbits	These orbits are unstable and are therefore not permanent	Asymmetry within the core of Mars can account for some irregularity in the same manner that asymmetry within the Earth's core has been proposed to account for irregular orbits of known man-made satellites
		The orbits are not of the type expected from symmetrical heavenly bodies orbiting about a symmetrical planet	There is no reason to think that natural heavenly bodies this small would be symmetrical

	Observation	Interpretation	Alternative explanation
Moon	Dark markings in the "seas" or "maria"	Organic carbon deposited on the floors of former actual seas when the moon was younger, still possessing an atmosphere and water	Even organic compounds could have a non-biological origin. Could have been splashed onto the moon by a very large meteor striking Earth's oceans
Remains of certain meteors known as "carbonaceous chondrites" composed of 1% organic matter	Spectral analysis of material from meteors yielding spectra similar to cytosine	This is one of the bases found in nucleic acids and could have been a breakdown product of nucleic acid from an organism which existed on a planet before it exploded into meteors	Contamination or non-biological origin
	Paraffinic hydrocarbons found in meteors	Produced by organism on some ancient planet before explosion	
	Deposits that look like fossils of single-celled organism		Could have a non-biological origin such as Fox's and Harada's (1963) microspheres
	Extraction of material which "grows" like bacteria	Living survivor from exploding planet	Contamination or some chemical process which is not well understood

* Some of these observations have been discussed in more detail in the articles by MacGowan (1962), Briggs (1962), Urey (1962), Zigel (1961), and Sagan (1964).

material is reported to have demonstrated a behavior similar to that associated with the growth of bacteria.

When man eventually reaches the other heavenly bodies (as scheduled for the Moon in 1970), attempts will be made to ascertain whether or not life is existing upon these new worlds. Even before a manned space ship can explore Mars, it has been proposed that an automated space ship might investigate the presence of life there. Such an automated space ship could place material sampled from the surface of the planet in a nutrient medium with the hope that microorganisms there could metabolize and release

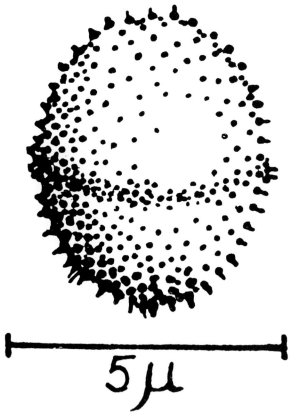

Figure 11-3. Drawing of organized, spine-covered element viewed in a section of a meteorite as drawn by Nagy *et al.* (1962). Nagy and co-workers suggest that this organized element represents the fossilized remains of some single-celled organism which existed on another planet. Others have suggested that this might represent an artifact composed of aggregated material or even contamination by a Terrestrial pollen grain.

detectable quantities of carbon dioxide. Various procedures for indicating the existence of life by the detection of animate motion in material sampled on Mars have also been put forward (Fig. 11-4).

Even if life does not exist on the other heavenly bodies of our Solar System, one cannot preclude its existence among the 10^{20} or so stars in the remainder of the universe. It has been estimated that from one in a billion to one in 20 of these stars possesses habitable planets orbiting about them (Shapley, 1958; Huang, 1959, 1960; Matsushima, 1964). Some of the assumptions used in attempting to evaluate the number of habitable planets are outlined in Table 11-5. The factors considered are sufficient stability of the planet to permit evolution, the nature of the atmosphere, and temperature conditions which would permit life based upon carbon and water. These assumptions would suggest that no habitable planet exists in association with our nearest star Alpha Centuri but that there are, within 10 light years of Earth, two stars which might possess habitable planets. Some methods for evaluating the existence of habitable planets are listed in Table 11-6.

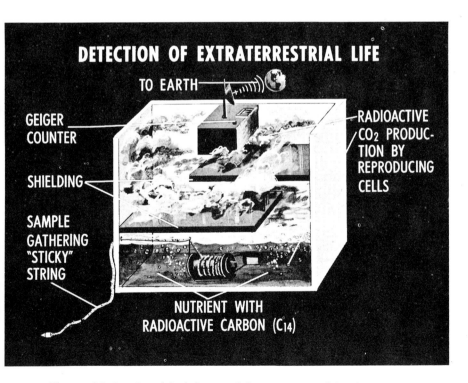

Figure 11-4. Simplified design of device proposed for detection of life on Mars. (*AIBS Bulletin, October 1962.*)

TABLE 11-5. Conditions for Habitable Planets*

Assumption	Justification	Implication	Factors Overlooked	Remarks
1. Time required for evolution of advanced forms of life (3×10^9 yr) is essentially the same as for Earth (4.5×10^9 yr)	Selection and evolution is a random slow process	Star would have had to possess nearly stable energy output for 3×10^9 yr Thus excluding stars brighter or larger than FO stars (10-fold greater mass and 2-fold greater brightness than our Sun)	Evolution might proceed at differing rates with exotic hereditary system Life might have migrated from another planet or star Only slightly higher temperature could decrease length of generations and thus permit faster selection and evolution	
2. Life based upon carbon atom	This atom is one of few capable of forming large, complex molecules	Temperatures not much greater than 290° K must be available on the planet Limit to maximum average separation of habitable planet from star (approximate distance from Sun to Mars for Solar System) which would increase with star's luminosity	Other possible types of life such as those based upon silicon overlooked	
3. Life with water as primary solvent	Most commonly encountered solvent on Earth	Temperatures not much lower than 273° K must be available on planet Limited to minimum average separation of planet from star (approximate distance from Sun to Venus for Solar System) which	Excludes possibility of other solvents such as ammonia or ethylene glycol. (Certain antifreeze-like solvents are known to exist in Terrestrial life.) Life which evolved upon another planet might be able to survive	Size of habitable zone should increase with star's luminosity and would therefore be so small with stars

4. Life unable to survive if temperature on planet's surface drastically departs from 273-290° K	Life not active on Earth at temperatures remote from these	Life would not be maintained on surface of planet with orbit so eccentric as to extend beyond the habitable zone	Possibility of dormant stage capable of survival. Many Terrestrial cells are believed capable of almost unlimited survival at very low temperatures	of Sun or mass less than 2/3 of Sun; i.e., beyond spectral type K5) that the slightest eccentricity of planetary orbit would place planet out of habitable zone
5. Local areas in planet unable to maintain adequate temperature for life if surface temperature is drastically altered	Same as above	When combined with assumption #4, planets with quite eccentric orbits would not support life. Therefore the possibilities of habitable planets associated with double or multiple stars would be remote. It would not be expected for our nearest star (Alpha Centuri, 4.3 light years away)	Life might survive in thermally insulated areas beneath the surface during extreme temperature. Natural or artificial means of locally modifying temperature in the vicinity of organisms might exist	
6. 1 through 5		Of the 41 stars within 17 light years of Earth only 2 (other than our Sun) are likely to have habitable zones: Epsilon Eridani (11 light years) and Tau Ceti (12 light years). Perhaps 5% of the stars could have planets where life might arise	Overlooks a number of possibilities	
7. Life could not evolve in a reducing atmosphere	Earth's atmosphere is an oxidizing atmosphere	Large planets (which could retain hydrogen) would not contain life	Chemical stages of biological evolution on Earth are believed to have started before this planet lost its reducing atmosphere	

* This information is obtained primarily from the discussion by Huang (1959, 1960) and Matsushima (1964).

TABLE 11-6. Proposed Methods of Detecting Habitable Planets beyond Solar System.

Portion of Electro-magnetic Spectra	Wavelength Which Will Penetrate Planetary Atmosphere	Proposed Wavelength for Investigation	Source of Signal	Status of Method	Reference
Radio waves	Those below one meter will experience little or no interference from galactic noise. Those above 0.3 mm will experience little or no interference due to absorption by the Earth's atmosphere	21 cm (1420.4 Mc/sec, the radio emission line of neutral hydrogen)	Transmitter constructed and manned by extra-Terrestrial intelligence	Project OZMA was organized with the use of an 85-foot radio telescope at the National Radio Observatory, Greenbanks, W. Va. This can detect signals from up to 10 light years away. However, within this range there are only about 40 stars and according to Huang (1960) only 2 of them are likely to support life. A radio antenna of 30-km diameter would be required to detect stars within 104 light years. (The distance proposed by von Hoerner, 1961, as the average postulated distance to the nearest 10 civilizations.) *No signals detected*	Drake, 1961
Infrared	8-12 μ	10 μ	Starlight which is converted to infrared as a by-product of an advanced society	Proposed	Dryson, 1960
Visible	Throughout visible range		Eclipse of star by planet	Proposed as feasible for a planet as small as 3 times the Earth's diameter by means of 16-inch Earthbound telescopes for a range of 1500 light years (10^4 stars within observable range). Range increases in proportion to telescope's aperture	Matsu-shima, 1964

Consequences of Interaction with Other Life

There are a number of consequences which may be expected to result from contact with a new form of life or intelligence. All of these consequences should be carefully weighed before any action which permits contact is pursued (Fig. 11-5). There is the possibility that contact will be beneficial and that man will gain knowledge not only by an exchange of information with some new intelligence but also from a study of the nature of new organisms. Learning the nature of present or past life on another world might give some indication of the characteristics which all types of life must possess. There is always the danger that this new form of life could harm us either by direct conquest and warfare or by contamination of our planet with undesirable parasites.

Whether or not a microorganism from another world could infect Terrestrial life is not really known. Although the conditions of another planet probably would not encourage the evolution of an organism ideally suited for the infection of man or some other Terrestrial organism, it is at the same time unlikely that the Terrestrial organisms would have developed any immunity to such exotic parasites. Even if an organism from another planet would not directly harm man, there is always the possibility that if by either accident or design some of these organisms are brought back to Earth they could breed rapidly in our environment and compete for food and other resources. Ecologists who consider this problem remind us of the manner in which the rabbits multiplied on the continent of Australia in the absence of any natural enemies. It is not unreasonable that either a new form of life introduced to this planet or an organism from this planet introduced to a new planet could drastically alter the balance of nature presently in existence.

The primary fear regarding biological contact with another planet is that microorganisms from Earth could destroy the life which exists on the new planet or any organic remains of past life. The loss of potential scientific information resulting from such an infection is almost incalculable. Essentially all of the components of a space probe could carry infection. Many of these components are of a type not normally sterilized. Some of the components would be destroyed by heat, which is the most commonly employed agent presently used in the sterilization of instruments. Other sterilizing agents may not penetrate all of the inaccessible areas. The advantages and disadvantages of various sterilizing agents which might be used in sending an unmanned exploratory capsule to the surface of another planet are tabulated in Table 11-7. There are certain disadvantages to any sterilizing agent which might be employed; however, ethylene oxide would appear to be the best agent thus far considered. Due to the expense and possible deleterious effects of complete sterilization, compromises with respect to the degree of sterilization will probably be necessary. There is evidence (as summarized by Packer et al., 1963) that some bacteria can survive and possibly multiply in a Martian environment.

Planets which are presently uninhabitable to man might be converted into habitable areas. The present evidence indicates that the surface of the planet

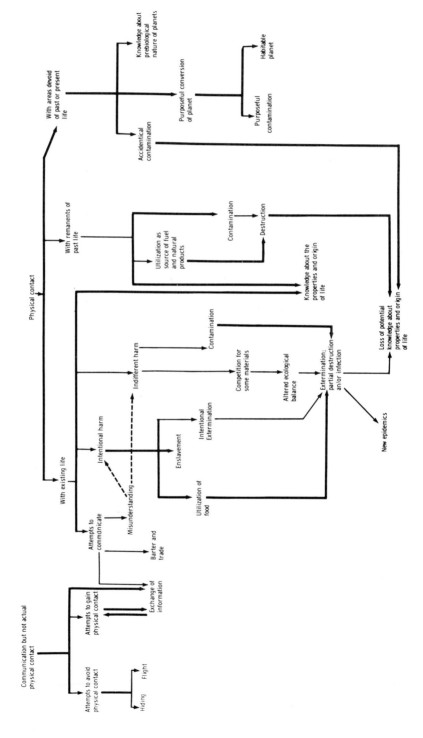

Figure 11-5. Possible consequences of contact with extra-Terrestrial life.

TABLE 11-7. Agents for Sterilization of Space Vehicles*

Agent	Disadvantage	Advantage	Remarks
A. Sterile assembly of sterilized components	Greater expense requiring individual assembly of otherwise readily available components	Perhaps only method to guarantee sterility of delicate components not readily exposed to agents listed below	
B. Terminal sterilization			
1. Heat	Many of the components in present payloads would be damaged	Dry heat could penetrate entire assembly	
2. Radiation	Some components such as transistors and mercury cells cannot tolerate this treatment	Could penetrate some otherwise inaccessible areas	
3. Gaseous or vaporous disinfectants			
a. Formaldehyde	Damages materials and leaves a film		
b. β-propiolactone	Does not readily penetrate; requires high humidity	No known damage to equipment, 25 times more effective than formaldehyde, 4000 times more effective than ethylene oxide, nonflammable	
c. Ethylene oxide	Flammable but can be used in a non-flammable mixture with dichlorodifluoromethane and trichloromonofluoromethane	Highly penetrating, soluble in oil and water, not known to damage materials, can be used in presence of air	Most likely to be used
	Requires several hours to disinfect		

* Based primarily upon the article by Wynne (1961).

Venus is too hot for Terrestrial forms of life and that there is little or no oxygen in the atmosphere. Presumably there is a large quantity of carbon dioxide in the atmosphere which prevents Venus from emitting energy absorbed from the Sun in the form of radiant heat. This type of heating is referred to as the "greenhouse effect." The earlier atmosphere of the Earth was believed to contain a high concentration of carbon dioxide with little or no oxygen. As plant life evolved, the process of photosynthesis converted the carbon dioxide to yield molecular oxygen. Sagan (1961a) has proposed that the same objective might be accomplished by seeding the atmosphere of Venus with one of the bluegreen algae, *Nostocaceae*. Although the surface of the planet is too hot for our forms of life, the higher reaches of the atmosphere would be cooler and the algae might survive there for a long enough period of time to convert the carbon dioxide into oxygen and as a result eliminate the greenhouse effect. If such a proposal proves feasible, Venus then could be converted to a planet quite similar to our own.

Although there are reasons for believing that life might exist in the planets beyond the atmosphere of the Earth, there are other reasons for doubting its existence. At this writing, no one can say with authority that there is or is not extra-Terrestrial life. Knowledge of this nature is necessary in designing the most fruitful and least destructive exploration and utilization of other planets. This information might also prove essential in avoiding repercussions which would imperil the existence of human life on our own planet.

Bibliography and References

ANDERS, E., DuFRESNE, E. R., HAYATSU, R. (1964): Contaminated meteorite. *Science 146*, 1157-1161.

ARRHENIUS, S. (1908): "Worlds in the Making." Harper, New York.

ASIMOV, I. (1963): "View from a Height." Doubleday, New York.

BRIGGS, M. H. (1962): The distribution of life in the solar system: an evaluation of the present evidence. *J. Brit. Interplanetary Soc. 18*, 431-437.

BRIGGS, M. H., AND KITTO, G. B. (1962): Complex organic micro-structures in the Mokoia meteorite. *Nature 193*, 1126-1127.

CALVIN, M. (1962a): The origin of life on Earth and elsewhere. *In* "Advances in Biological and Medical Physics" (C. A. Tobias and J. H. Lawrence, eds.), *Vol. 8*, pp. 315-342.

CALVIN, M. (1962b): Communication: from molecules to Mars. *AIBS Bulletin, October*, 29-44.

DRAKE, F. D. (1961): Project OZMA. *Physics Today 14 (4)*, 40-46.

DRYSON, F. J. (1960): Search for artificial sources of infrared radiation. *Science 131*, 1667-1668.

DU NOÜY, L. (1949): "Human Destiny." Signet Books, New York.

FITCH, F., SCHWARCZ, H. P., AND ANDERS, E. (1962): 'Organized elements' in carbonaceous chondrites. *Nature 193*, 1123-1125.

FOX, S. W., AND HARADA, K. (1963): Experiments related to the chemical origins of proteins. *In* "Medical and Biological Problems of Space Flight" (G. H. Bourne, ed.), pp. 261-270. Academic Press, New York.

GILVARRY, J. J. (1960): Origin and nature of lunar surface features. *Nature 188*, 886-891.

HASS, S. L. (1961): Mars as an astronautical objective. *Advances in Space Science and Technology 3*, 151-193.

HUANG, S. S. (1959): Occurrence of life in the universe. *American Scientist 47*, 397-402.

HUANG, S. S. (1960): Life outside the solar system. *Scientific American 202 (4)*, 55-63.

JACKSON, F. L., AND MOORE, P. (1962): "Life in the Universe." W. W. Norton and Co., New York.

JONES, H. S. (1952): "Life on other Worlds." Mentor Books, New York.

LEDERBERG, J. (1960): Exobiology: approaches to life beyond the Earth. *Science 132*, 393-400.

LEDERBERG, J., AND SAGAN, C. (1962): Microenvironments for life on Mars. *Proc. Natl. Acad. Sci. 48 (9)*, 1473-1475.

MacGOWAN, R. A. (1962): On the possibilities of the existence of extraterrestrial intelligence. *In* "Advances in Space and Technology" (F. I. Ordway III, ed.), *Vol. 4*, pp. 39-110. Academic Press, New York.

MASON, B. A. (1963): Organic matter from space. *Scientific American 208 (3)*, 43-49.

MATSUSHIMA, S. (1964): Astronomical limitations on detecting habitable planets beyond the solar system. *Proc. Ia. Acad. Sci. 71* (in press).

NAGY, B., CLAUS, G., AND HENNESSY, D. J. (1962): Organic particles embedded in minerals in the Orgueil and Ivuna carbonaceous chondrites. *Nature 193*, 1129-1133.

NAGY, B., MURPHY, M. T. J., MODZELESKI, V. E., ROUSER, G., CLAUS, G., HENNESSY, D. J., COLOMBO, U., AND GAZZARRINI, F. (1964). Optical activity in saponified organic matter isolated from the interior of the orgueil meteorite. *Nature 202*, 228-233.

OPARIN, A. I., PASYNSKII, A. G., BRAUNSHTEÏN, A. E., AND PAVLOVSKAYA, T. E. (eds.) (1959): "Proc. of the First Intern. Symposium on the Origin of Life on the Earth, held at Moscow 19-24 August 1957." *Vol. 1*, I. U. B. Symposium Series. Pergamon Press, New York.

PACKER, E., SCHER, S., AND SAGAN, C. (1963): Biological contamination of Mars II: cold and aridity as constraints on the survival of Terrestrial microorganisms in simulated Martian environments. *Icarus 2*, 293-361.

PONNAMPERUMA, C., SAGAN, C., AND MAINER, R. (1963): Synthesis of adenosine triphosphate under possible primitive Earth conditions. *Nature 199*, 222-226.

QUASTLER, H. (ed.) (1953): "Essays on the Use of Information Theory in Biology." University of Illinois Press, Urbana.

REA, D. G., O'LEARY, B. T., AND SINTON, W. M. (1965): Mars: the origin of the 3.58- and 3.69 micron minima in the infrared spectra. *Science 147*, 1286-1288.

ROSS, H. H. (1962): "A Synthesis of Evolutionary Theory." Prentice-Hall, Englewood Cliffs, N. J.

RUDAUX, L., AND DE VAUCOULEURS, G. (1959): "Larousse Encyclopedia of Astronomy." Prometheus Press, New York.

SAGAN, C. (1960): Indigenous organic matter on the moon. *Natl. Acad. Sci. 46*, 393-396.

SAGAN, C. (1961a): The planet Venus. *Science 133*, 849-858.

SAGAN, C. (1961b): Interstellar panspermia. (Paper delivered at AAAS Meeting, Denver, December 1962.)

SAGAN C. (1964): Exobiology: a critical review. *In* "Life Sciences and Space Research II" (M. Florkin and A. Dollfus, eds.), pp. 35-53. North-Holland Publishing Co., Amsterdam.

SALISBURY, F. B. (1962): Martian biology. *Science 136*, 17-26.

SCHRÖDINGER, E. (1947): "What is Life?" Cambridge University Press, New York.

SHAPLEY, H. (1958): "Of Stars and Men." Beacon Press, Boston.

SIMPSON, G. G. (1964): The nonprevalence of humanoids. *Science 143*, 769-775.

SMOLUCHOWSKI, R. (1965): Is there vegetation on Mars? *Science 148*, 946-947.

UREY, H. C. (1962): Origin of life-like forms in carbonaceous chondrites. *Nature 193*, 1119-1123.

VON HOERNER, S. (1961): The search for signals from other civilizations. *Science 134*, 1839-1843.

WYNNE, E. S. (1961): Sterilization of space vehicles: the problem of mutual contamination. *In* "Lectures in Aerospace Medicine" (Paper No. 16). School of Aerospace Medicine, Brooks AFB.

ZIGEL, F. (1961): There is intelligent life on Mars. *Space World 1, March*, 20.

AUTHOR INDEX

ABELSON, 270
Ackerman, E., 177
Adler, H. F., 95, 97
Akhlebininskiy, S. S., 108, 253
Allen, S. C., 238
Allison, N., 159
Altman, P. L., 85
Armstrong, H. G., 154
Arrhenius, S., 11, 265
Arsen'yeva, M. A., 23
Asimov, I., 264

BAHADUR, 270, 272
Balbiano, 270
Barnett, C. H., 136
Barnett, S. M., 254, 255
Barnothy, J. M., 185
Beischer, D. E., 185, 186
Berglund, R. A., 63
Bernard, Claude, 13
Berry, C. A., 23, 159, 168, 233
Birkhead, N. C., 159
Black-Schaffer, B., 84
Bongers, L. H., 240, 253
Bourne, G. H., 157
Bozajian, J., 42
Brannon, E. W., 159
Briggs, M. H., 42, 275, 277
Brooks, B., 159
Brooks, W. A., 77
Brown, F. A., Jr., 206
Buckheim, R. W., 85
Burton, A. C., 96
Burton, R. R., 142
Bussard, R. W., 228
Bychkov, V. P., 253

CAIN, C. C., 23
Calvin, M., 268, 274

Campbell, P. A., 20
Capotosto, A., Jr., 240
Carlson, L. D., 24
Catterson, A. D., 159, 168
Cavagna, G. A., 176
Clamann, H. G., 239
Clark, B., 159
Clarke, A. C., 37, 76, 231
Clynes, M., 233

DEITRICK, J. E., 159
de Vaucouleurs, G., 275
Dodge, C. H., 171
Dose, 270
Drake, F. D., 282
Dryden, H. L., 29
Dryson, F. J., 282
Duguid, R. H., 119
du Nouy, L., 265

EBERSOLE, J. H., 117
Eccles, J. C., 159
Edwards, B. F., 155
Elliott, D. R., 165

FLINN, D. E., 232
Fox, S. W., 268, 270, 272, 277

GAUER, O. H., 157, 167
Gazenko, O. G., 133, 159, 171
Geiser, M., 159
Generales, C. D. J., Jr., 59, 65, 157
Gerathewohl, S., 156
Gilbert, D. L., 11, 14
Gilvarry, J. J., 275
Glembotskiy, Ya. L., 23
Gold, T., 42

289

SUBJECT INDEX

ABLATING materials in heat shields, 77, 79
Absolute pressure, effects of, 103
Absorbents for removal of carbon dioxide
    during space flight, 236. See also
    Carbon dioxide, removal of.
Absorption
    atmospheric, of some types of radiation,
      196
    in change in some quantity, 107
    of carbon dioxide. See *Carbon dioxide,*
      removal of.
    of sound, 174
    photoelectric, ionizing radiations and,
      212
Absorption coefficient, 197, 203, 204, 216
Absorption properties of ionizing radia-
    tions, 212-215
Acceleration, 140. See also *Centrifugation;*
    Centrifuge; Gravitation; Gravity.
    acute
      "black-out" with, 151
      effect of
        upon brain, 149
        upon cardiovascular system, 150
        upon consciousness, 149, 151
        upon eyeball, 150
        upon man, 150 (table)
        upon respiration, 151
        upon vision, 149, 150
      responses of circulatory and respira-
        tory systems to, 149
    angular, effect of, upon arterial blood
      pressure, 154
    as hazard in space environment, 54
    centrifugal, 124
    centripetal, 124
    changes in absolute pressure due to,
      effects of, 99
    Coriolis, 125
    description of, 122

Acceleration (*continued*)
    direction of, 152
    effect of
      upon blood pressure, 149, 153
      upon heart, 149, 153
      upon vision, 149, 153
    for orbit and escape of manned rockets,
      146, 149
    for reentry of manned rockets, 149
    gravity and, quantities related to, 122-
      131 (table)
    in centrifuge, physiological events dur-
      ing, 153
    intense, atelectasis and, 117
    negative, 141, 150, 152
    pattern of, for orbit and escape of
      manned rockets, 146, 149
    positive, 150, 152
    rocket, total field in, 144
    significance of, 122
    tolerance to, 139, 149
    transverse, 152
    vector quantity of, 122
    vibratory, values for, 176
Acclimate, 67
Acclimatization, 67
Accretion in change of some quantity, 107
Acid(s)
    amino. See *Amino acids.*
    aspartic, synthesis of, 271
    deoxyribonucleic. See *Deoxyribonucleic*
      acid.
    diaminosuccinic, synthesis of, 271
    glutamic, synthesis of, 271
    nucleic. See *Nucleic acid.*
    organic, in creation of life on Earth or
      Earth-like environment, 268, 274
    oxalic, synthesis of, 271
    ribonucleic, in Terrestrial life, 265
Acosta, José, 17